THE LITTLE GIANT ENCYCLOPEDIA OF *Puzzles*

THE LITTLE GIANT ENCYCLOPEDIA OF *Puzzles*

THE DIAGRAM GROUP

Sterling Publishing Co., Inc. New York

Library of Congress Cataloging-in-Publication Data
Available

10 9 8 7 6 5 4

Published 1996 by Sterling Publishing Company, Inc.
387 Park Avenue South, New York, N.Y. 10016

Distributed in Canada by Sterling Publishing
c/o Canadian Manda Group, One Atlantic Avenue, Suite 105
Toronto, Ontario, Canada M6K 3E7

Distributed in Australia by Capricorn Link (Australia) Pty Ltd.
P.O. Box 6651, Baulkham Hills, Business Centre, NSW 2153,
Australia

Manufactured in the United States of America

Sterling ISBN 0-8069-4258-4

Foreword

Puzzles have existed for more than 4,000 years. One of the oldest is the Cretan labyrinth. According to Greek mythology, it was built by Daedalus for King Minos of Crete, who wanted to capture the minotaur, a creature that was half man, half bull. Legend has it that Theseus, another king's son, went into the labyrinth and killed the minotaur; he then found his way out of the twisting paths by following a thread he had unwound as he entered.

The labyrinth is one type of the amazing variety of puzzles to be found in this illustrated encyclopedia. The more than 300 puzzles reflect not just a range of the best-loved puzzle types but also a balanced mix of the simple and the complex. But don't be fooled – a puzzle you might think looks simple could have you racking your brains!

There are:

- Puzzles of logic that test your wits:

  To what question must you always answer yes?

- Maze puzzles that can put you in a twist.

- Number puzzles that challenge your ability to make complex calculations in your head – and really make you think!

- Visual puzzles, where the eye deceives the brain.

- Activity puzzles, where the doing is the proof, requiring you to work through a sequence of steps to find the solution.

No matter how taxing they might be, all the puzzles *can* be solved. You'll find the answers at the end of the book – but try not to peek!

1

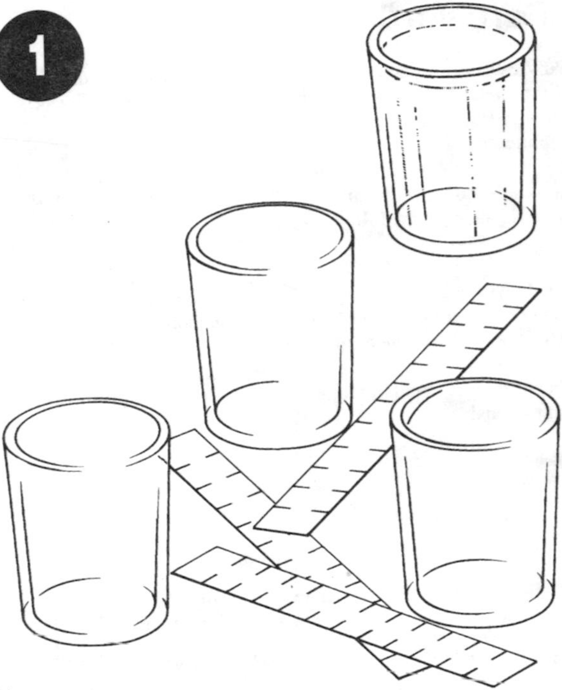

Three empty glasses are each 13 inches apart. If we gave you three 12-inch-long rulers, could you make a bridge between the empty glasses that was strong enough to support a fourth glass – which is full of water? You may not empty out the water first!

Can you rearrange the fruit so that you have a row alternating apples and oranges? You have four moves and may pick up two adjacent pieces of fruit in each move.

2

3 **A farmer had seven daughters, and they each**

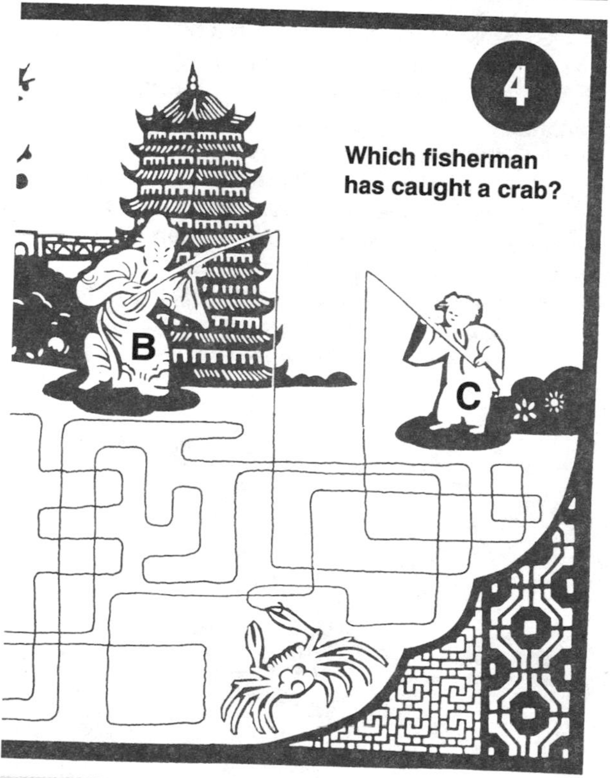
4
Which fisherman has caught a crab?
B
C

had a brother. How many children did he have?

5 Researchers working on a new heat exchanger developed this experiment to compare the efficiency of different coolants. Hot water (in the black pipes) carries heat into the system at a steady 111 units per hour. The various test coolants flow through the surrounding pipes and remove heat at rates dependent on their own thermal properties. Given that the heat input of each black pipe must be balanced by the heat removal capacity of its ring of coolant pipes (see below), can you fill in the missing values on the full-scale test rig on the opposite page?

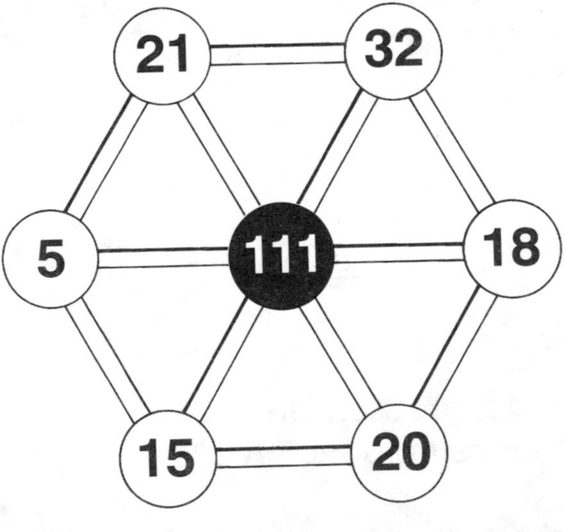

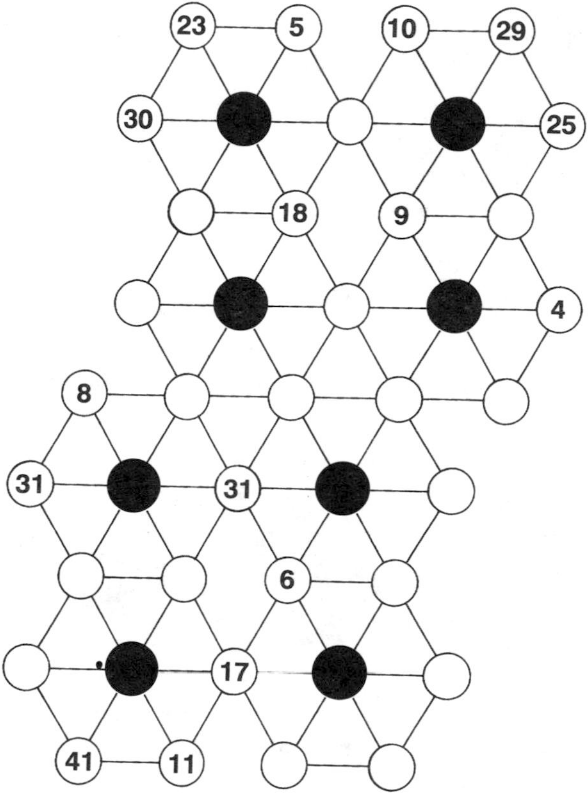
23
5
10
29
30
25
18
9
4
8
31
31
6
17
41
11

6

This arrangement of matches represents, in Roman numerals, the fraction one-seventh. By moving any one match, except the horizontal fraction bar, can you change it to an arrangement representing a fraction equal to one?

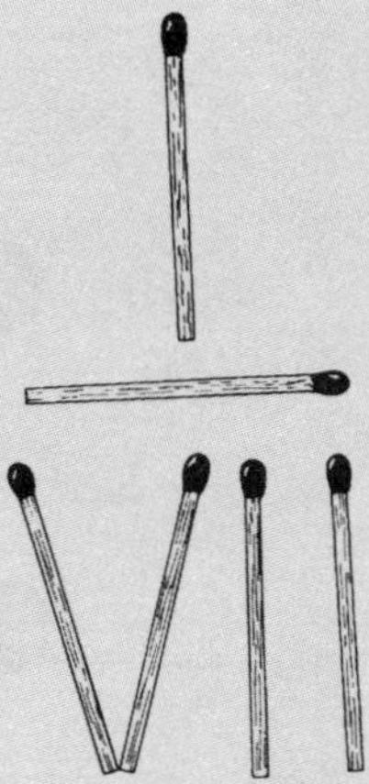

7

A clever but idle mathematician was watching his wife pick apples and thought up this puzzle. He noticed that the number of apples in her basket doubled every minute and that it was full at precisely 12 noon. At what time was the basket half full?

1	23	6	14	19	2	24	10	7
9	8	7	12	24	6	18	5	16
3	4	24	8	7	1	6	24	12
6	5	12	6	8	10	15	12	6
12	2	7	21		6	15	30	7
11	6	5	6	10	12	9	6	11
12	8	11	30	15	18	6	24	9
2	13	24	6	12	8	6	7	18
9	8	12	10	9	7	15	3	8

8 Starting at any edge, and not using diagonals, can you get to the middle, passing only through rooms with even numbers divisible by three?

9 If a project takes me $7\frac{1}{2}$ hours to complete, and you can complete it in 5 hours, how long would it take us to tackle the project together?

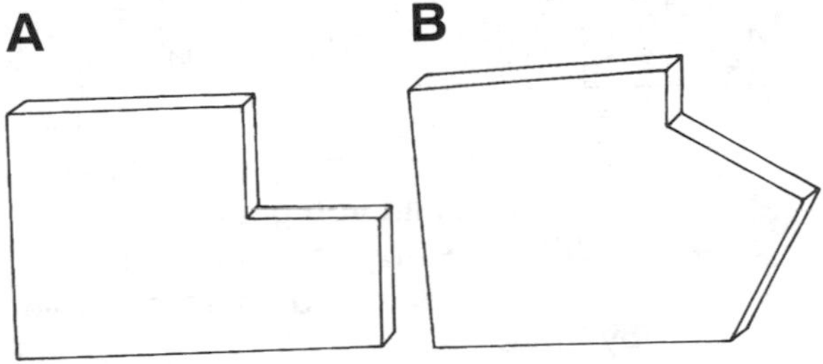

10 Each of these wooden shapes can be sawed into three pieces, which can then be rearranged to form perfect squares. Where would you make the cuts?

11

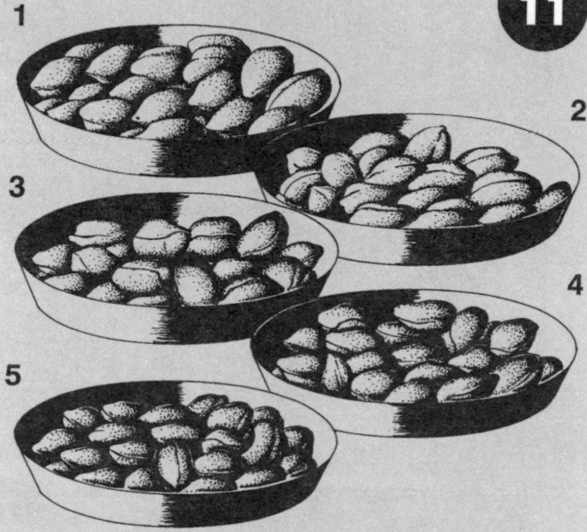

Here we have 100 nuts in five bowls. The first and second bowls together hold a total of 52 nuts; the second and third, 43 nuts; the third and fourth, 34; and the fourth and fifth, 30. How many nuts are in each bowl?

12 "Guess who's coming to dinner?" said Mrs. Street. "I've invited as few people as possible. As well as my husband and I, there will be my sister, Mrs. Road, her brother-in-law and his wife

Charlotte, my daughter Primrose, my lawyer Percy and his wife and daughter, and then I've invited Mrs. Hill, the widow who lives next door, and her Aunt Alexandra, who's staying with her. . . . How many places should I set?"

(5 5)
(5 5)
=100

13 To make his sum work, Little Boy Blue has to write in +, −, ×, or ÷ signs between the numbers on his slate (left). Can you write them in for him?

14

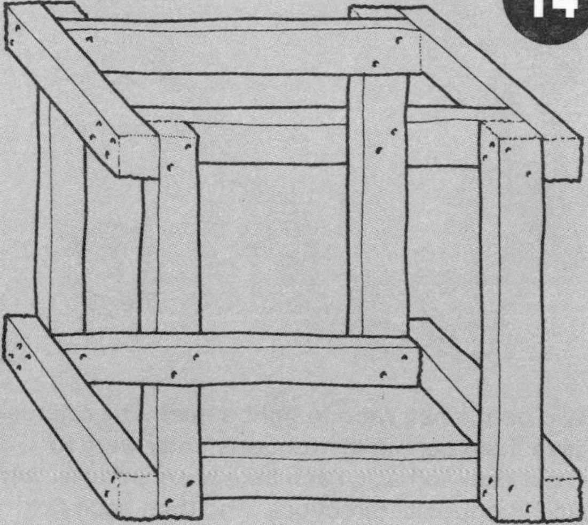

Can you make this object from twelve pieces of wood?

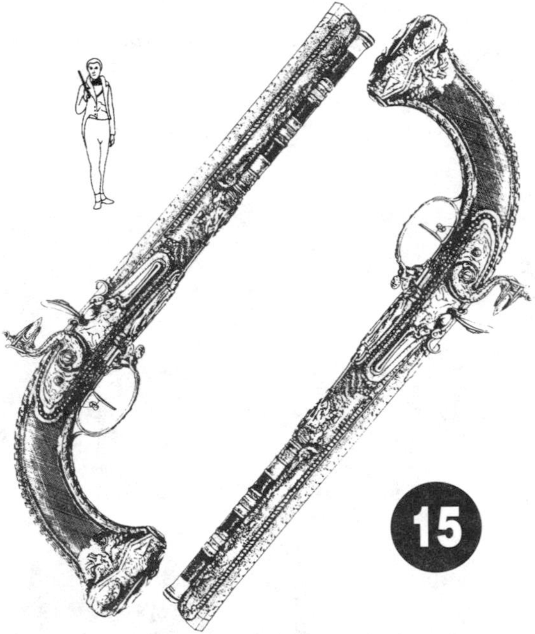

15

Two gentlemen were to fight a duel. The referee gave them careful instructions: they were to stand back to back, each take twenty paces, turn, face in opposite directions, and then each fire one shot. The duelists protested that they could not fire at each other if they were facing in opposite directions. The umpire maintained that they could. Who was right?

16

Trolls enjoy eating people for dinner but always pretend to give them a chance at escaping their fate. The hapless victim is offered a choice of two slips of paper and told that one says "Dinner" and the other "Freedom." If they choose the slip saying "Freedom," the troll releases them. But because trolls also enjoy cheating, both slips of paper actually say "Dinner" – so no one should ever escape.
But one peasant boy had been warned about this habit of the trolls by his fairy godmother, and he managed to work out a way of getting away from them uneaten. How did he do it?

17 **The secret agent stole the plans to an enemy spy school but made 18 mistakes when he copied them.**

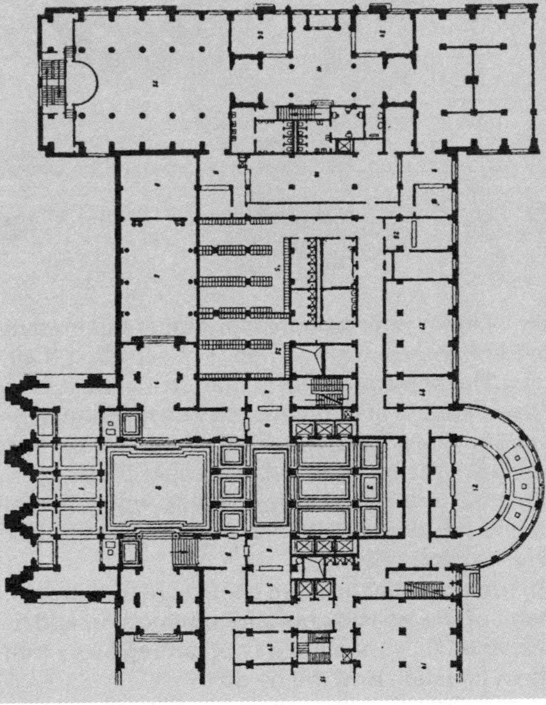

Can you find all the differences?

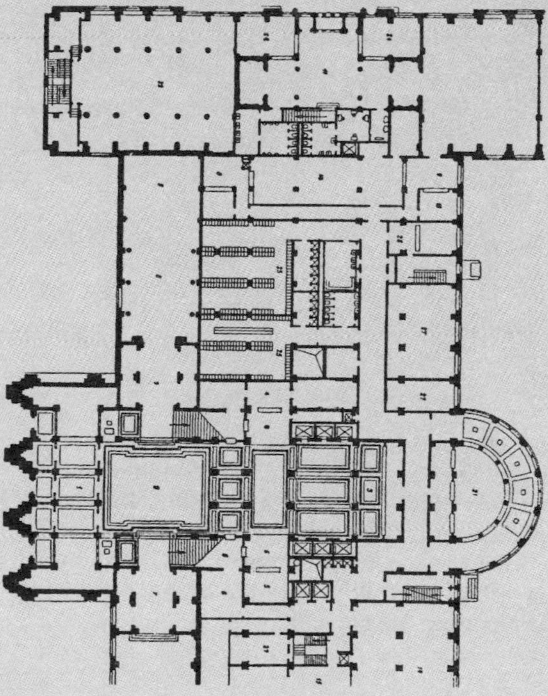

Alan, Bill, and Charlie were being questioned by the police about the theft of Mr. Tebbit's bicycle. Alan said that Bill had stolen it; Bill said that he was innocent; Charlie said that he was not the thief. The police knew that only one of the three was telling the truth – both the others were lying. So who stole the bicycle?

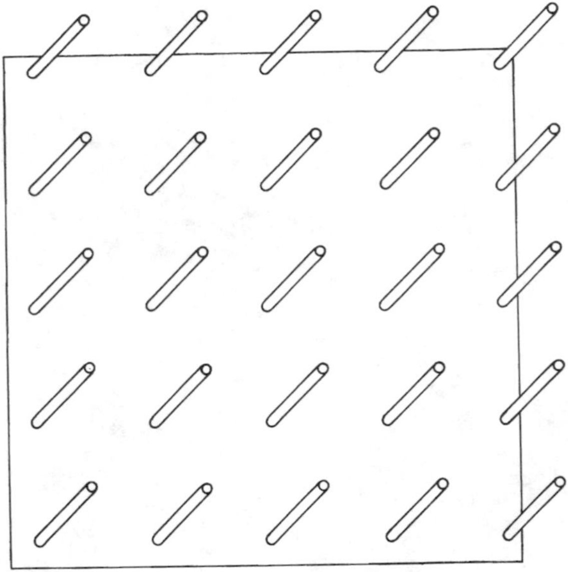

19 A serious accident at a remote civil engineering site left four men in urgent need of hospital treatment. The helicopter pilot asked for the largest possible red cross to be marked on the ground near the pick-up point. The only materials available were the builders' survey posts, laid out in a square grid, and a large roll of red masking tape. What did the site foreman do?

20

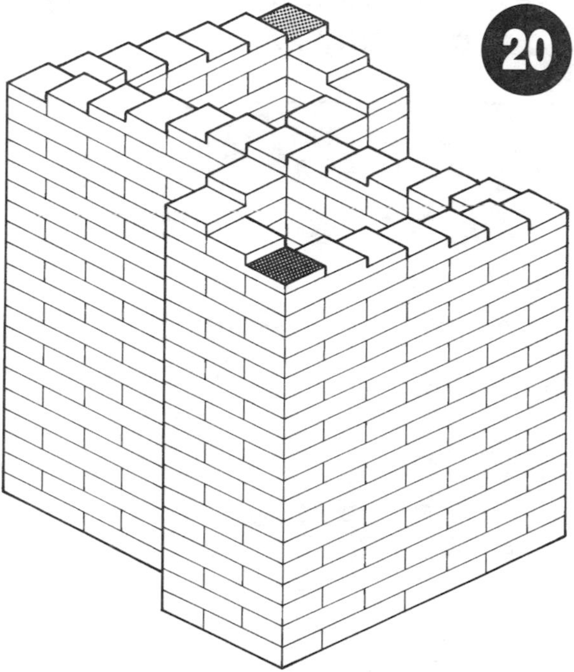

As soon as he had captured the castle, the victorious commander sent two of his men to the top of the walls with orders to raise his banner from the highest point. One claimed the flag should fly from the far corner, the other insisted that the near corner was higher. Who was right?

21 Look at this picture very carefully . . .

. . . then turn to the next page.

Can you remember ...

a) How many people are being chased by the bull?

b) Who is the man talking to?

c) What did the fisherman catch?

d) How many people is this man talking to?

e) How many ostriches are pulling this cart?

What does this message say?

22

23

Identifying the 12 animals opposite should not be too difficult, but 11 of these have something the 12th does not have. Which is the odd one out and why is it different?

24

It took a computer only a fraction of a second to identify all the triangles hidden in this figure. Human brains and eyes work a little slower; how many triangles can you locate in exactly one minute?

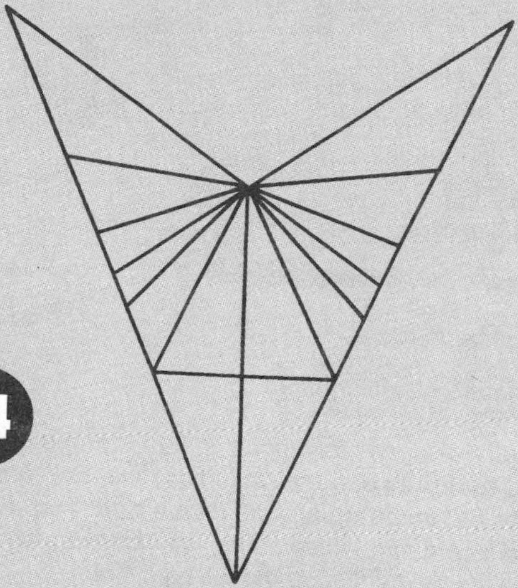

25

A very disorganized camper had lost his lighter and had only one match left. He wanted to light both his camping stoves (one a double burner and one a single gas ring), his camping lamp, and his cigar. Which did he light first?

26

Hi Team,
Wish you were here - just bought some cherries from George Washington's own tree. You know, when his parents accused him of cutting it down, he said "I cannot tell a lie - I did it with my little hatchet." They taste delicious!
Bart
Sue & the girls at
Diagram
11½ Adeline Place
Bedford square/London
WC1B 3JR
ENGLAND
FREDERICKSBERG
U.S.A.
POSTAL
US
7¢
AIR MAIL

Is Bart as truthful as George Washington?

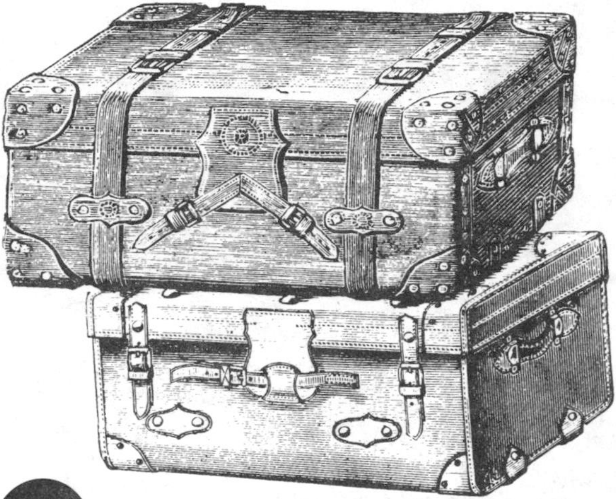

27

If the large trunk can hold twice as many books as the small trunk and the small trunk can hold 14 books, how many books can be put into both trunks?

28

How much earth is there in a hole 2 yards wide by 2 yards long by 2 yards deep?

29

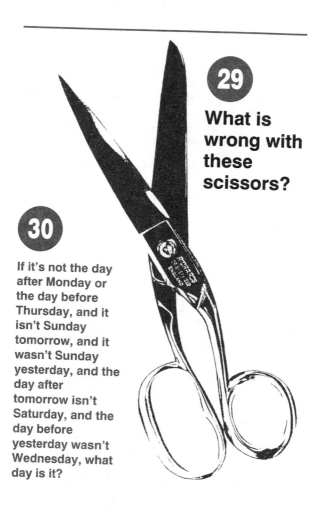

What is wrong with these scissors?

30

If it's not the day after Monday or the day before Thursday, and it isn't Sunday tomorrow, and it wasn't Sunday yesterday, and the day after tomorrow isn't Saturday, and the day before yesterday wasn't Wednesday, what day is it?

31 **Father Ignatius was learning to draw. For practice, he copied pictures of his favorite saints. When he copied**

this frieze of eight saints, he made 24 mistakes. His copy of the frieze is on the next pages. Can you find all the mistakes he made?

This is Father Ignatius's copy of the frieze.

S.Colomānus Martyr apud Stokherau passus
S.Leopoldus Princ pius Marchio aust.
S.Poppo Marchio orientalis Archiepiscopus Traueirensis.
S.O Marchio orientalis Episcopus Frigensis

32 How many unit measures must the bartender pour into the empty glasses to ensure that each row of glasses contains a total of 26 units?

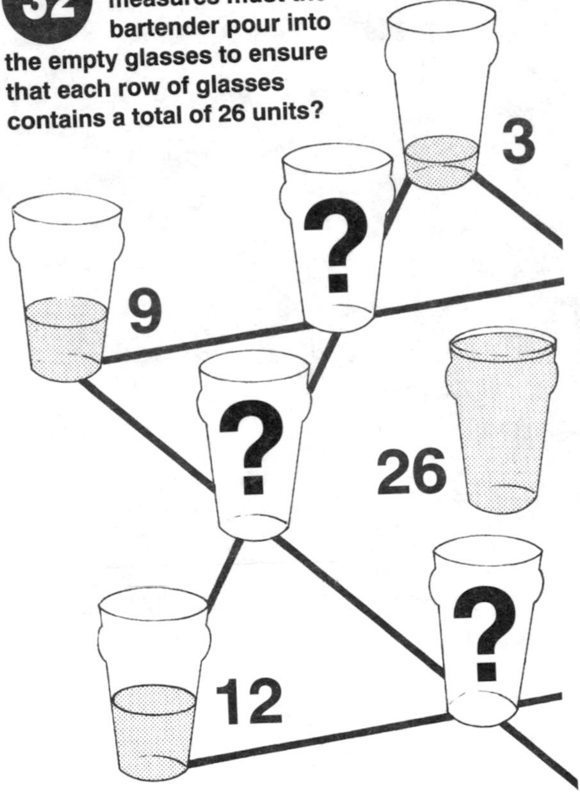

33

If you cut a cake straight across through the middle four times, how many pieces will there be?

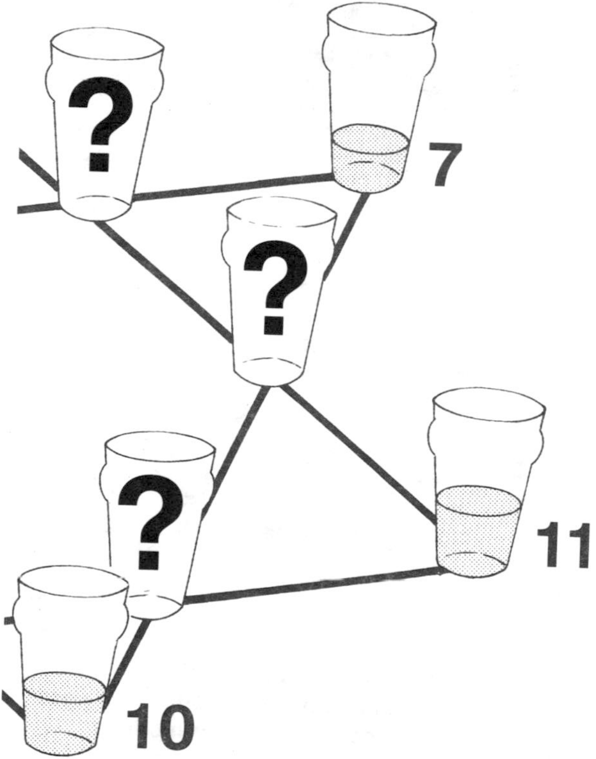

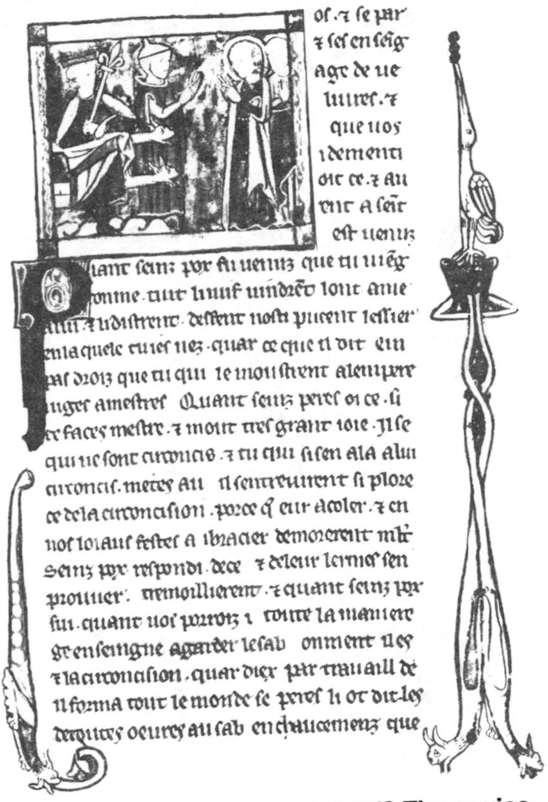

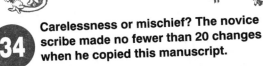

34 **Carelessness or mischief? The novice scribe made no fewer than 20 changes when he copied this manuscript.**

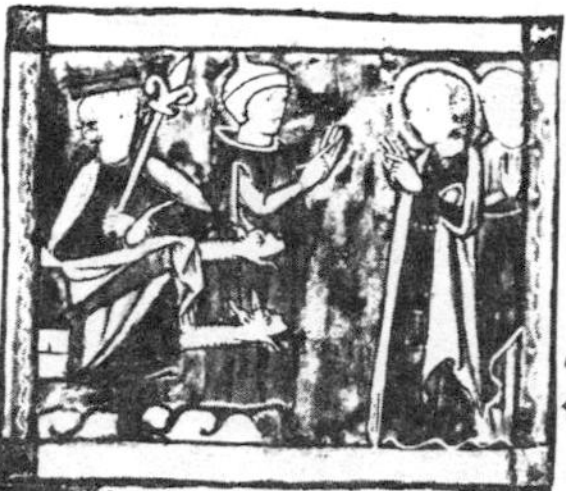

os. ⁊ se par
⁊ ses en seig
age de ue
lunres. ⁊
que nos
i dementi
oit ce. ⁊ au
ent a seit
est uenuz

P seinz seinz por fu uenuz que tu ineg
onne. tuit li iuif uindrēt lont anie
auui ⁊ li distrent. aucun nostr pucent lessier
en la quele tu ies nez. quar ce que ti dit drein
pas droiz ioie tu qui le moustrent a leur pere
uges a mestres. En dem seinz peres oi ce. si
te faces mestre. ⁊ moult tres grant par. Il se
graue sont circoncis. ⁊ tu qui si sen ala alui
circoncis. acoler au il sentreuinent si ploro
ce de la circoncision. por ce est eur acoler. ⁊ en
nos loiaus festes a ibracier demorerent mlt
Seinz por respondi. quil ⁊ de leur lermes sen
prouuer. tremoillierent. ⁊ quant seinz por
sui. quant uos porroiz i toute sennmanier
gr en seingne a garder le sab onment il es
⁊ la circoncision. quar diex par trauaill de
il quan tout le monde se peres li ot dit les
derquires oeures au sab en chaucemenz que

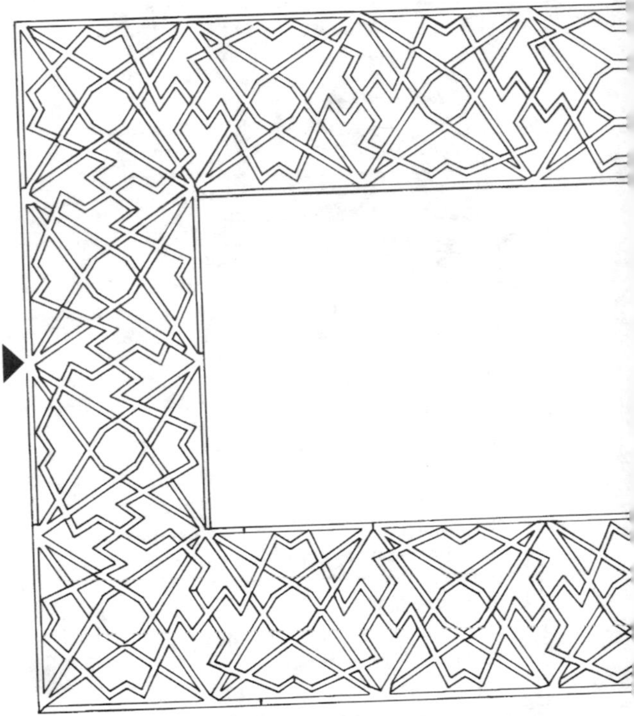

35 **The designer of this Moorish floor pattern always incorporated a puzzle in his work. In this particular**

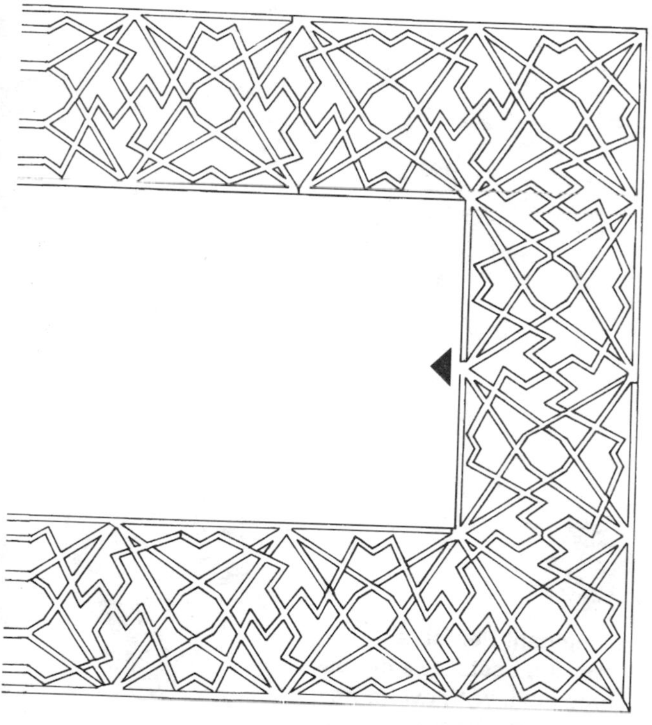

pattern, he hid a route, following the narrow paths from the edge of the room to the middle. Can you find it?

36

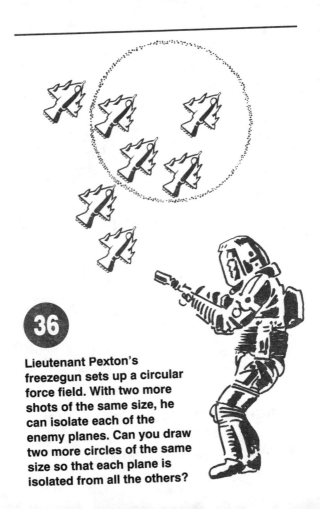

Lieutenant Pexton's freezegun sets up a circular force field. With two more shots of the same size, he can isolate each of the enemy planes. Can you draw two more circles of the same size so that each plane is isolated from all the others?

37

Janet has 6 blue stockings and 6 green stockings all mixed up in her drawer. If she closes her eyes, what is the minimum number of stockings she must take out to make sure that she has a pair that matches?

38

Can you arrange these pictures (left) into the five most logical pairs? All the pictures must be used, and each may be used only once. All the pairs must make sense! When you have produced one set of five pairs, try rearranging them to make a second set.

39

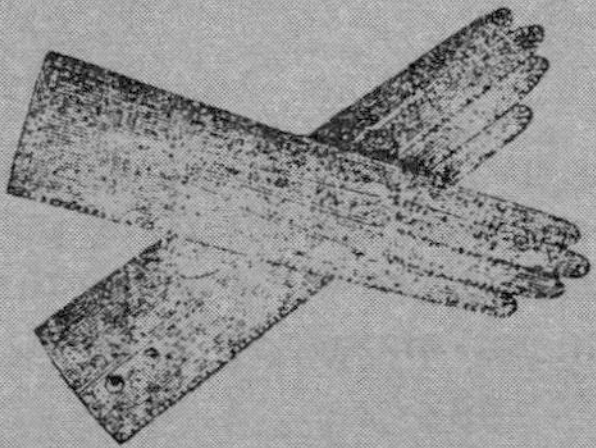

Some pairs of gloves – like the ones shown on the right – are made of leather. All leather goods feel somewhat stiff when new, but some grow more supple with age. Therefore:

a) All gloves are somewhat stiff when new
b) Some gloves grow more supple with age
c) Only supple aged leather is used to make gloves

True or false?

40

The pieces of the magic egg shown below can hatch into the pelican shown above left or the dove shown above right. Can you make both of them, using all the pieces of the egg?

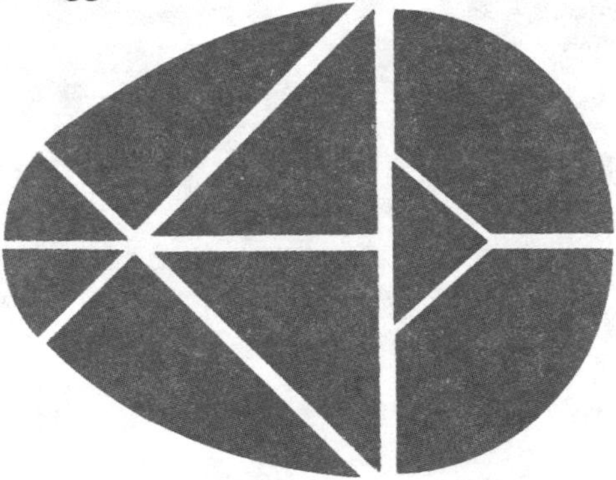

The diagram below will help you make your own magic egg from a piece of cardboard, or you can trace ours.

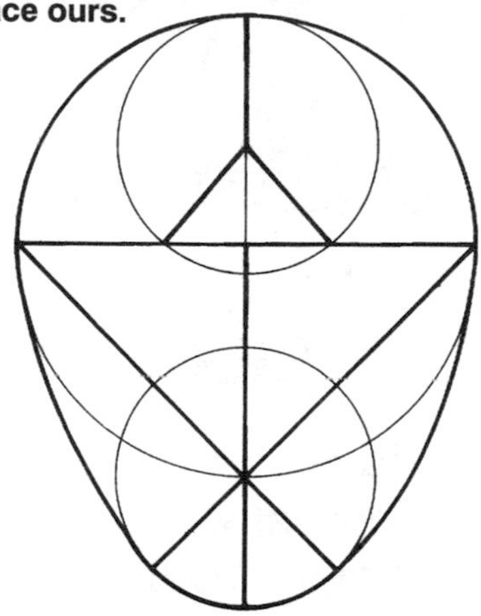

The Pharaoh asked,
"Who is the greatest of the gods?"
"I am not," said Horus.
"Anubis is," said Isis.
"Isis is lying," said Anubis.

The Pharaoh knew that only one of the gods was telling the truth – the other two were lying. Who is the greatest of the gods?

42 These hunters are searching for 23 creatures that are hiding in the forest.

Can you find them all?

43 The computerized range finder on the wildlife filmmaker's camera told him that the gazelle started 60 leaps ahead of the pursuing cheetah, that the cheetah took 2 leaps to every 3 made by the gazelle, but that the cheetah's stride covered as much ground in 3 leaps as the gazelle covered in 7. How many leaps did each take before the cheetah brought down the gazelle?

44

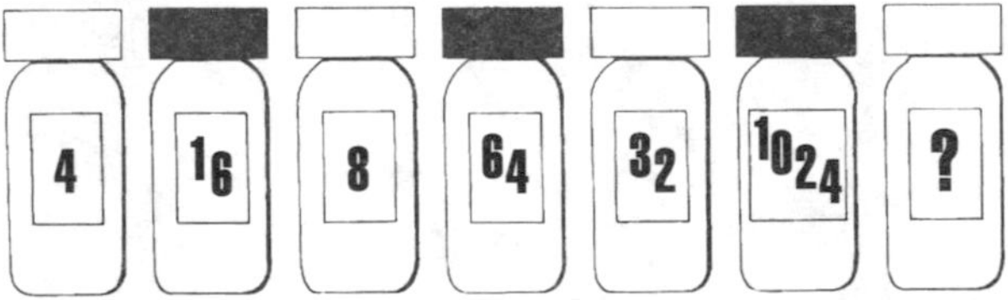

The pharmacists' annual party had all the usual games, including a competition to guess the number of pills in a bottle. However, this year guesswork was not required; the answer was there for anyone smart enough to spot the numerical sequence on the labels.

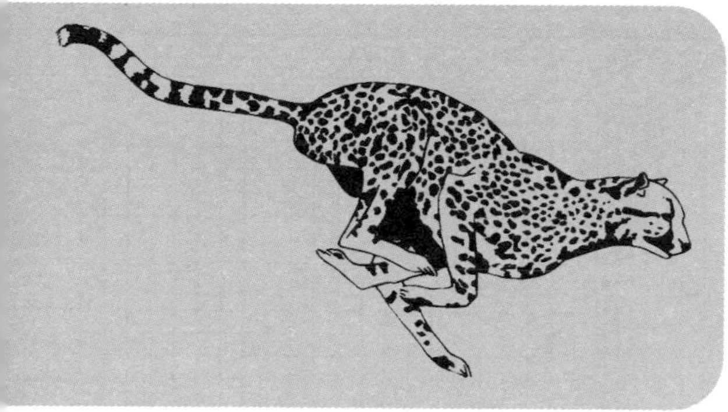

45

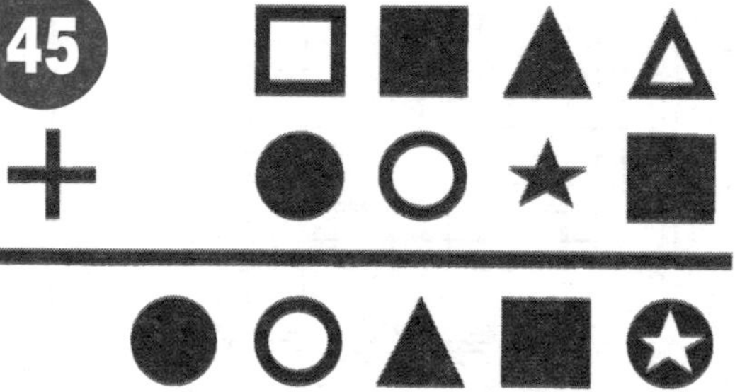

The visual display unit on a new data presentation system developed a fault and used symbols instead of numerals when asked to display a simple numerical addition. Can you work out the correct numerical values?

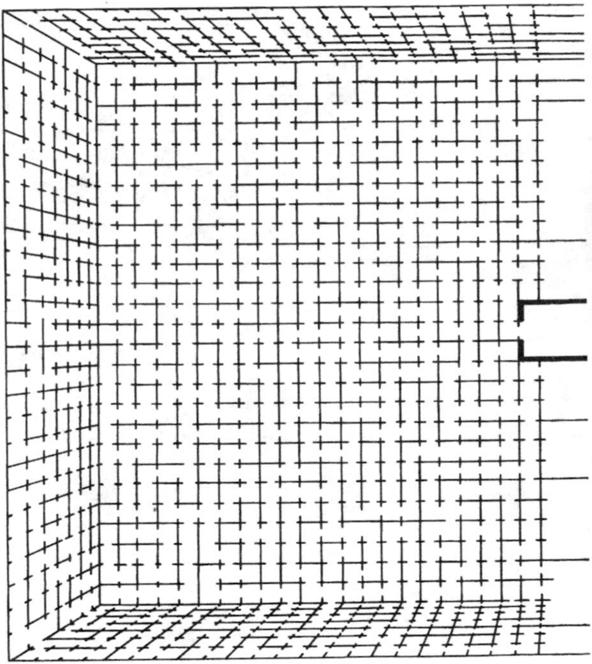

46 A condemned Roman slave was allowed one more chance before being thrown to the lions! He was shut into this room and given an hour to trace a path from the marked corner to the middle. Would you have managed it?

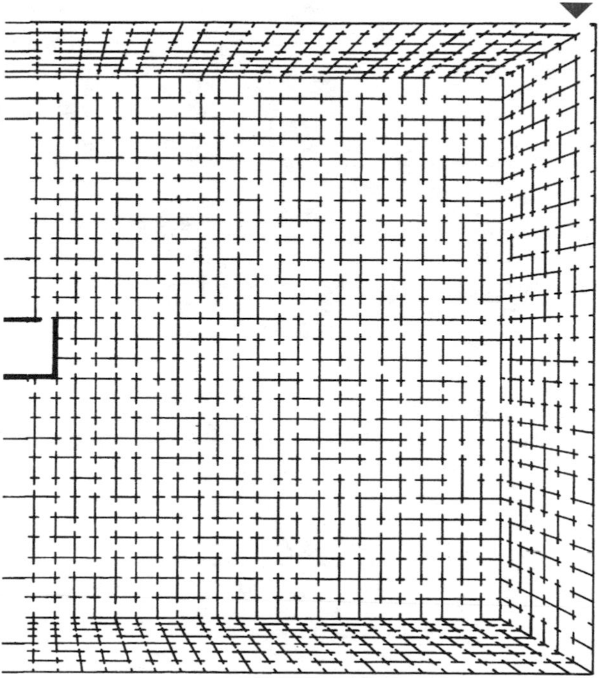

47

Having discovered a way of constructing hexagons, the mathematician drew this figure. How many regular hexagons does it contain?

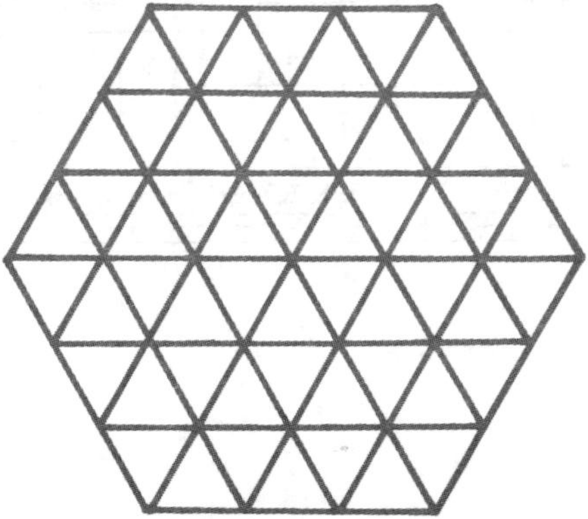

48

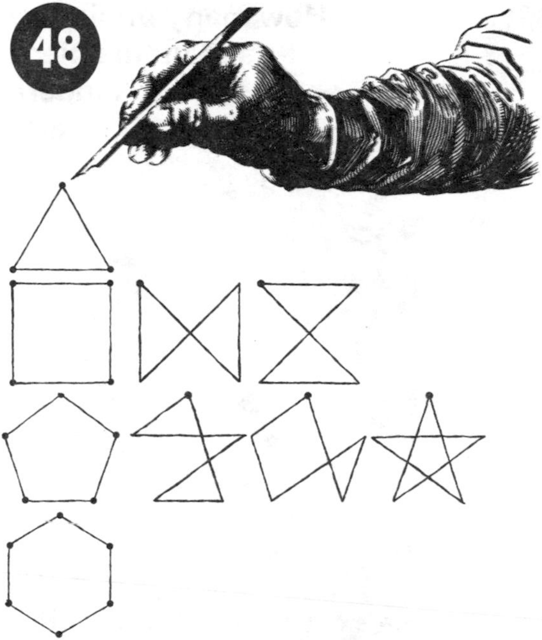

The same mathematician would have enjoyed this one. There is only one way of joining three dots with a continuous series of straight lines finishing at the starting point. There are three ways of joining the four dots at the corners of a square and four ways of linking the points of a pentagon. How many ways can you find of joining the six points of a regular hexagon?

49

How many bricks are used in this piece of modern art?

Each evening the four wizards asked each other the question, "What do you take off last before you get into bed?" Do you know the answer?

50

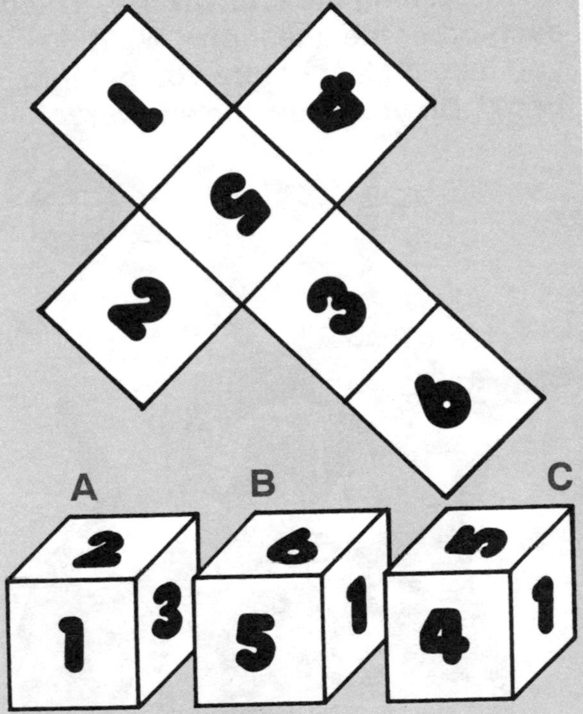

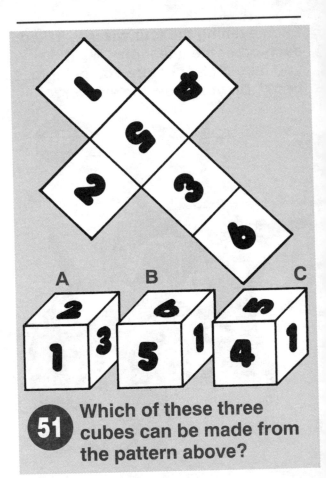

51 Which of these three cubes can be made from the pattern above?

52 **Cynthia Smythe-Summers sketched Timothy Thompson-Tweedale six times. Which of her drawings is the odd one out?**

The livery stable has just bought at least three new horses, but we know very little about them. We have heard that:

53

a) All the new horses are chestnuts
b) One or more of the new horses are chestnuts, but not all of them
c) One or more of the new horses are not chestnuts

Which two of the three statements may both be true, but cannot both be false, and which two may both be false, but cannot both be true?

54 **What is the nearest thing to a cat with its nose pressed against the window watching a bird?**

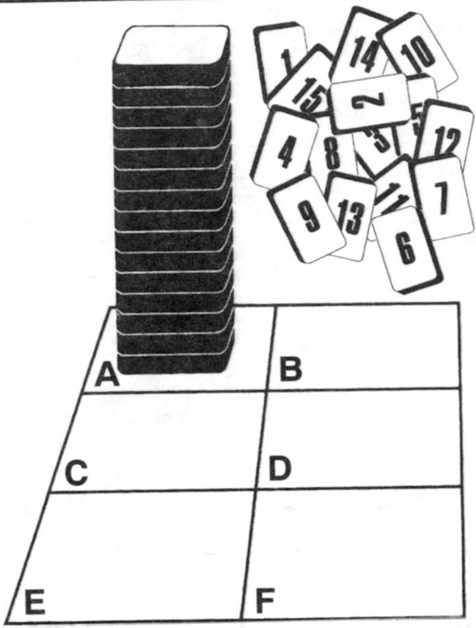

55 Make 15 cards, numbered 1–15, and stack them in numerical order (with 15 at the bottom) on a board divided into six lettered squares, as shown. Now transfer the whole stack to Square F, moving only one card at a time. You may move any card to any square, providing that you do not put it on another card showing a lower number. So you may put the 3 on the 4, but not the 4 on the 3. What's the minimum number of moves you need?

56

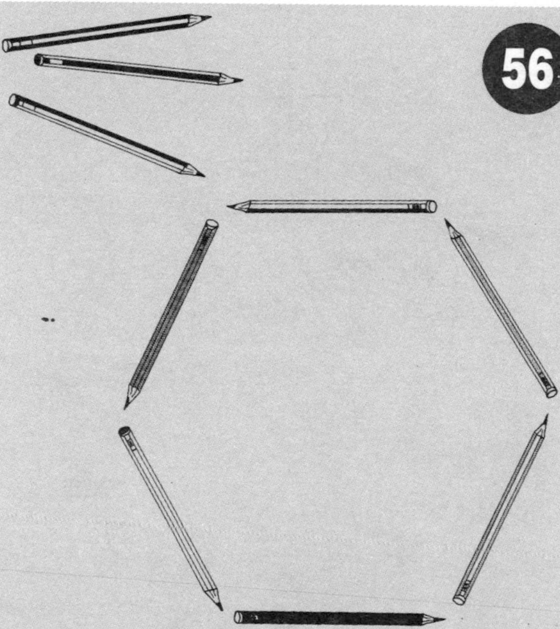

These six pencils make a six-sided figure, a regular hexagon. Add another three pencils and try to arrange all nine to show another regular six-sided figure.

57

Sam Loyd's "Get Off the Earth" paradox, which he patented in 1896, is one of the most famous of all visual puzzles. A card, free to revolve around a central pin, bears partial images of 13 Chinese warriors. The remaining parts of the images are on the fixed background card.

Rotate the card slightly and one of the warriors will disappear completely. Which one has vanished, and where did he go?

58 Starting from the letter A in the middle (left), find a way to Z moving only to adjacent letters in alphabetical order.

59

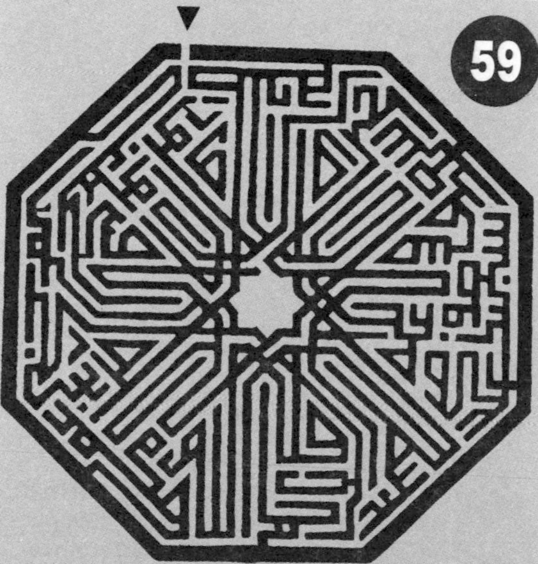

The Sultan has placed his harem in the middle of a room with an ornately patterned floor. He has hospitably offered his guests the freedom of the harem if they can reach it without crossing a black line. Is this possible?

60 The new "Two-Six Security" internal telephone featured a remarkable push-button system: four round, four oval, and four square buttons, numbered 1 through 12 in an apparently random arrangement. However, the alarm could be raised by tapping out any horizontal row, any vertical row, or all the buttons of the same shape. How were the buttons numbered?

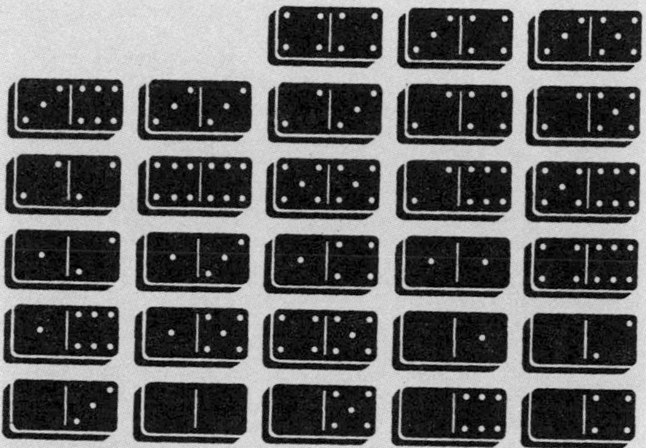

61

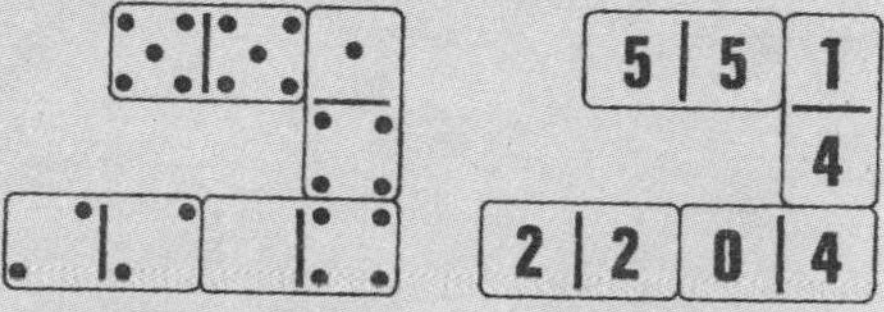

As shown here, 4 dominoes may be arranged so that their pips represent the numbers in a multiplication problem. Starting with a full set of 28 dominoes, see if you can arrange them to form 7 such problems. (Blanks represent 0 and cannot therefore appear at the start of a number.)

62

Can you rearrange the letters of the words BURNS ME THERE to spell out three numbers?

63

This toucan bird has a 6-inch-long bright orange beak. How many toucans can you put in an empty cage that measures 2 yards by 2 yards by 2 yards?

64 The three fragile parcels on the bottom shelf have been stacked in the correct order but in the wrong place. The truck driver has been told to move them up to the top shelf. He knows that he is never allowed to put a large parcel on top of a smaller one, and his forklift truck can only lift one parcel at a time. He had the parcels in the correct order on the top shelf in seven moves. How did he do it?

65

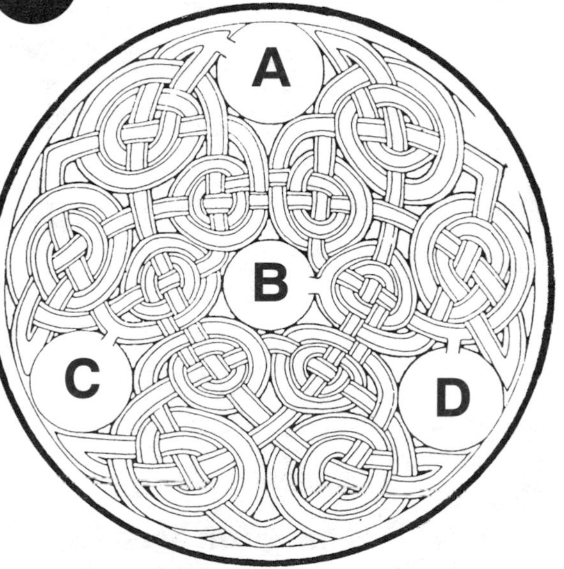

Can you work out which letters in this pattern are linked together?

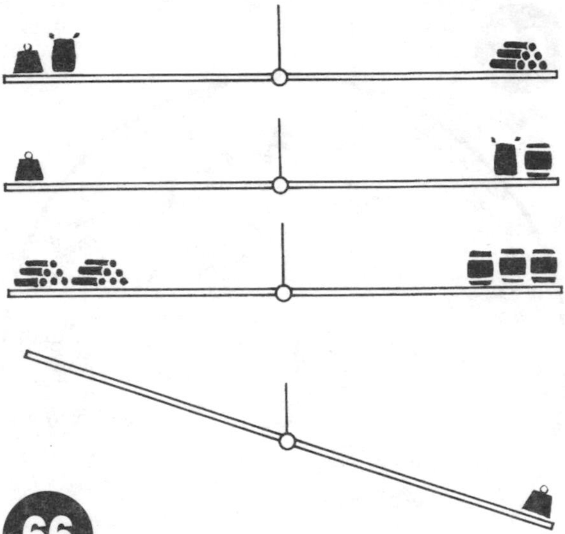

66

The steelyard has been used for centuries to weigh market produce. Using the information given in the first three weighings, can you work out how many sacks would balance the iron weight in the last situation?

67

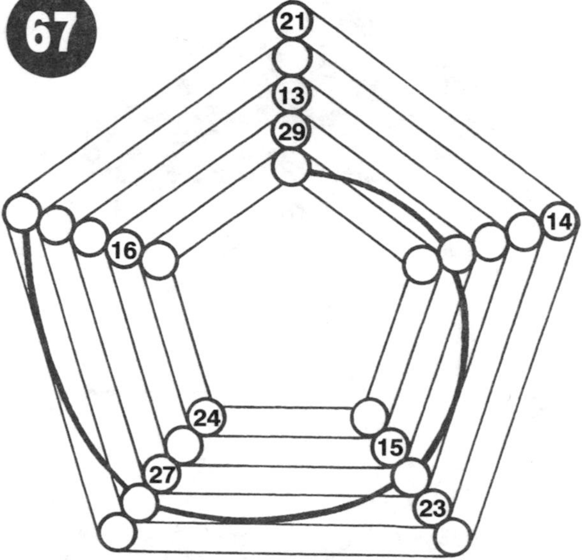

Complete the magic pentagon so that the numbers in any radial line add up to 90, the numbers in each of the five shells total 90, and the numbers on any spiral pathway through the shells also total 90.

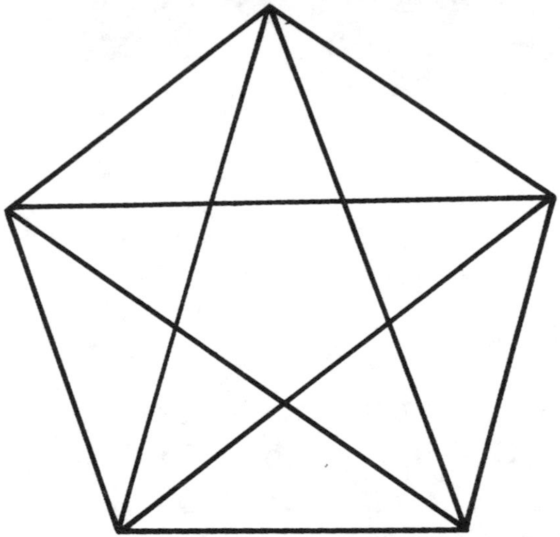

68 **Phineas O'Flaherty was driven insane trying to count the number of triangles in this pattern. How many are there?**

69

For his final examination, this draftsman produced perfectly accurate drawings of the front and side views of a solid object. What shape was the object?

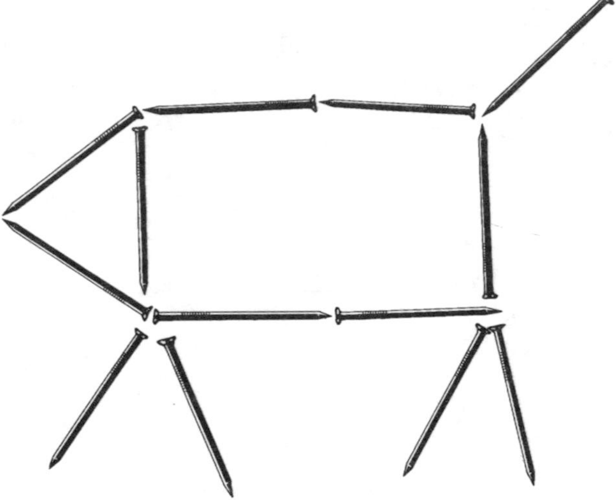

70 If you move just two nails, can you make this dog face the other way – and still keep his tail in the air?

71

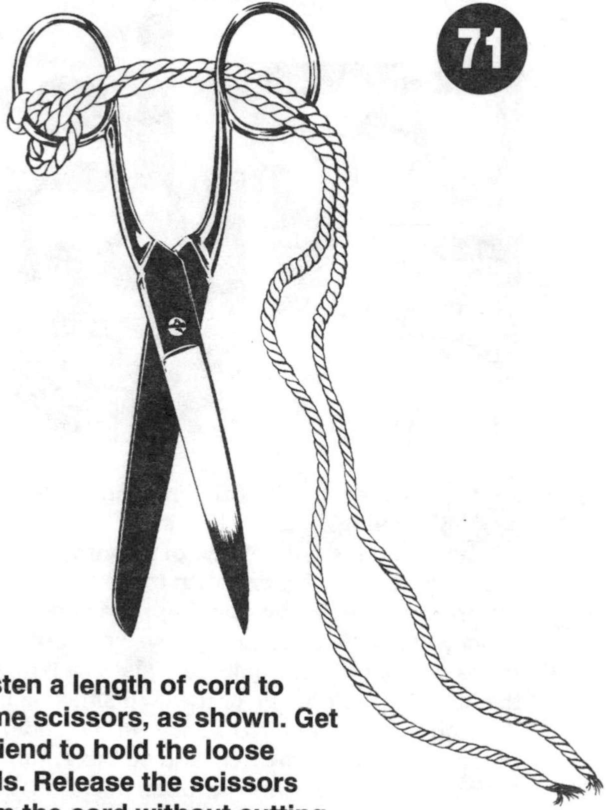

Fasten a length of cord to some scissors, as shown. Get a friend to hold the loose ends. Release the scissors from the cord without cutting either the cord or your friend!

72 An equatorial shipping company was having difficulty loading a large crate into the hold of one of its cargo boats. The crew couldn't lower it with the crane because the crate and the hatch opening were almost exactly the same size, so there was no room for ropes or chains. Nor could they just line it up with the hatch and drop it in, or it would smash a hole through the ship's bottom. They were standing around the dock in the heat and considering taking up the deck planking when one of them had a good idea. Soon after, the crate was safely installed in the hold without a plank being lifted. How did they do it?

73

All fencers in the eighteenth century enjoyed dueling. Some eighteenth-century fencers were French aristocrats. Some French aristocrats were killed in the French Revolution of 1789. Therefore:

a) All fencers in the eighteenth century were French aristocrats

b) All those killed in the French Revolution were duelists

c) Some French aristocrats enjoyed dueling

d) All fencers in the eighteenth century were killed in the French Revolution

Which of these conclusions are true, and which are false?

74

The potter had said that each one of his pots was unique – but he must have been lying! Can you spot two pots that are the same?

75

One of the apple trees had only green apples, and the other tree had only red apples. The village boys picked all the apples from both trees, and found that there were 5 red apples for every 4 green apples. Between them, the boys then ate 16 red apples and 16 green apples. When they counted the apples that were left, they found there were 3 red apples for every 2 green apples. How many apples of each color were there on the trees in the first place?

76 To allow for any required level of "graduated response," the eighteen missile batteries are individually rated at 1 kiloton through 18 kilotons of fire power. But for more drastic

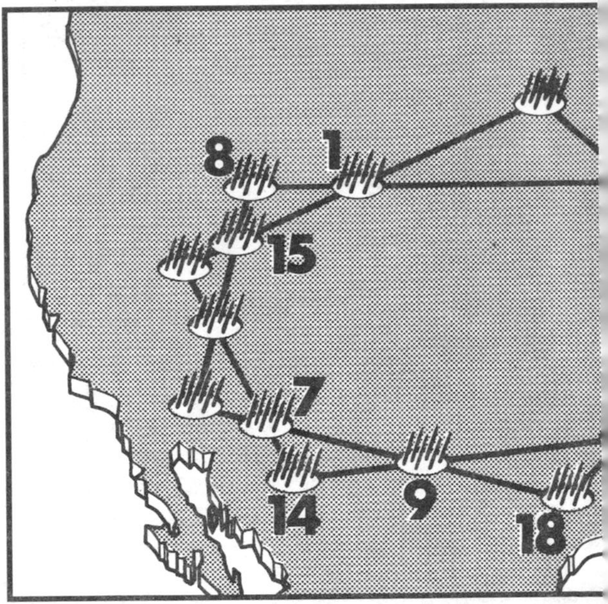

retaliatory action, any one of the nine four-battery straight-line fire groups can unleash a salvo of missiles with an aggregate of 38 kilotons of strike power. Can you fill in the rest of the missile-deployment pattern?

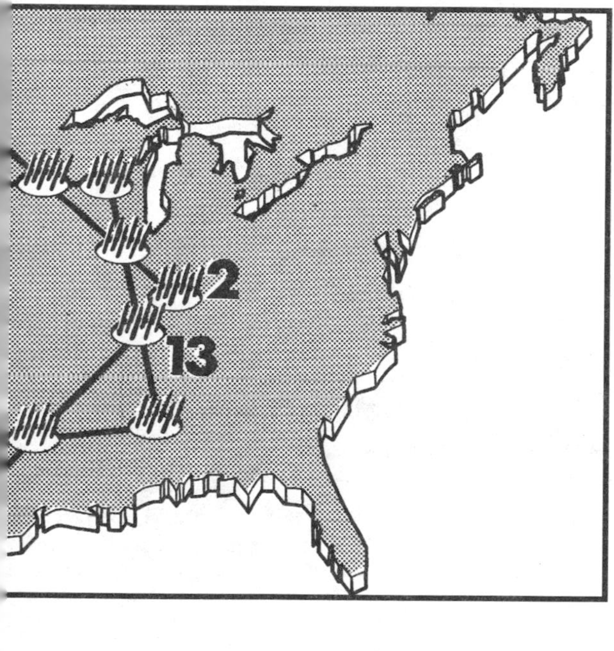

77

These five pictures tell a story. Can you put them in the right order?

C

D

E

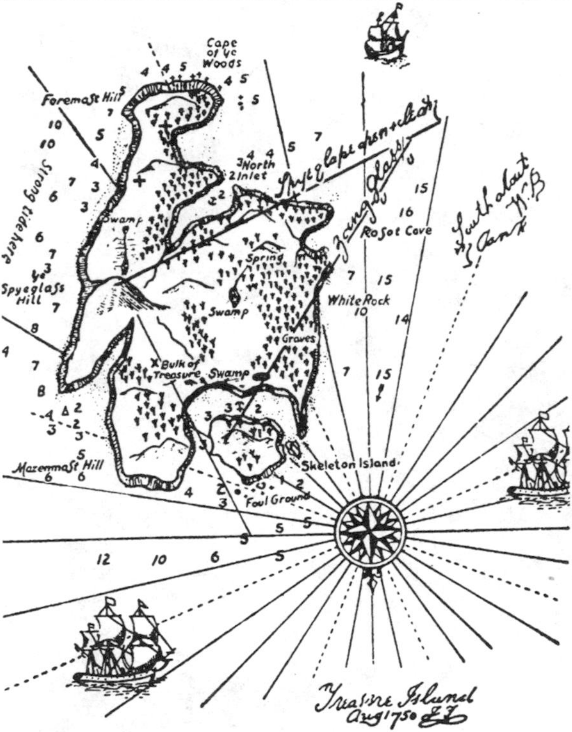

78 **When his crew mutinied, Blackbeard the pirate was forced to give them a copy of his map of**

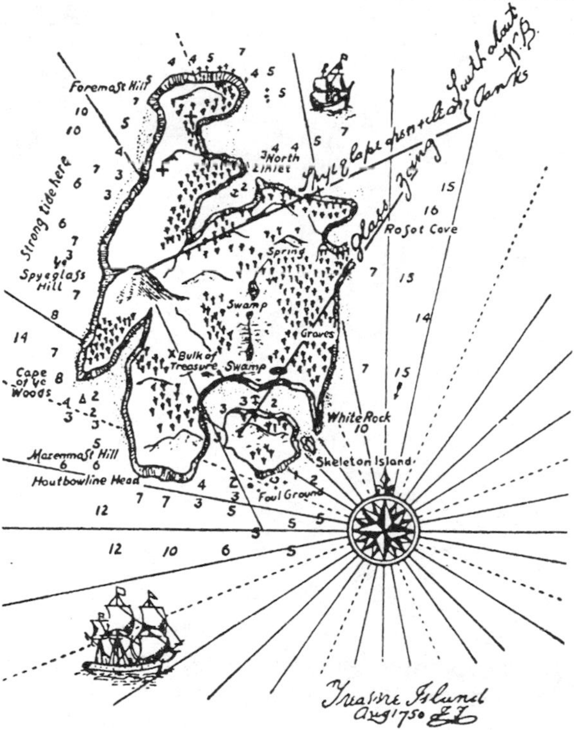

Treasure Island. To stop them from finding the treasure, he altered the map in 13 places. Can you find all the changes he made?

79

How did the crafty farmer guarantee himself $34 for each lot of 4 price-branded pigs – irrespective of whether the buyer took a horizontal, vertical, or diagonal row, the 4 outside corner pens, the inner block of 4, or one of the 4 "corner groups" of 4 pens?

80 Five competitors in a recent marathon finished together. An observant race official spotted that their race numbers formed a simple mathematical sequence. What number was the fifth man wearing?

81

Can you arrange the ace to nine of hearts in three rows of three cards so that the pips in each row – horizontal, vertical, and diagonal – add up to 15?

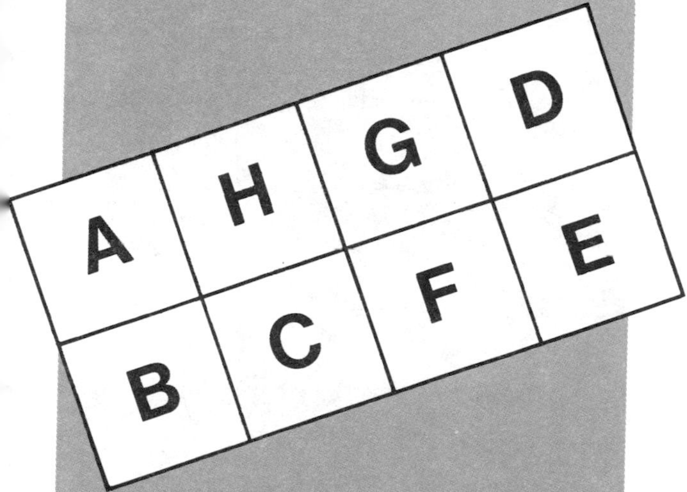

82 Take a rectangular sheet of paper and mark it into eight lettered squares, as shown. Can you fold this sheet into a packet that is the size of one of the lettered squares, with the letter A face up on top and all the other letters in alphabetical order underneath?

83

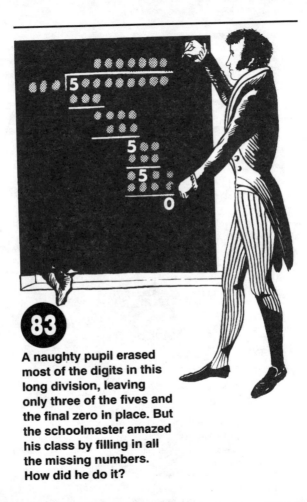

A naughty pupil erased most of the digits in this long division, leaving only three of the fives and the final zero in place. But the schoolmaster amazed his class by filling in all the missing numbers. How did he do it?

84

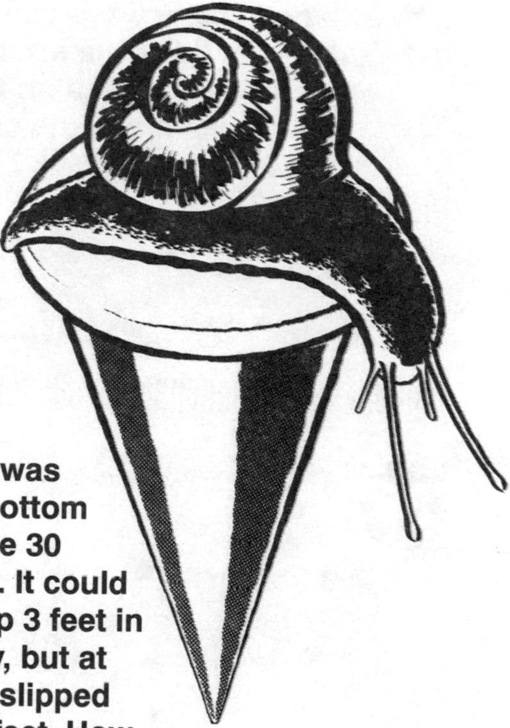

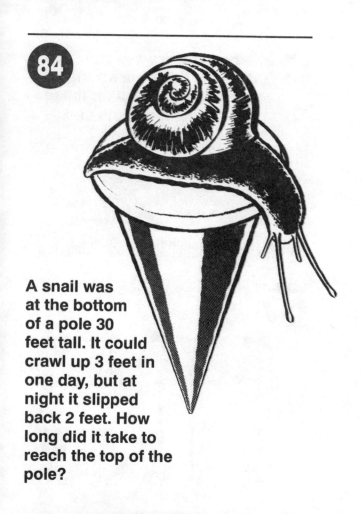

A snail was at the bottom of a pole 30 feet tall. It could crawl up 3 feet in one day, but at night it slipped back 2 feet. How long did it take to reach the top of the pole?

85 In how many ways can the driver of this train arrange these four wagons on these four tracks if he puts one wagon on each track?

86

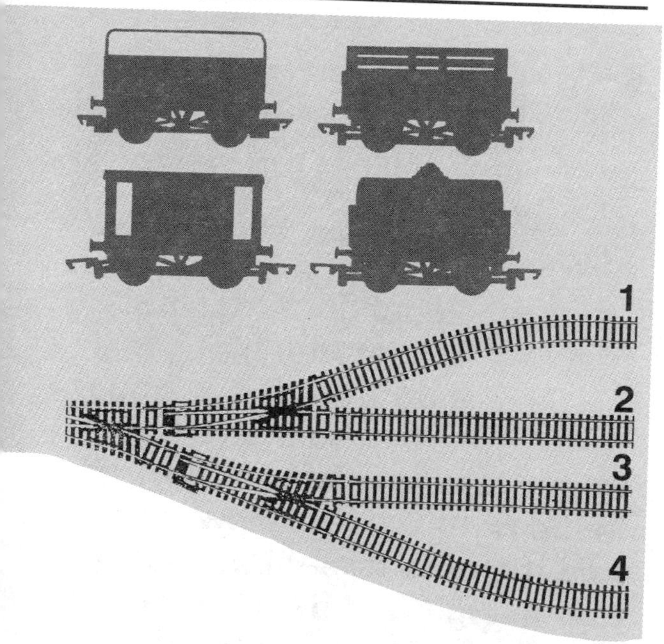

The officer was trying to work out how long it would take to get his soldiers to the battle, so he asked his sergeant, "If 5 soldiers can march 1/5th of a mile in 5 minutes, how many soldiers would it take to march 4 miles in 100 minutes?" What did the sergeant say in reply?

87

Most countries have banknotes that carry a portrait of a famous person. Hold one of these notes so that the portrait is the right way up. Now try to fold the note three times (down to one-eighth of its original size) so that when you unfold it the famous person is standing on his or her head. You may not, of course, simply turn the folded or unfolded note upside down!

88 Without tracing a path through this labyrinth, can you work out if the ant can crawl out of it without crossing a single line?

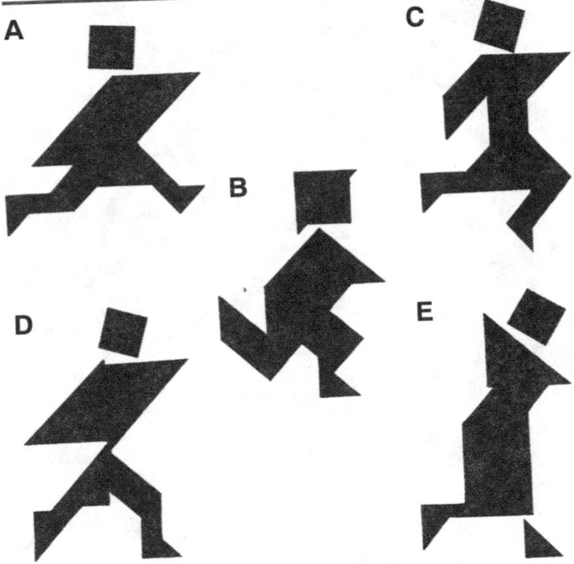

89

Some tangram puzzles. Try to make this series of running men. Remember, each figure must use all seven tangram pieces. Follow the diagram on the right to make your own tangram from a piece of thin cardboard. It's quite difficult to reassemble the square from the separate pieces without the diagram. Try it and see!

F

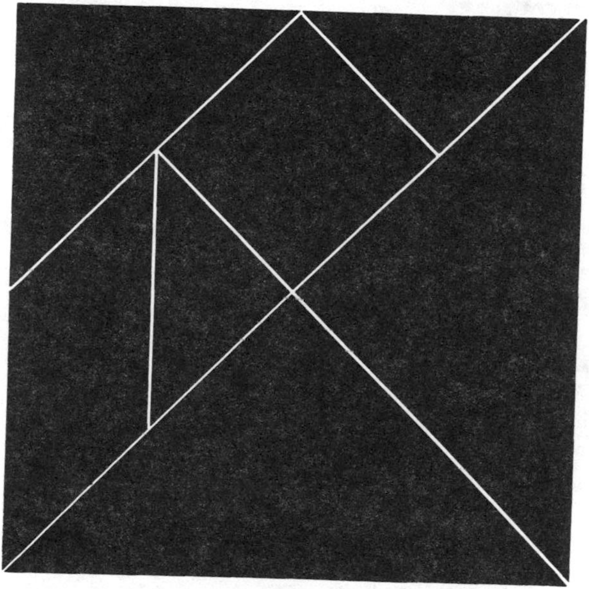

90 Can you give each of the guards a mug of

coffee without going through the same alley twice?

91

One morning the soldier who had been on sentry duty the night before asked to see his centurion. "Last night I dreamed that hordes of barbarians would sweep down from the north and attack our fort tonight," he reported. The centurion wasn't quite sure that he believed in prophetic dreams, but decided to double the patrols just in case. That night, the barbarians made their attack, but thanks to the extra patrols they were easily defeated. After the battle, the centurion thanked the soldier for his warning and then confined him to barracks until the Ides of March as a punishment. Why?

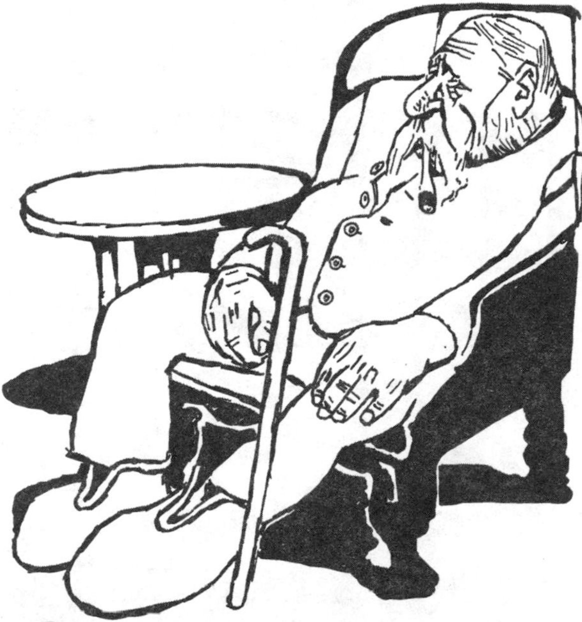

92 The elderly gentleman had enjoyed his after-dinner drink. Deciding to have another, he inspected his glass, but was unable to remember what had been in it. He said to the waiter, "If this was brandy, I want port, and if this was port, I want madeira, and if this was madeira, I want brandy." The waiter brought him a glass of port. What had the gentleman been drinking originally?

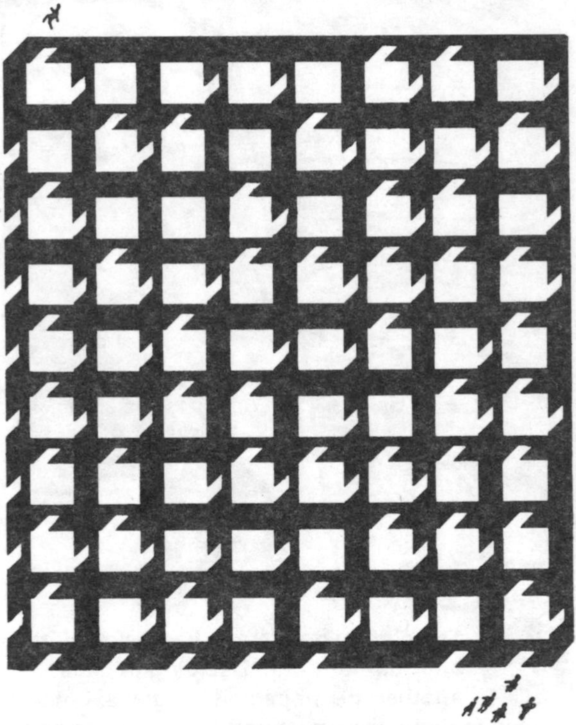

93 **Enter this building through any of the doors at the bottom, find your way through, and leave by a door at the top.**

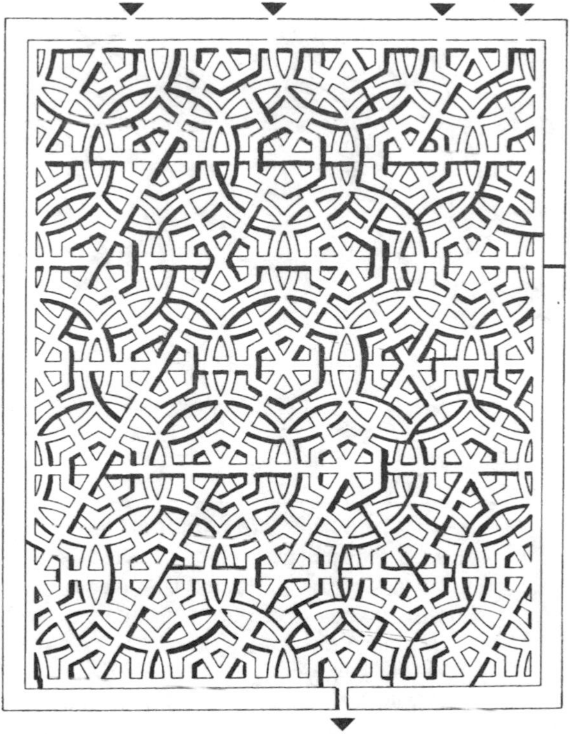

94

Can you find a way through the circles and hexagons of this design?

95

96

Kate and Alice are identical twins who enjoy practical jokes. On one vacation, they decided that Alice would always tell the truth, whatever question she was asked, while Kate would always lie. How could you find out which twin you were talking to by asking her only one question?

Which creature is
the odd one out?
5
6

97

Wee Willie Winkie needs a new candle every night to light him around the town. He can make one new candle from every 5 candle ends he collects. If he manages to collect 25 candle ends, how long will his supply of new candles last?

How could a boy be born in May, although his birthday was in June, and then grow up and marry his mother?

98

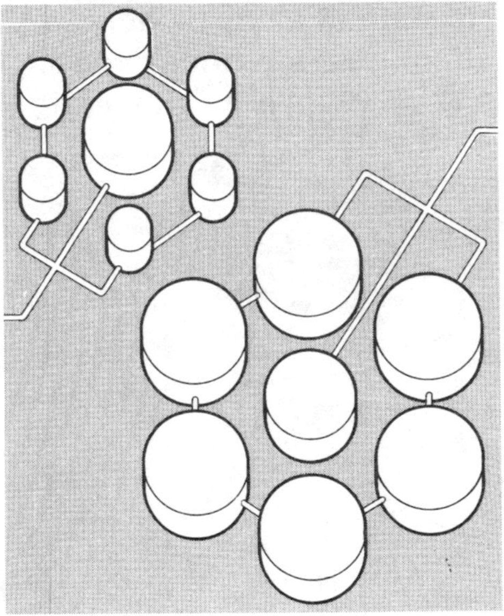

99

Intelligence reports indicated that only the two central tanks of the enemy's fuel dump still contained aviation fuel, and the pilots were given orders to destroy them. Unfortunately, only one aircraft succeeded in getting through, and he had only one rocket left. Which tank should he have attacked to destroy the largest quantity of fuel?

100

In these architects' models, each cube represents one apartment. The contract went to the architect whose building offered more apartments. Was it building a or building b?

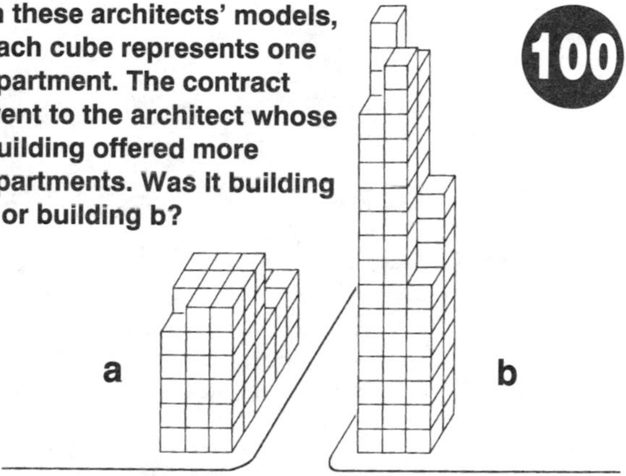

101

"The Kid" thought he was heading for a big win until he realized that several cards in his straight flush had been tampered with. Can you spot them?

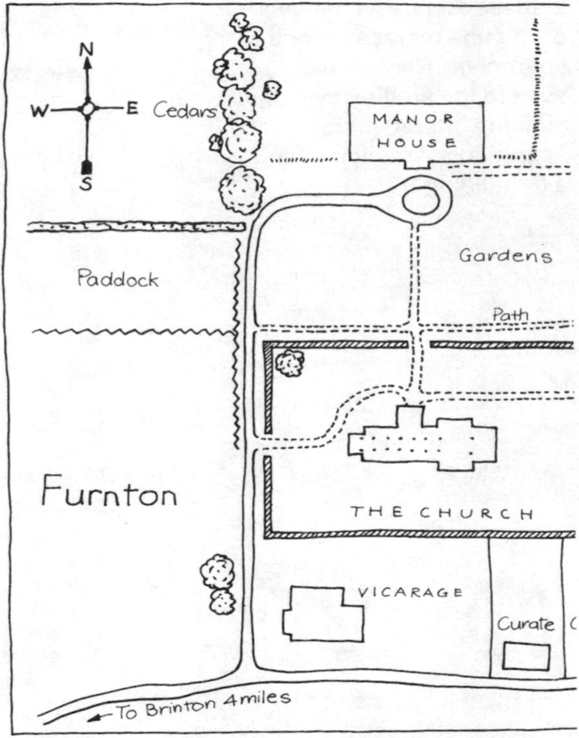

102 **If you follow these directions carefully, you should be able to find the hidden treasure. Marking your route on the map with a pencil will help. Starting at the manor house entrance, move due east**

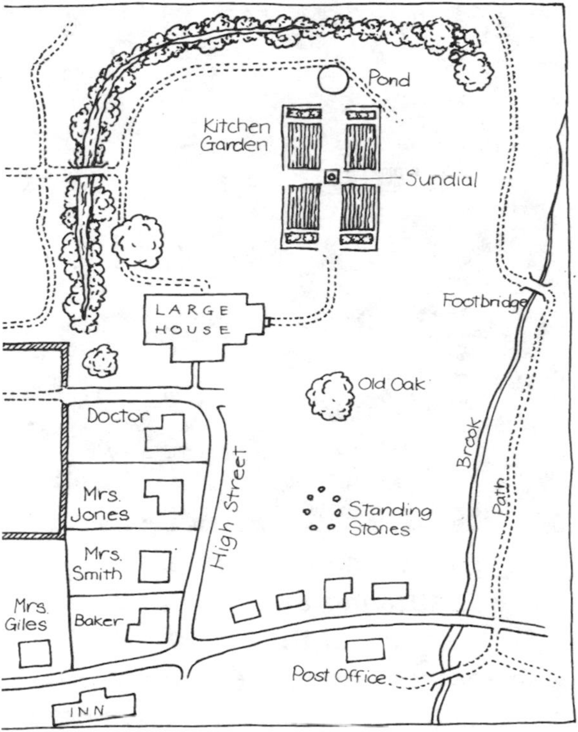

to the sundial; move due north to the pond; move southeast to the footbridge; move southwest to the standing stones; move north to the old oak; move west to the church door; move back to the manor house entrance. Where is the treasure?

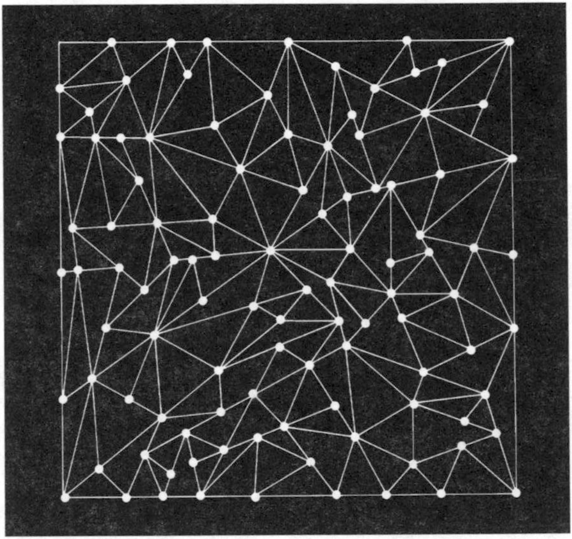

103 After many years spent studying one little-known sector of the sky, an astronomer suddenly discovered a constellation of ten stars forming a perfectly symmetrical five-point star shape. He promptly named the constellation "The Great Star." Can you find it?

104 By the time the sailing ship had made five voyages, it had carried a total of 500 passengers. There were 190 passengers altogether on the first two voyages, 155 passengers altogether on the second and third voyages, 210 passengers altogether on the third and fourth voyages, and 225 passengers altogether on the fourth and fifth voyages. How many passengers were on the ship on its third voyage?

105

The Swiss Family Robertson had eggs for breakfast every day, even though they didn't keep chickens. But they never bought any eggs, never borrowed any eggs, were never given any eggs by anyone else, and certainly none of them would ever steal an egg. So how did they manage?

106 The archer has shot two arrows into the tree. The head

107

Here are six ribbons, each in the shape of a

of one of the arrows has broken off. Which arrow is still intact – A or B?

letter S. Which S matches ribbon number 6?

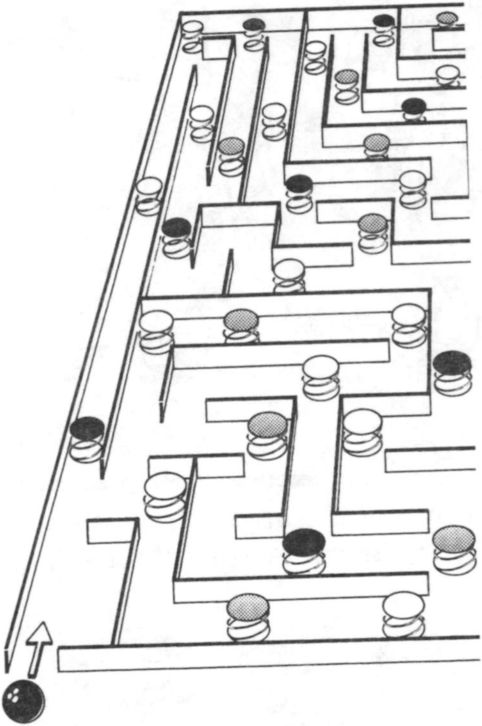

108 The spring-loaded stops in this maze can be lowered to let the ball through on whatever route the player chooses. But on passing

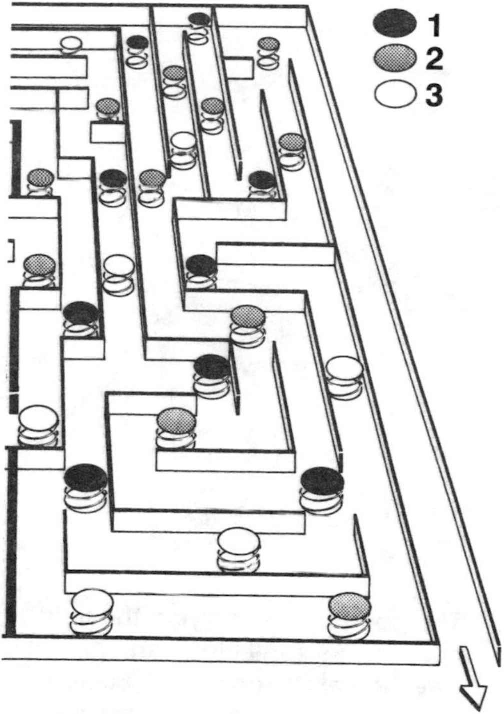

over each lowered stop, the ball incurs penalty points in accordance with the key at the top right. Which route earns the lowest number of penalty points?

109 The goods train carrying the gold bullion was 1 mile long and traveling at its top speed, 60mph. The driver was worried that there

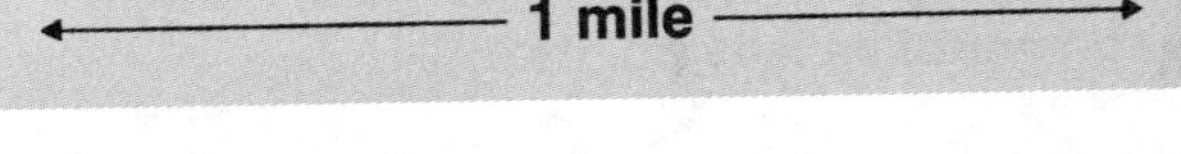

On the galleon there were a number of ship's cats, a number of pirates, the cook, and the one-legged captain. Altogether there were 15 heads and 41 legs. How many ship's cats were there?

might be an ambush in the 1-mile-long forest ahead. How long did it take for the train to pass completely through the forest to safety on the other side?

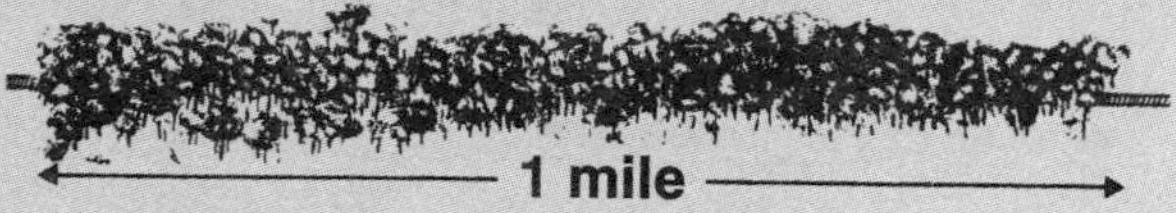

"All farmers are equal, but some are more equal than others." The commissar had to divide the land into small farms. To maintain productivity, he wanted the farms to be as large as possible, but local tradition demanded that the farms should be perfectly square! Without subdividing the small squares, what is the smallest number of farms he could allocate?

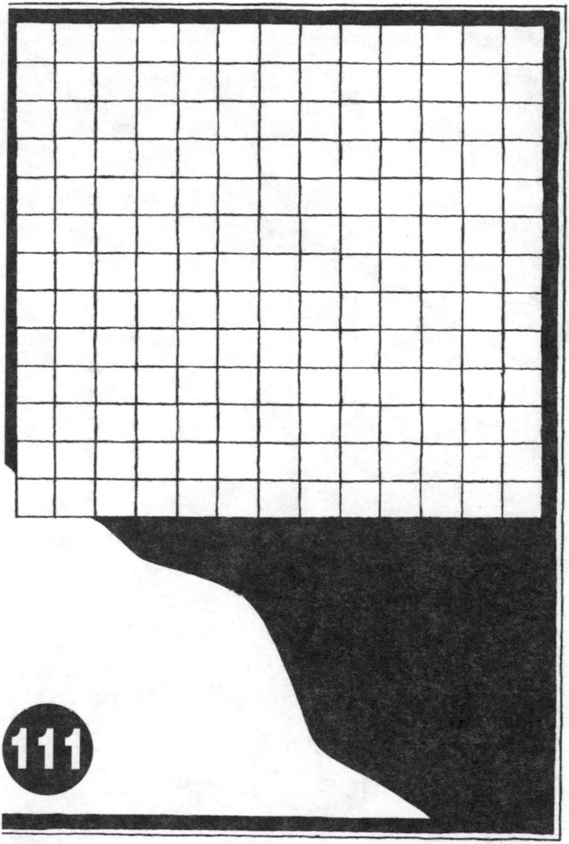

111

112

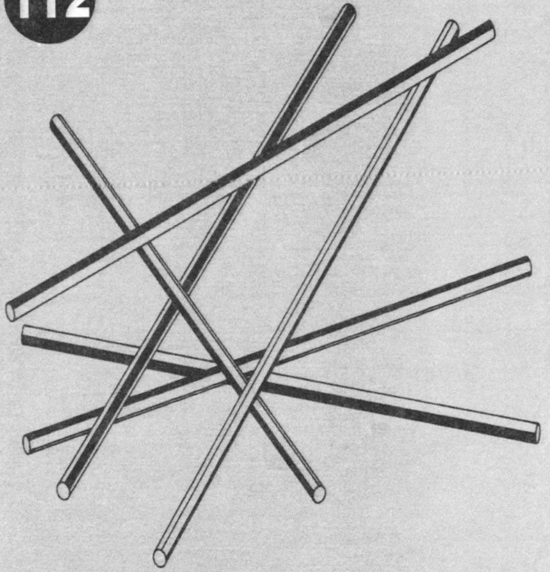

Can you arrange six drinking straws to make four triangles, all with sides of the same length?

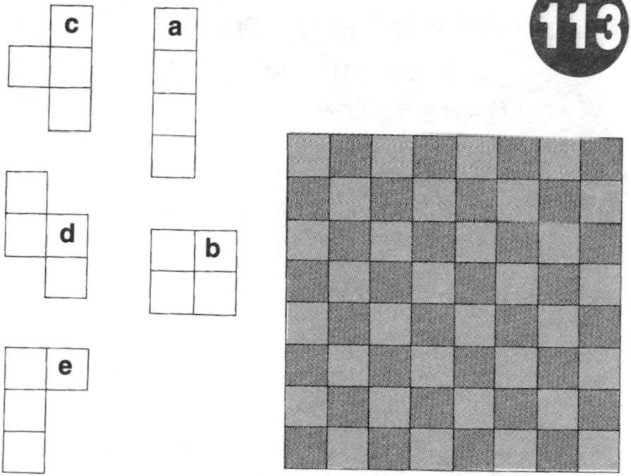

A tetromino is made up of four squares, and so can have five different shapes, as shown. Four of the shapes can be used as repeating tiles to cover a standard chessboard – but not the fifth. Which is the odd one out? Remember to use each shape separately (you will need 16 of each) and not to mix them on the same board.

114

Pick one of the squares in the top left-hand corner to start your search for the shortest route to the bottom right-hand corner. The number

5	3	4	1	2		3		5
		3						4
2	1			3			2	
2	2	2	1			1	4	
	2	4	3		2	5		4
3			2		1			
1	4	4	3			4		3
	5	2	5	1			2	1
4	3		4			2	3	
2	1		5		3			
		2			4	2	5	
3	4				3			1
		5	3		2		3	3
	1	3				4	1	
5	3			5			3	
					1	1	5	5

in the square tells you how many squares you can move. Your first move must be downward, but after that you may move vertically or horizontally. Each move must be in a straight line from one numbered square to another. You may not cross your own path.

2		4	2	**3**	3		**1**
	3		1	5		2	
3		2	3			5	
5					2		2
	2	5	4	3		1	
1						3	
3	**4**		5	**2**		**1**	4
		3	2	1			**2**
	2						
1	**5**		4		1		3
3	3	1					
		4		3		2	**4**
	1		**4**				2
5			4		4		**1**
		3	1				
4			1	4	2		

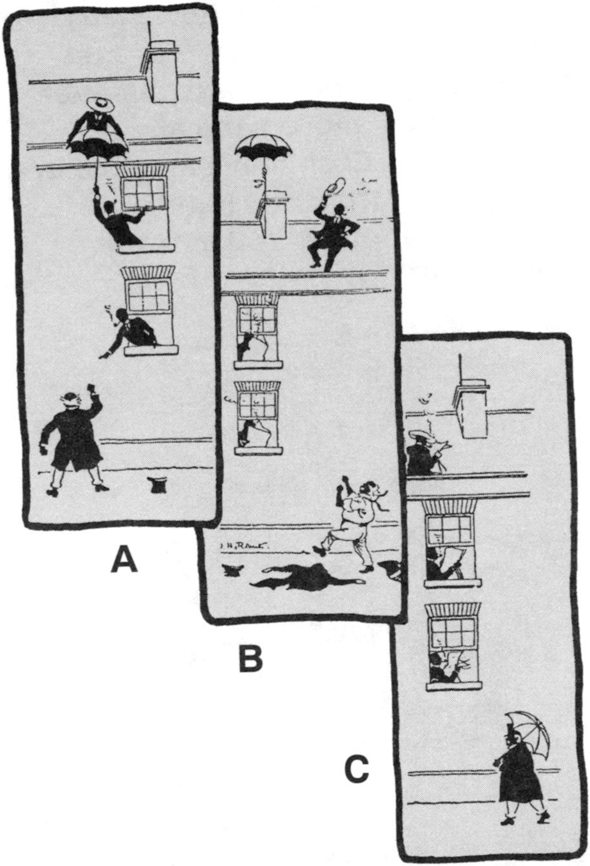
A
B
C

115 **These five pictures tell a story. Can you put them in the correct order?**

D

E

116 Ingrid and Siegfried each made mistakes when they wrote out the alphabet. Ingrid's alphabet is on the right, and Siegfried's is on the next page.

In Ingrid's alphabet . . .

1) Which letter is used twice?
2) Which letters are missing?
3) What is wrong with the W and the Z?

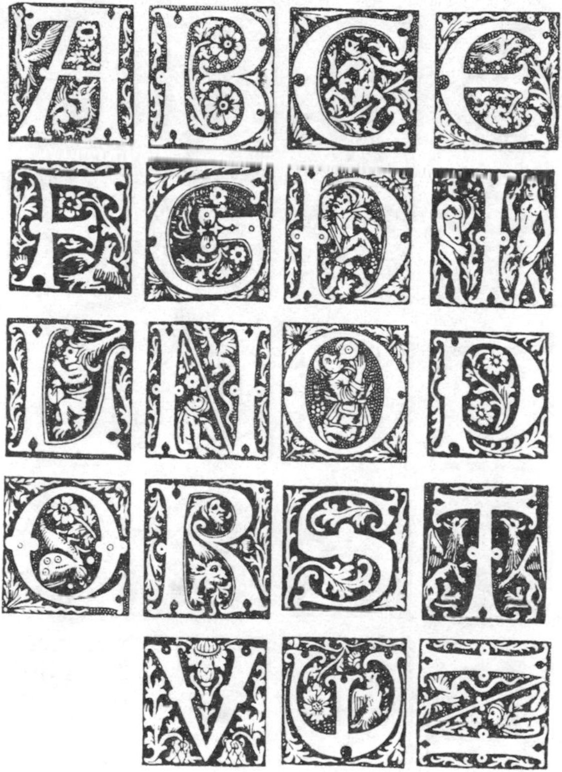

INGRID'S ALPHABET

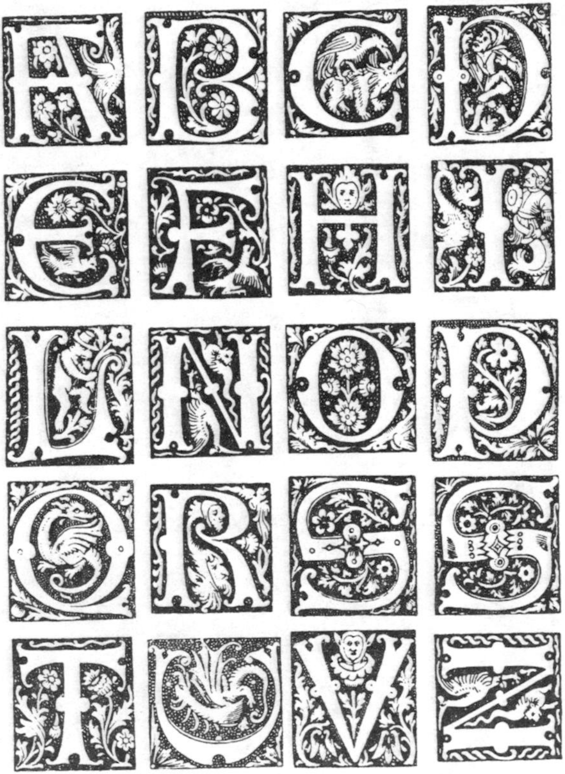

SIEGFRIED'S ALPHABET

In Siegfried's alphabet . . .

1) Which letter is upside down?
2) Which letters are missing?
3) Can you find three more mistakes?

117

The rancher offered to sell the cowboy 4 cows and 3 horses for $37 or 3 cows and 4 horses for $33. How much does one horse cost? One cow?

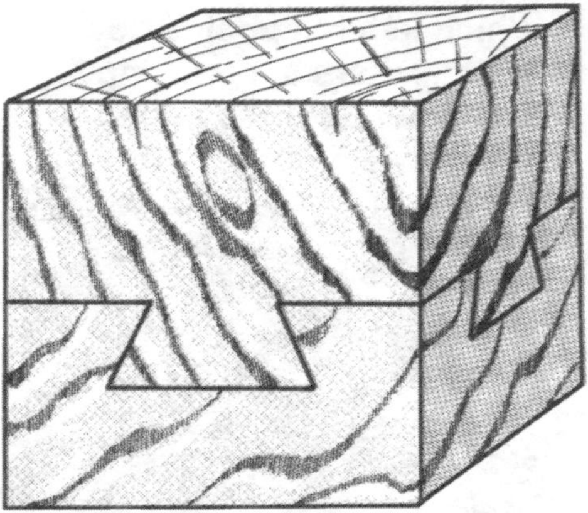

118 Woodworkers delight in showing off their ingenuity. One old cabinetmaker offered his apprentice a new set of chisels if he could make a cube from two pieces of wood dovetailed together exactly as shown in this sketch. He added that the two hidden faces looked just the same as the two drawn. The lad won his chisels. How?

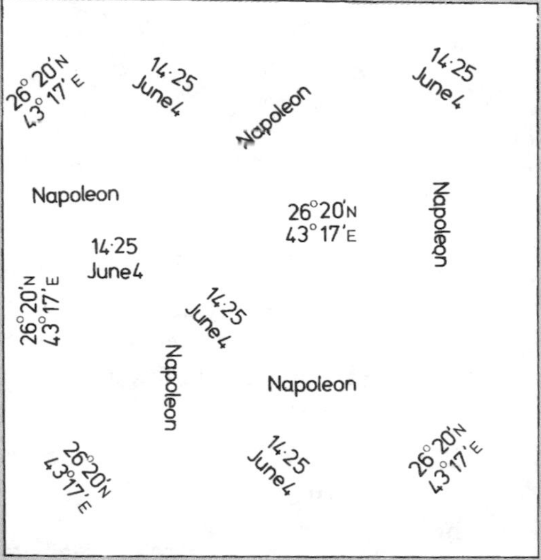

119 Just before his capture, master spy Boris wrote down the time, place, and code word for the next meeting for each of his five accomplices. For extra safety, he wrote the key words at random and then tore the sheet of paper into five pieces, each bearing the essential information. How quickly can you spot how he tore the paper?

120 In one of their more complex routines, the college band ends up with a different number of players in each row. There are half as many in the first as in the

121 Mushrooms on a culture bed double the area that they cover every 24 hours. From the appearance of the first mushrooms to the time the bed is totally covered is 60 days. On what day is it half covered?

last, and three less in the second than in the third. The total of musicians in the first and last rows is twice the number in the third row. How many players are there in each row?

Alf, Bert, and Colin are each trying to be the first to score 50 bull's-eyes. Two of them are already in double figures. Alf has scored half as many again as Bert would have scored if Bert had scored half as many as Colin. Colin has scored half as many again as Alf would have scored if Alf had scored half as many as Bert. Who is winning so far?

122

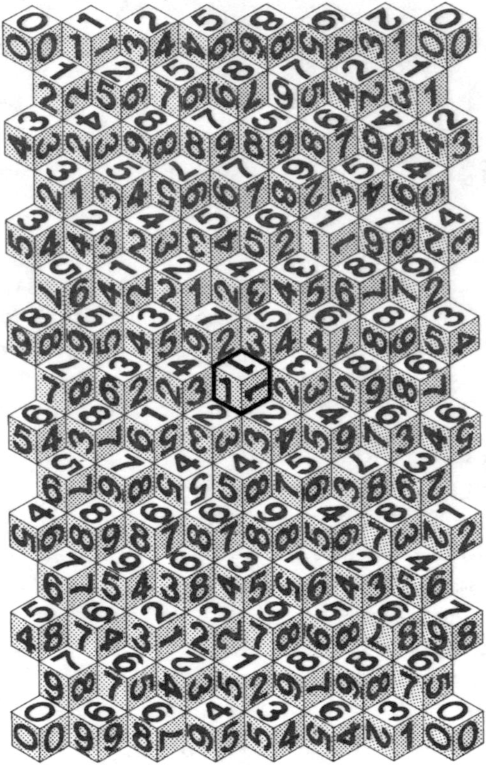

123 Starting from 1 on the middle cube, move through adjacent faces counting up to 9, then back to 1, up again to 9, and so on, to end by counting down from 9 to 0.

124 Can you find the way that sound travels along the continuous black line of cells from this man's left ear to the middle of his complex brain?

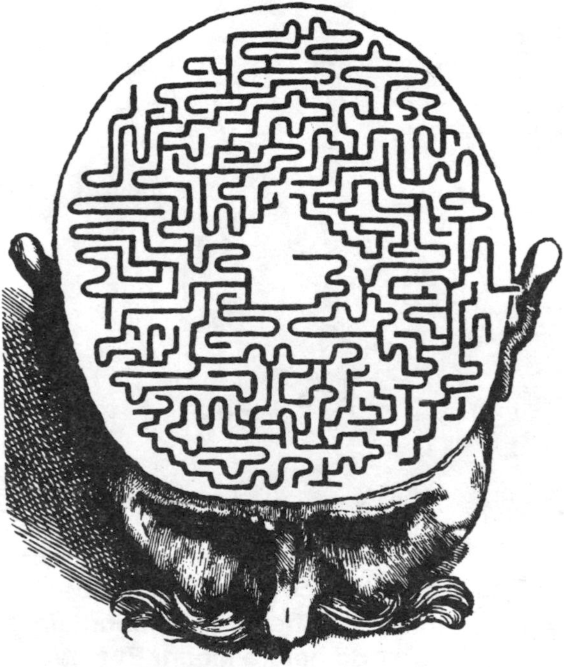

125 **Henry just could not remember which was the highest mountain in the world before Mount Everest was discovered. Do you know?**

126

A way must be found through the blocked corridors of the bunker. Can you help the troops get to the center?

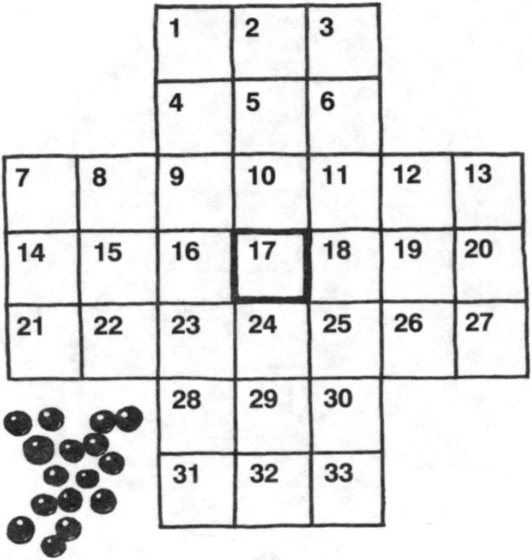

127 You can try this puzzle on your peg solitaire board, or copy our board and use beans, pennies, or buttons as your counters. Use 16 markers in the pyramid pattern shown and try to jump until there is a single marker in square 17. You are allowed the normal solitaire moves: each jump moves a marker over any adjacent marker into an empty space, and markers that have been jumped are removed from the

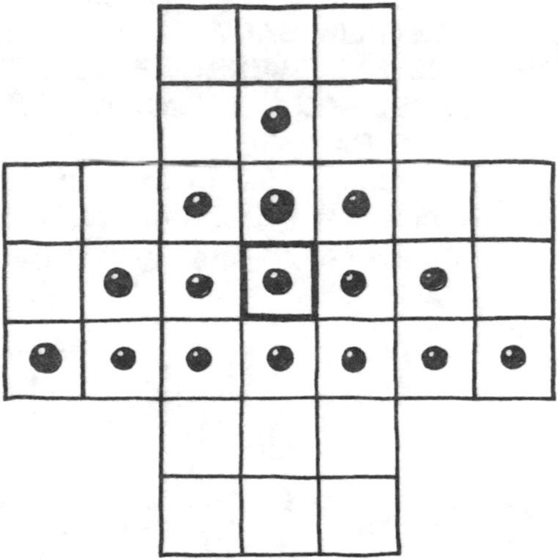

board. Jumps may be horizontal or vertical, but never diagonal. We give a solution in 15 separate jumps – can you beat us?
(And if you have never solved the traditional solitaire puzzle – starting with all the squares occupied except number 17, and ending with a single marker on 17 – we've given one of the many solutions for that as well.)

128

The last names of 11 famous people – CHAPLIN, DARWIN, DICKENS, EINSTEIN, EISENHOWER, GANDHI, GARBO, KENNEDY, NAPOLEON, NERO, PICASSO – are hidden in this square. They may read forward, backward, up, down, or diagonally. Can you find them all?

C	R	D	A	R	N	H	G	C	E	A	I	S
D	E	F	K	C	K	O	S	S	A	C	I	P
I	W	C	U	J	N	R	E	Q	F	N	L	I
C	O	E	G	B	L	E	D	L	I	G	D	N
C	H	A	P	L	I	N	F	E	O	H	C	A
A	N	A	G	I	W	G	T	K	E	P	P	G
I	E	K	B	A	M	S	B	A	K	D	A	H
U	S	E	N	F	N	O	B	R	A	G	S	N
R	I	N	G	I	O	D	G	A	J	R	H	M
D	E	N	E	K	W	T	H	L	C	I	D	S
W	H	E	D	K	S	R	I	I	E	T	Y	T
E	N	D	R	L	C	O	A	R	A	M	O	S
T	B	Y	A	G	T	I	J	D	P	Y	A	F
I	A	I	K	E	L	S	D	I	D	X	N	Z

129 There is an animal with a head like a cat, a tail like a cat, and a liking for cat food. But it's not called a cat. What is it called?

130 **What is it that was given to you, that still belongs to you, that you have never lent to anyone, but that is used by all the people you know?**

131

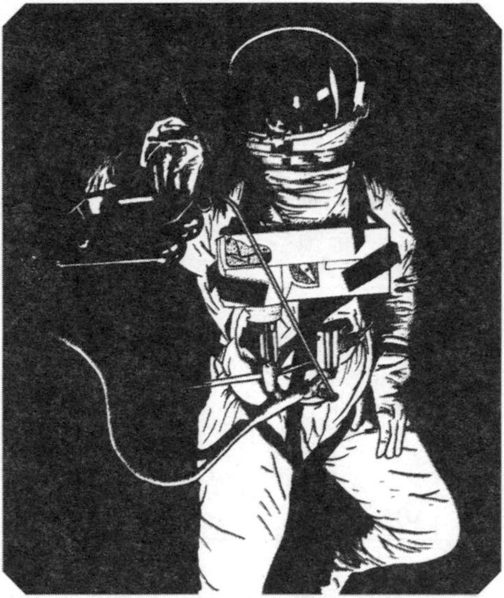

The astronaut reported back to base that he had found a strange galactic object. It was a perfectly symmetrical solid figure which presented exactly the same appearance on whichever face it stood. At least it did before the astronaut touched it. Now three of the faces are pulsing with red light, three with blue light, and the other six with green light.

The scientists at base headquarters are still trying to work out what the lights mean, but they do know the shape of each of the faces. Do you?

132

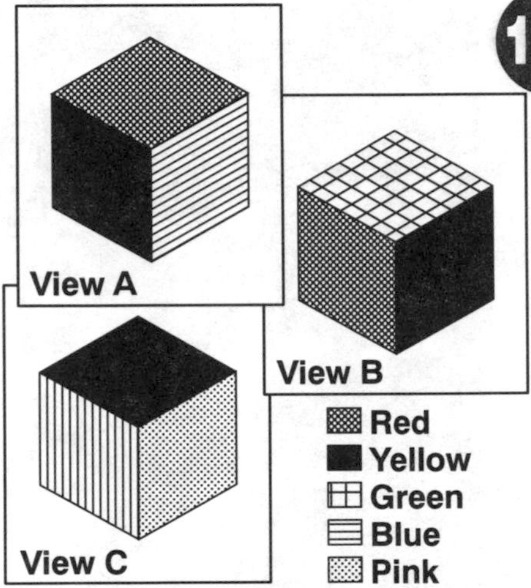

An advertising agency sent these design sketches to a packaging supplier, leaving him to work out what shade should appear on the face directly opposite the yellow face in view C. He telephoned the next day. What was his query?

133

Calligraphy requires great care. If a student loses one mark for each error in copying the upper (right) inscription, what mark did this candidate receive out of 25?

東志各笑露鎗
份爭起術創造
葳亞家池的擔
梅蘇好人礦隄
惦冶台被終城痹

東志各笑露鎗
份爭起術創造
葳亞家池的擔
梅蘇好人礦隄
惦冶台被終城痹

134

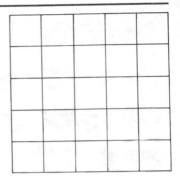

You are given 25 square tiles, numbered 1 through 25 without gaps or repetitions. Can you place them on the grid so that the horizontal rows, vertical rows, and long diagonals all add up to exactly 65?

135

Can the number eleven thousand eleven hundred and eleven be divided by three? (The child's fishing net might suggest a small catch somewhere!)

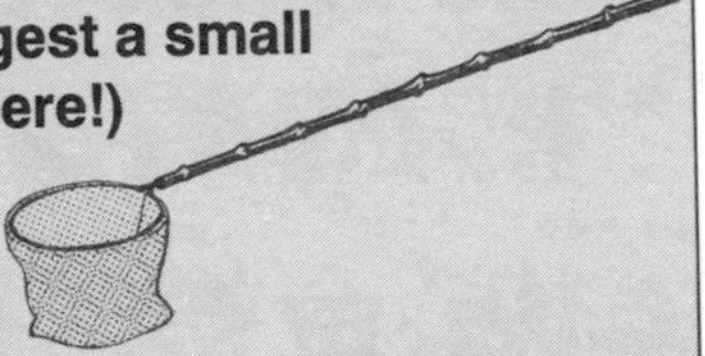

136 In the park this morning, I saw dogs, cats, and people. There were more dogs than people. The dogs and people between them had 100 heads and feet, and the dogs and people together were three times as numerous as the cats. How many cats did I see?

987654321=100

By inserting plus or minus signs in the sequence of numbers, make a mathematical expression equal to 100. What is the minimum number of signs with which a solution can be made? **137**

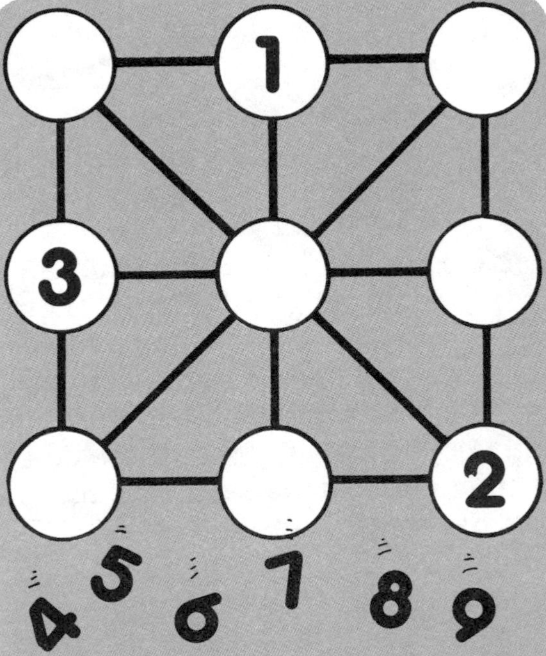

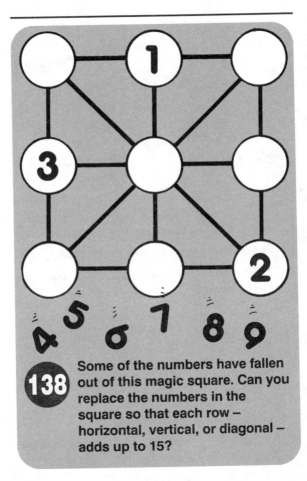

138 Some of the numbers have fallen out of this magic square. Can you replace the numbers in the square so that each row – horizontal, vertical, or diagonal – adds up to 15?

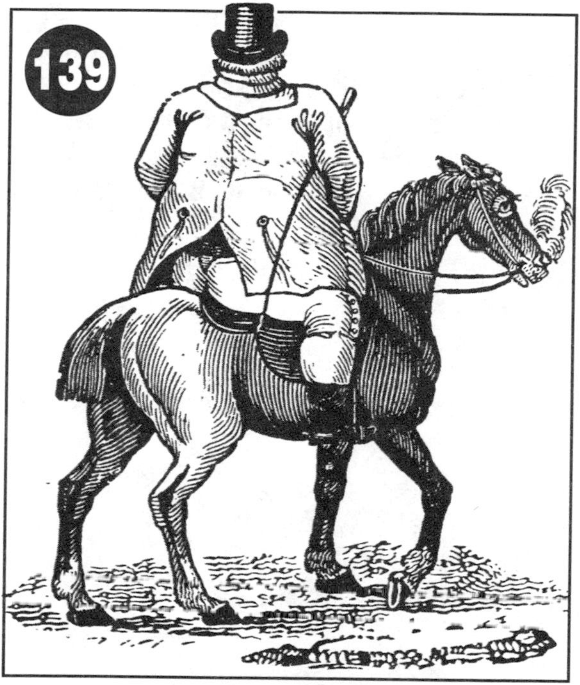

"I've got some birds in my farmyard," said Farmer Finkel. "They're all ducks but two, all chickens but two, and all geese but two. How many birds have I got?"

140 To ensure that finding a way out of the labyrinth would not be a problem, Ariadne gave Theseus a ball of thread to mark his path. But how did he find the way into the middle of the labyrinth where the Minotaur raged?

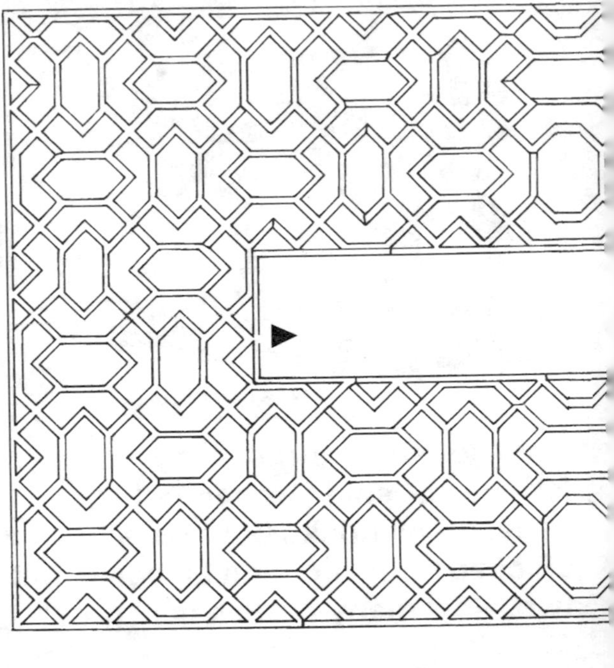

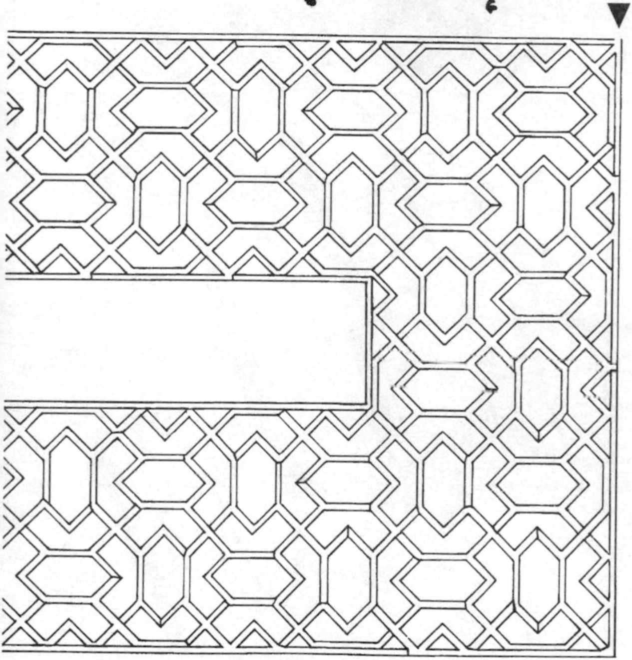

141 Take three coins and arrange them in a row with their edges touching. Now try to move coin A so that it is between coins B and C – without touching coin C or moving coin B!

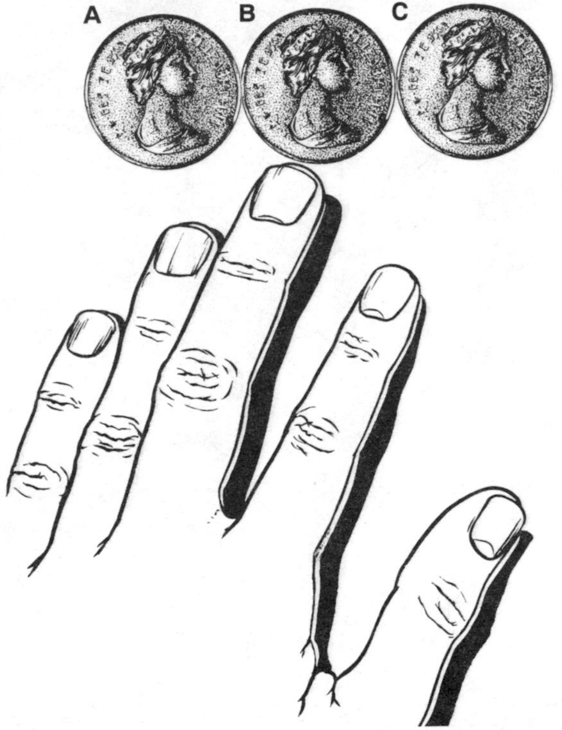

142 Each member of the group of four coins shown here is touching the other three. Can you take five coins and arrange them so that they are all in direct contact? Remember, each coin must touch all of the other coins!

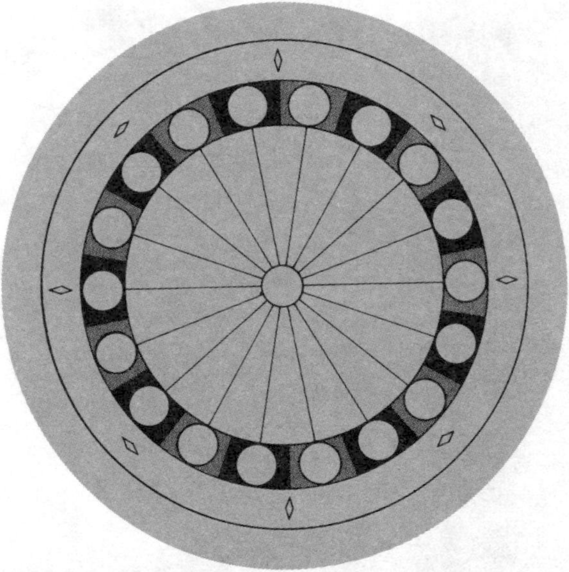

143 As a novelty feature, one of the roulette tables in a Las Vegas casino introduced a most unusual wheel having eighteen numbers around the rim and a single number in the middle. The numbers were arranged so that any three lying on a line through the middle would add up to exactly 30. Can you fill them in?

144

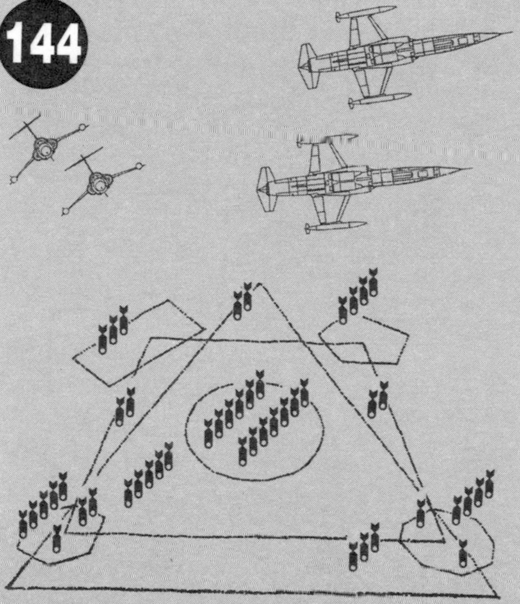

Bomber pilots flew over the area shown by the grid. How many bombs fell in the square? How many fell in the hexagon and octagon, but not in the square? How many fell in the triangle but not in the circle within it? How many fell in the pentagon, rectangle, and triangle?

145 **Can you spot 25 differences between these two plans of the same building?**

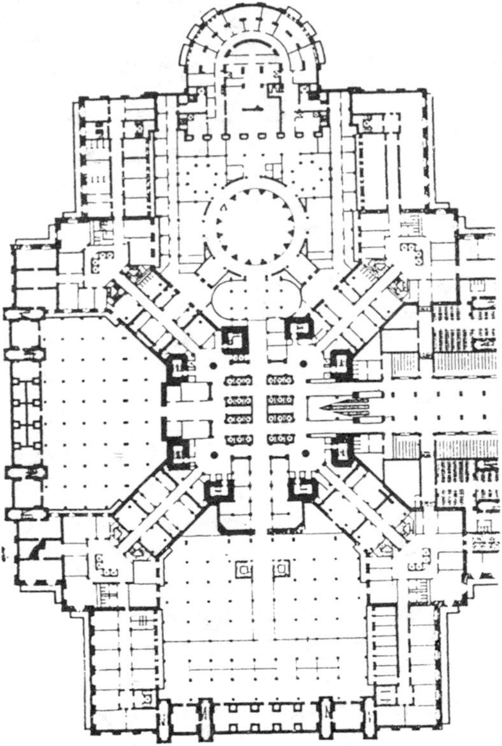

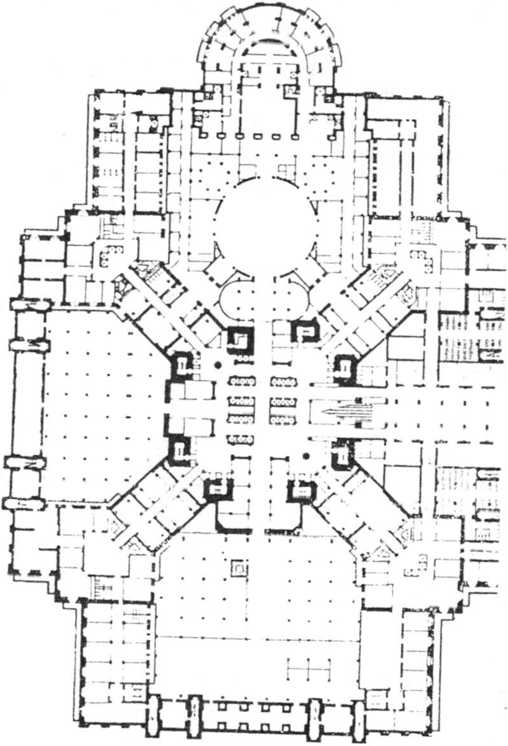

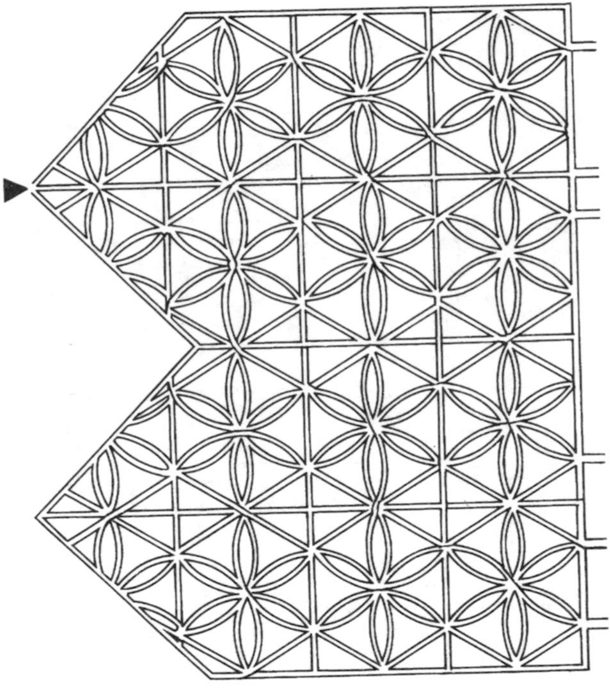

146 **The architects designing the new civic building came up with a tubular-frame roof structure that was**

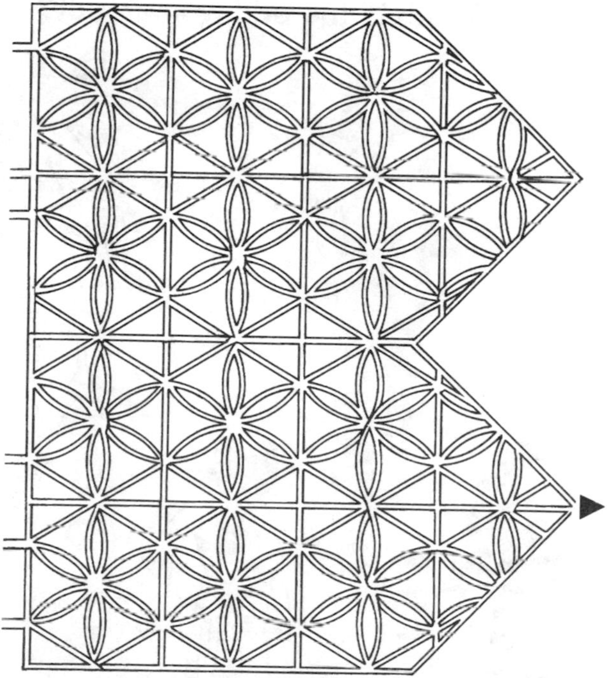

strong, light, and decorative. It even contained one continuous open tube to carry the electric lighting cables. Can you find it?

147 Which is the odd woman out?

148 Three women were waiting at the baker's. The first bought half the bread on the shelves and half a loaf more. The second and third women did the same. When they had all gone, the baker shut up shop, as he had sold out. And he hadn't needed to cut a single loaf in half. How many loaves did he have on his shelves to begin with?

149 **Sergeant Snodsip painted this sign on the barracks window. What does the sign say? And can you find the mistake he made with one of the letters?**

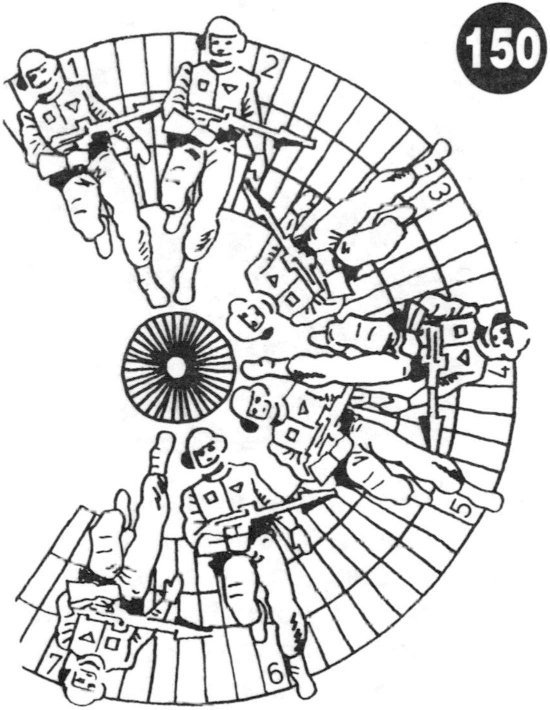

Zargon's time viewer showed him seven views of Barkov. Only one was real – the others were all reflections in time. Which is the real Barkov?

151 This vintner normally sells his wine in 30-ounce and 50-ounce quantities, and so naturally only has measuring jugs in those sizes. One day, a customer asked for just 10 ounces of wine, as he had very little money. The vintner agreed to sell him the wine, and measured it out with his two jugs. How did he do it?

152 Ruth, Debbie, and David run a race every day before breakfast. At the end of September, they realized that since the beginning of the month, Ruth has finished before Debbie more often than after her, and that Debbie has finished before David more often than after him. Is it possible that David has finished before Ruth more often than after her?

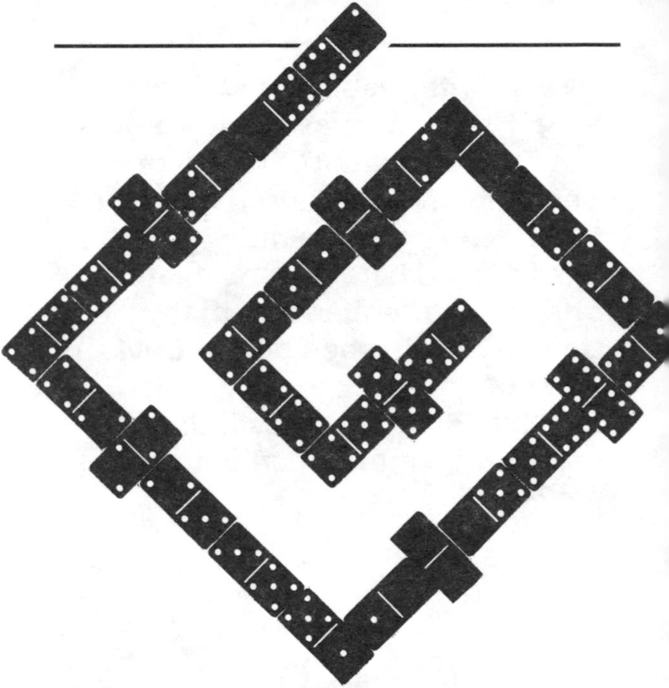

153

In the illustration above, a full set of 28 dominoes has been laid out end to end in a continuous series, and the chain has then been broken into four lengths, each of seven dominoes. In this case, the total number of spots in each row is different. Can you find a solution in which the spot total is the same in each row?

47

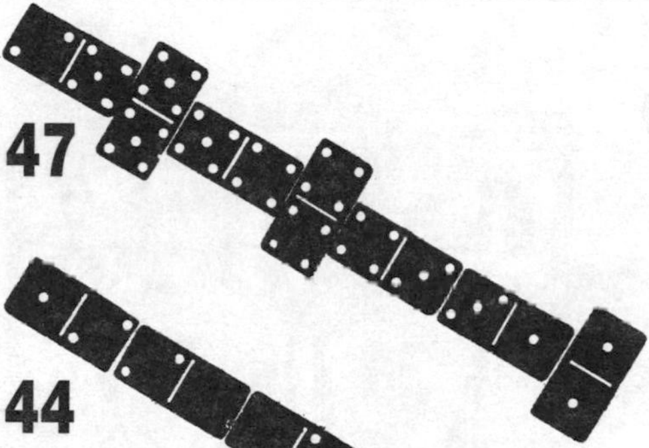

44

29

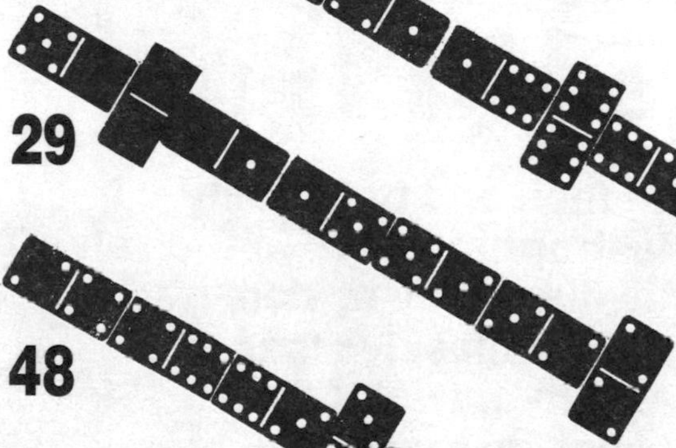

48

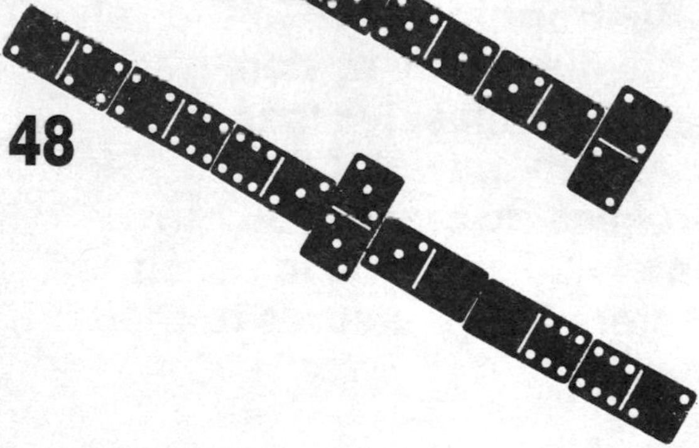

154

A sudden and potentially catastrophic failure in the valve-activating relay system has caused a massive loss of pressure in two of the processing tanks. You have barely 30 seconds in which to restore the pressures to their correct levels.

89				
			86	
16		0		
		66		
	10			96

155

Using only the numbers 1, 6, 8, 9, 0, the two boys completed the electronic game so that each row and each column added up to 264. But their pleasure turned to amazement when their friend leaned through the window and said, "That solution works from this side as well, and it even has the same constant – 264!" Can you work out the boys' solution?

156 Everyone was very pleased with the new signs for the big

157 The teacher had to buy 34 new numbers for the school lockers, numbered from 1 to 34. How many plates with the figure 1 on them did he buy?

exhibition. But one of the signs is an odd man out. Can you see which one?

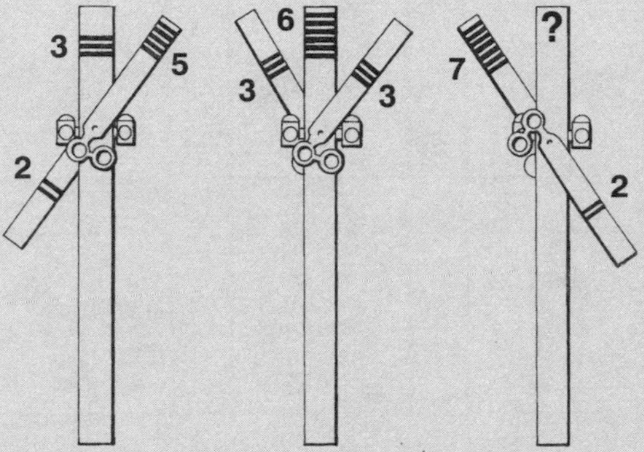

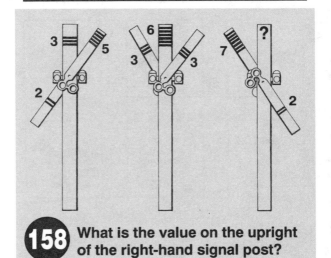

158 What is the value on the upright of the right-hand signal post?

159

Eight trees are growing in a line at intervals of three yards. What is the distance between the two end trees?

160

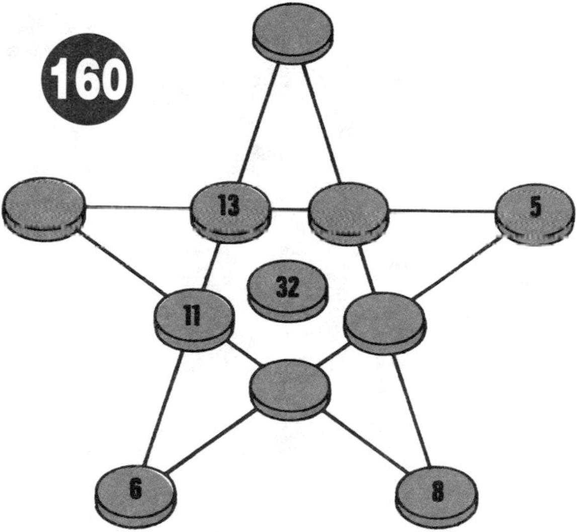

Fill in the missing numbers so that the sum of the numbers in each straight line equals the total in the middle.

161

A father is aged 62 when his daughter is 36. How many years is it since she was exactly one-third his age?

162 Cynthia Smogtrout noticed that if she covered over exactly half of the dial on her watch, the covered numbers added up to the same total as the uncovered numbers. Which half of the dial did she cover up?

163 Cynthia put a new battery in her watch a million seconds ago. So has she had the new battery for more than a day, more than a week, or more than a year? (Try to work it out without using a calculator!)

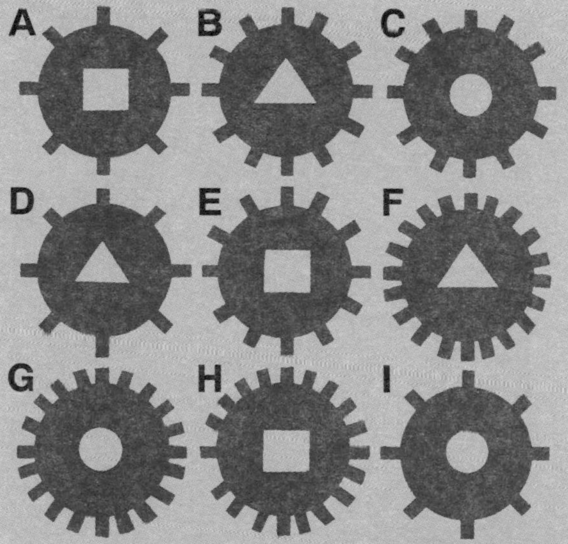

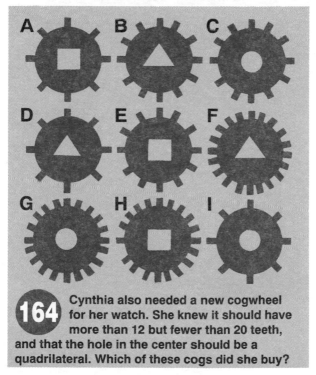

164 Cynthia also needed a new cogwheel for her watch. She knew it should have more than 12 but fewer than 20 teeth, and that the hole in the center should be a quadrilateral. Which of these cogs did she buy?

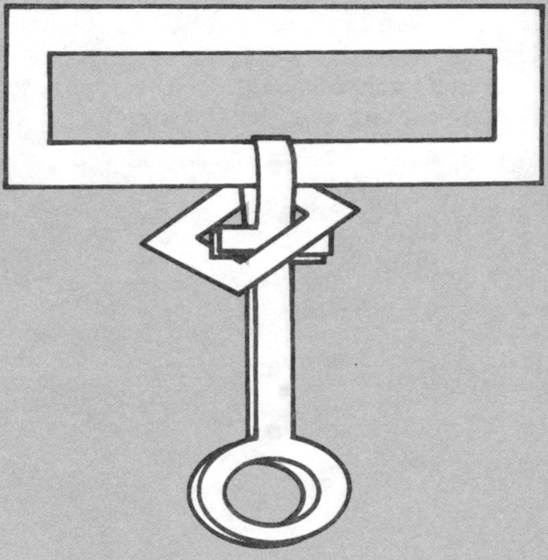

165 Starting from a single sheet of paper, can you construct this double key ring? You may cut out the two rectangles and the pair of keys separately, but you may not make any tears or joins when you assemble them.

166

Can you arrange the queen of hearts, the king of spades, the jack of diamonds, the queen of clubs, the king of hearts, and the queen of spades so that all the following conditions are met:

a) The queen of hearts is two away from the queen of clubs, which is immediately on the left of the queen of spades

b) The jack of diamonds is next to the king of spades, which is two away from the queen of clubs

c) The queen of hearts is between the jack of diamonds and the king of hearts

167 **Sherlock Holmes instantly saw how many ways the word MADAM could be read from this pattern. Can you work out how many? You can go in any direction, but you must keep to the pathways.**

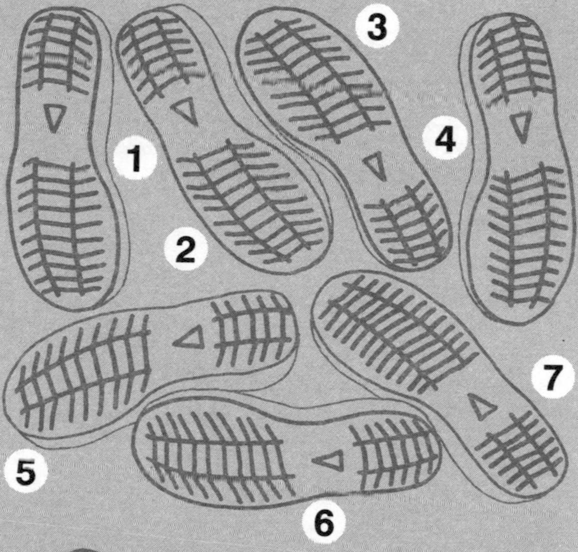

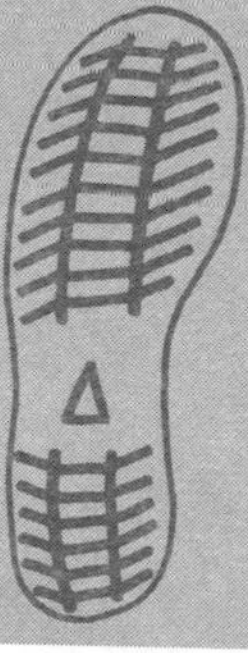

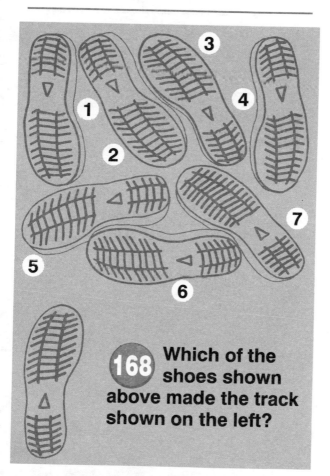

168 **Which of the shoes shown above made the track shown on the left?**

169 Can you draw a circle with a dot in the middle – without lifting your pencil from the paper or using an eraser?

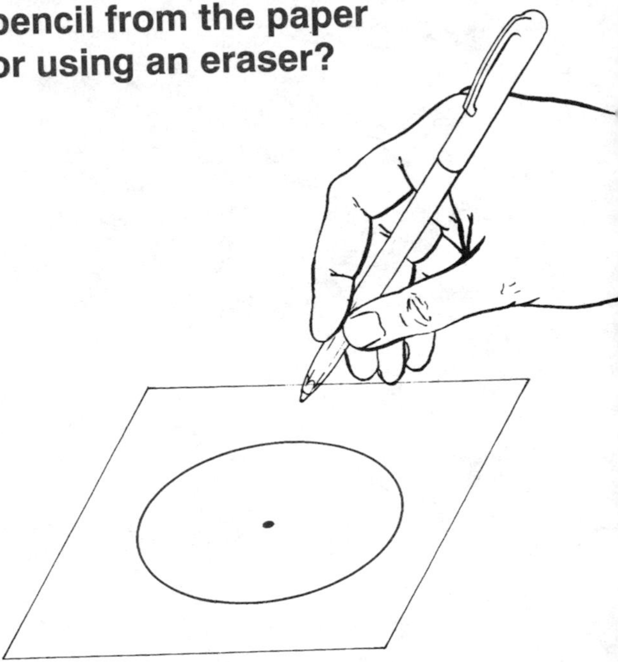

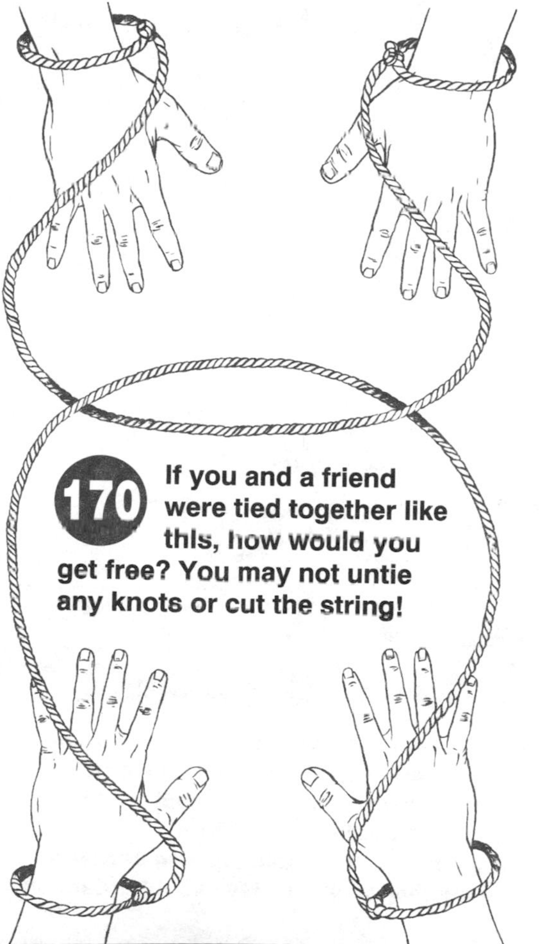

170 If you and a friend were tied together like this, how would you get free? You may not untie any knots or cut the string!

171 **An alien has taken over one of the cabins in the intergalactic cruiser, shown above. He telepathed his location back to his home planet.**
"My cabin and the captain's cabin border on the same number of cabins. My cabin borders on

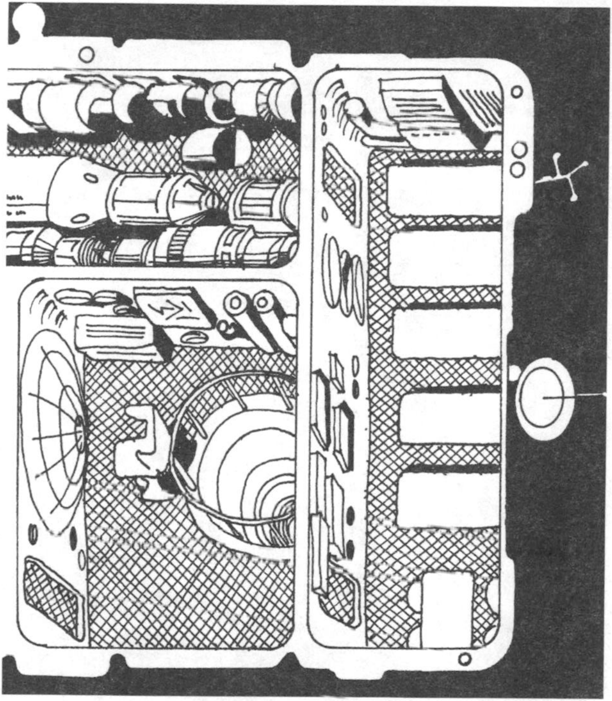

Lovell's cabin and also on Armstrong's. Collins's cabin is the same size as Scott's. Lovell's cabin does not border on Collins's."

From this, his planetary controller was able to deduce the name of the cruiser's captain and the location of the alien's cabin. Can you?

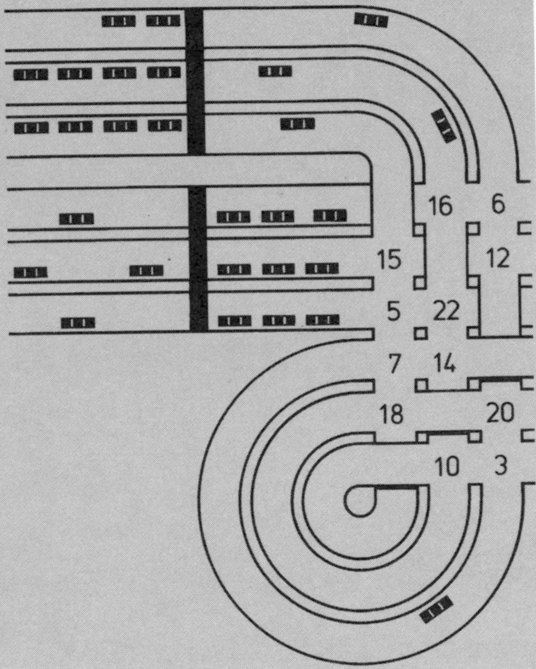

172 **Vehicles entering this interchange system are charged a toll for each flyover they cross. Although the toll**

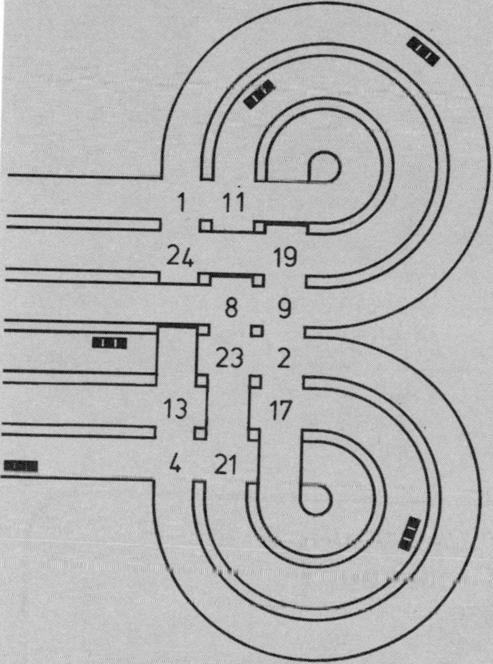

charges vary, each circuit of the clover leaf adds up to $100. Some of the toll flyovers are drawn in. Can you add the rest?

173

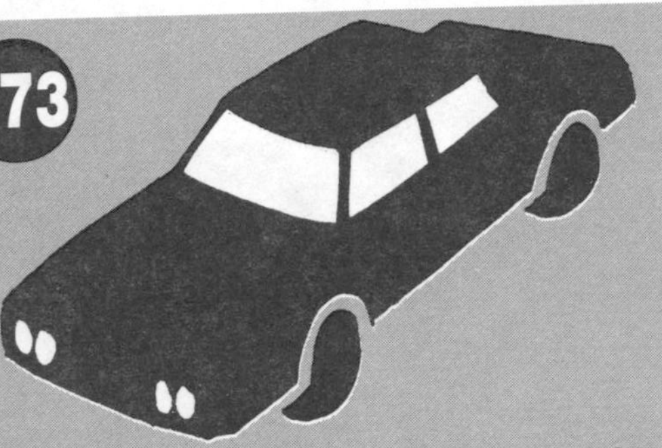

Thirty-eight people were stranded one night after their bus had broken down. A passing motorist offered to take them all to the nearest town but said he could only take a maximum of four passengers on each trip.
How many trips did he have to make?

174

Can you read this message?

175

Can you lead these three blind mice to the cheese?

176

Three men are playing a version of an old card game in which each player is dealt only one card. Each picks up his own card (without looking at it) and holds it against his forehead, face out, so that the other two players can see it. A player raises his hand if he sees a black card held by either of the other two men. The first player to be able to say whether his own card is red or black is the winner.

On this round all the men raised their hands. Within seconds, one man has come up with the right answer and won the game. How did he work it out, and was his card red or black?

177 Three tarot cards lie face down in a row. There is a queen on the right of a knight and a queen on the left of a queen. A card from the suit of cups is on the left of a card from the suit of swords, and a card from the suit of cups is on the right of a card from the suit of cups. What three cards would you see if you turned them face up?

178
True or false?
All Titans live on Titan.
All Titans are our enemies.
So all our enemies live on Titan.

179 How many squares has David the draftsman drawn?

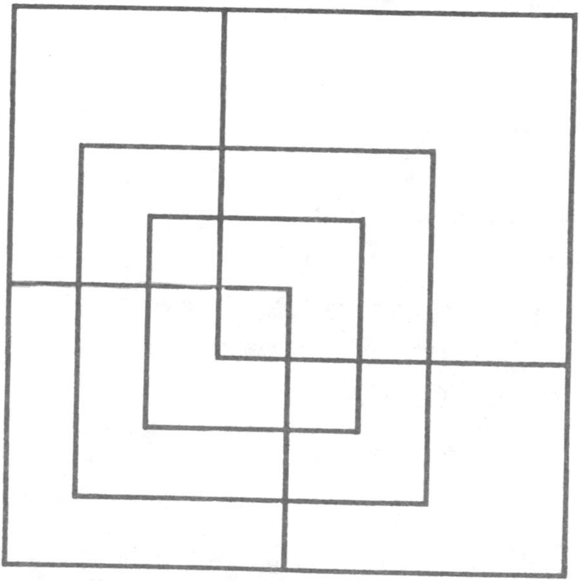

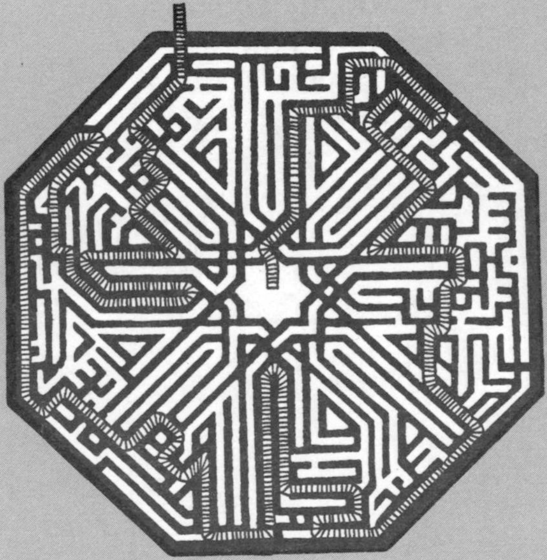

180 A maze has been built into each of these Arabic floor patterns. The route to the middle is shown on the first maze.

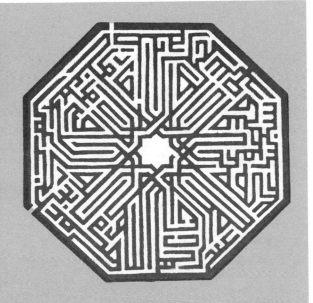

Can you spot the differences between the two mazes and find the route to the middle of the second maze?

There are 20 differences between these two drawings. Can you spot them all?

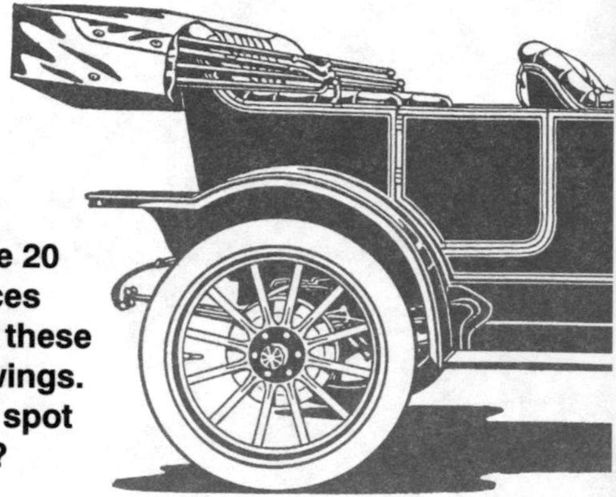

181

182 A rare edition of a 16th-century herbal encyclopedia came up for auction recently. A sharp-eyed assistant spotted the book as a clever fake

and proved his case by comparing it with the definitive work (left) from the library. He found 10 differences. Can you?

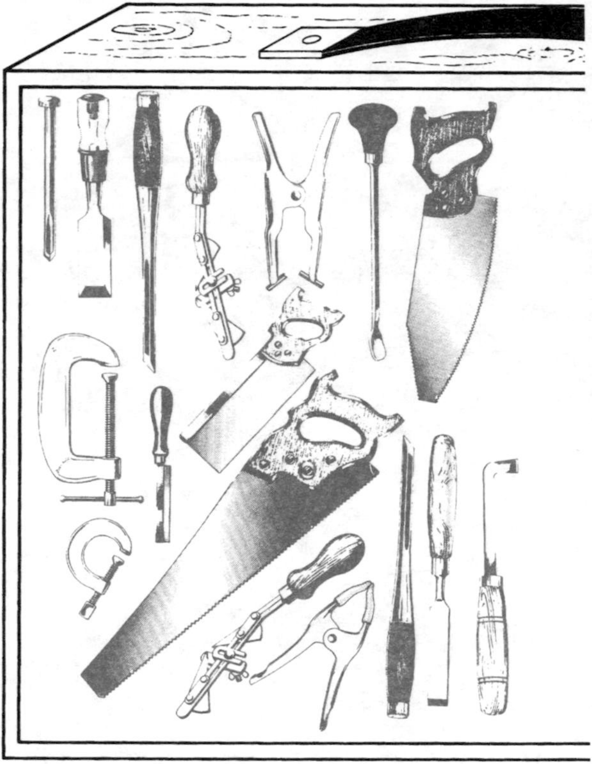

183 **Following an age-old custom, the carpenter kept two sets of his tools – one for himself and one for his apprentice.**

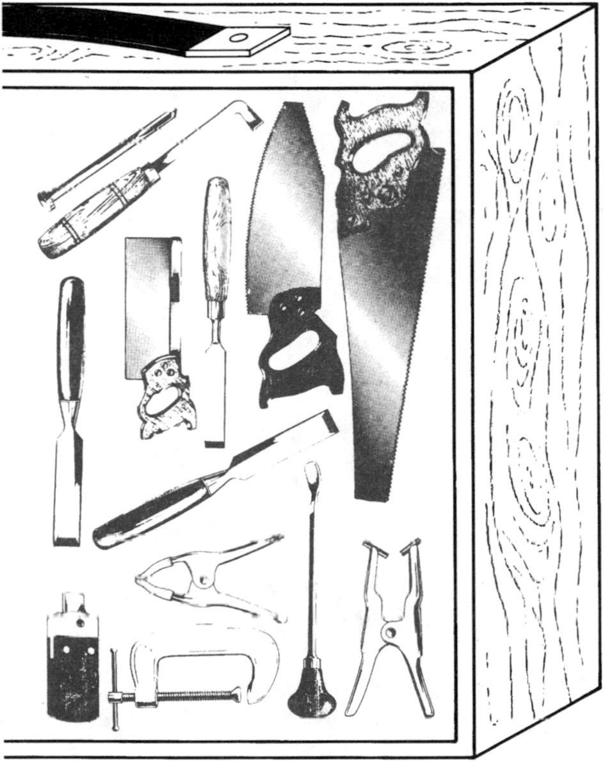

However, four of the master's tools were "off limits" to the junior. Can you spot them?

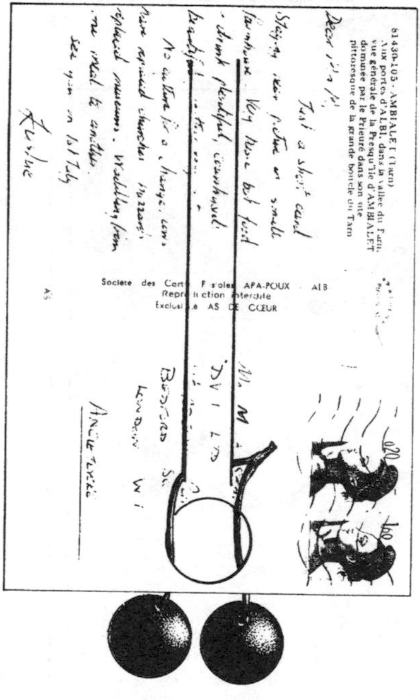

184 **This postcard has had two slits and a circular hole cut in it; the hole is smaller than either of the cherries. Can you separate the cherries and the postcard without damaging the card or the cherry stalks? Eating the cherries is cheating!**

185 "How many letters are there in the Greek alphabet?" asked the Sphinx. Ajax knew that the Sphinx was famous for asking trick questions, so he thought carefully and gave the correct answer. What was his answer?

186

It was midmorning on Cleopatra's birthday. The five of them were sitting aboard Cleopatra's present to herself – another new barge – sipping their drinks and reading the newspapers. Cleopatra was wearing two of her birthday presents – a new robe, and a gift from Mark Antony. Mark Antony was drinking beer, and one of his generals, a man called Ahenobarbus, was sitting next to him drinking wine. Cleopatra's son, Caesarion, was looking at the comic strip in the *Daily Sphinx*; he wasn't drinking water. The woman reading the *Pharaonic Times* was

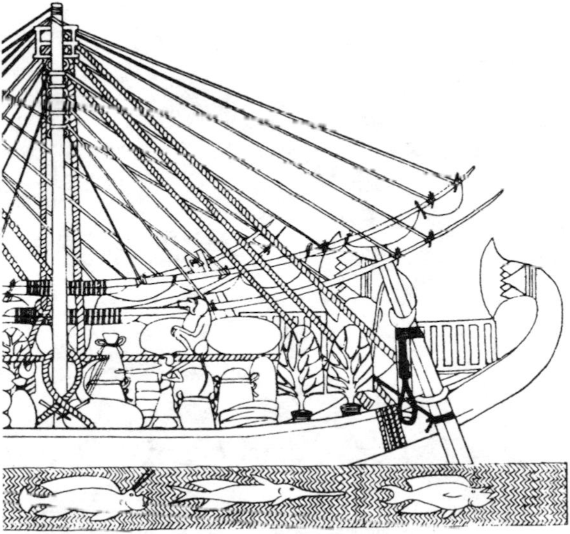

drinking asses' milk, but this wasn't Charmian, the handmaiden, who always thought it tasted like bathwater. Nor was Charmian drinking fruit juice – that was the person who had given Cleopatra the baboons. The person reading the *Ptolemaic Post* hadn't given the string of pearls, but the man reading the *Heliopolis Gazette* had presented the trees that the baboons were playing in.

Which of the five was reading the *Nile Street Journal*?

188

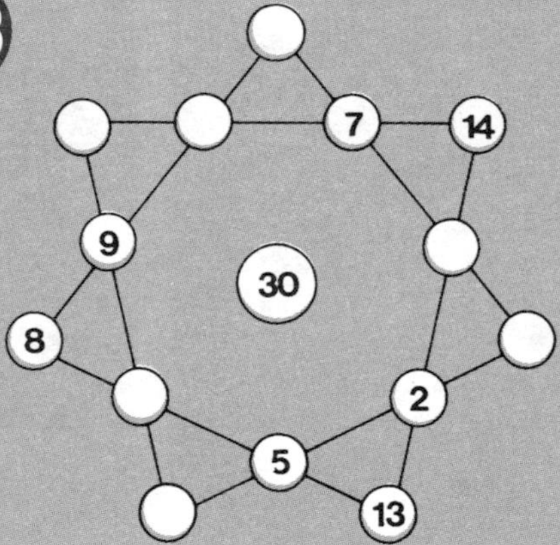

Fill in the missing numbers so that the sum of the numbers in each straight line equals the total in the middle.

187

To complete the sequence, what number should the middle car be carrying?

189

The storekeeper stared in amazement at the end of his calculation. What is so surprising about the total, and why was the storekeeper even more surprised when he took a second look at the individual rows of numbers?

1975308624
1728395046
1604938257
1234567980
0987654312
0864197523
0617283945
0493827156
0246913578
0123456789

TOTAL ?

190

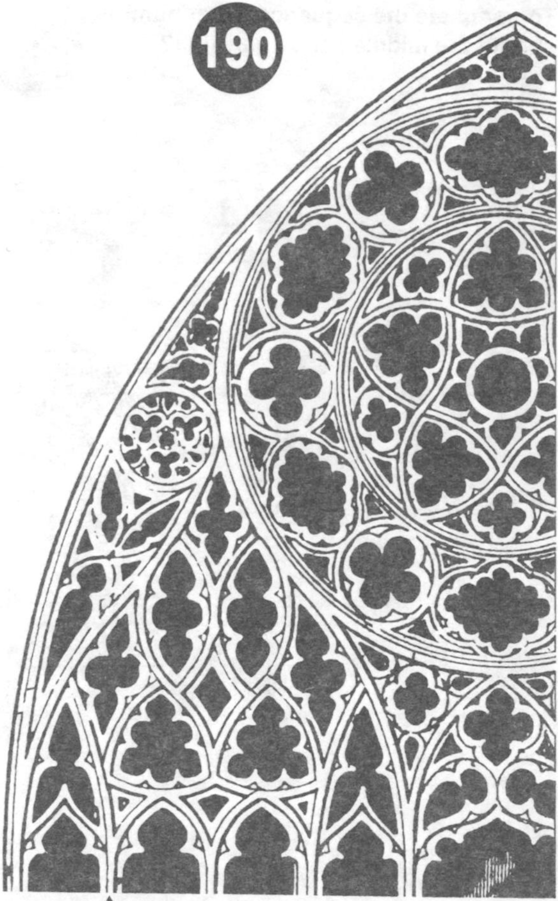

The stonework of this church window hides a path from the bottom left-hand corner to the central circle. Can you follow the path, keeping to the white lines of the stonework?

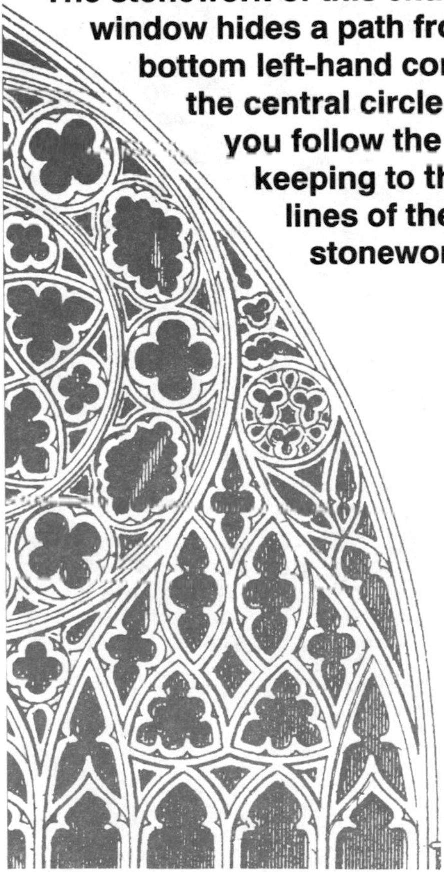

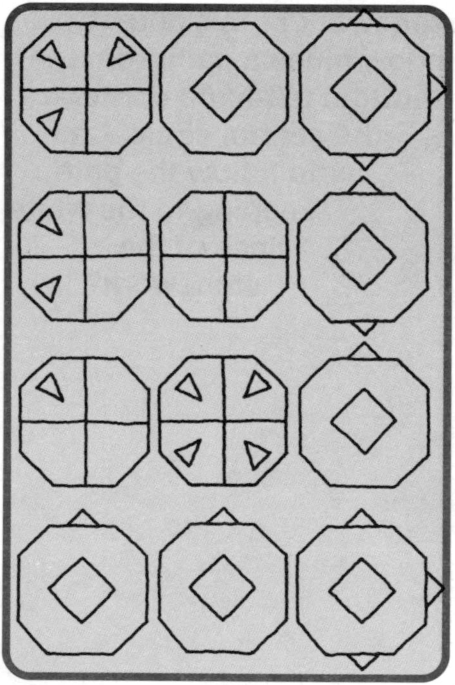

= 358

= 207

= ?

= ?

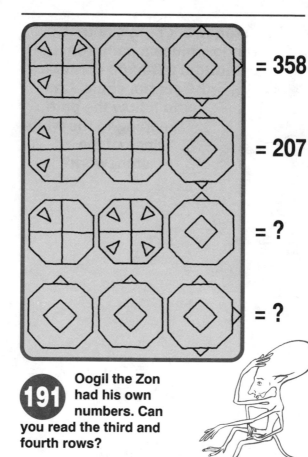

191 **Oogil the Zon had his own numbers. Can you read the third and fourth rows?**

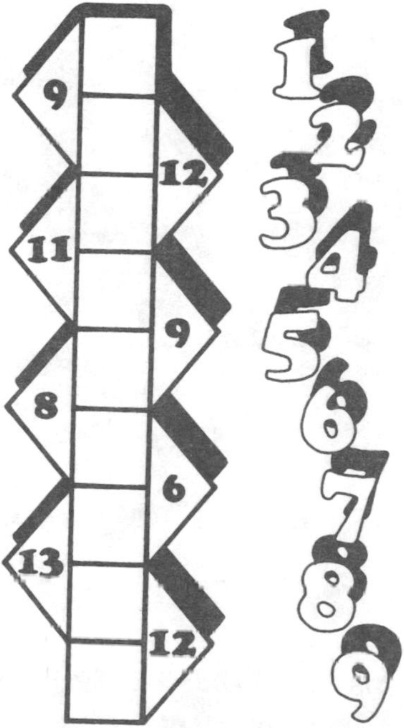

192 Arrange the numbers 1 to 9 in the squares so that the sum of the numbers in each pair of squares is the same as the number in the triangle that touches both squares in the pair. You may only put one number in each square, and you may use each number only once.

193 Although no one had touched the contents of any of the files, someone had switched all the labels! Joyce knew that all the filing had been done correctly and that all the letters had been individually stamped IN or OUT. She realized that by opening just one drawer and taking out just one letter she could easily correct the labels. How did she do it?

194

Why did the yachtsmen going to the auction think that only half the sails were worth bidding on?

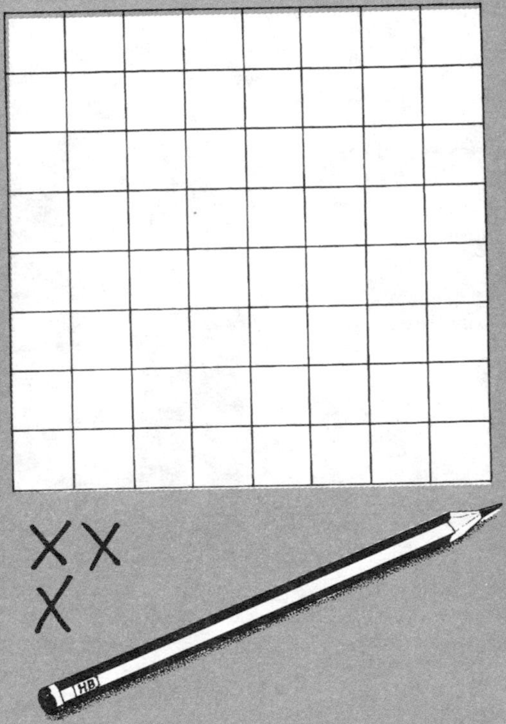

195 Can you mark eight crosses on this 64-square board so that no two crosses are in the same horizontal, vertical, or diagonal line?

196

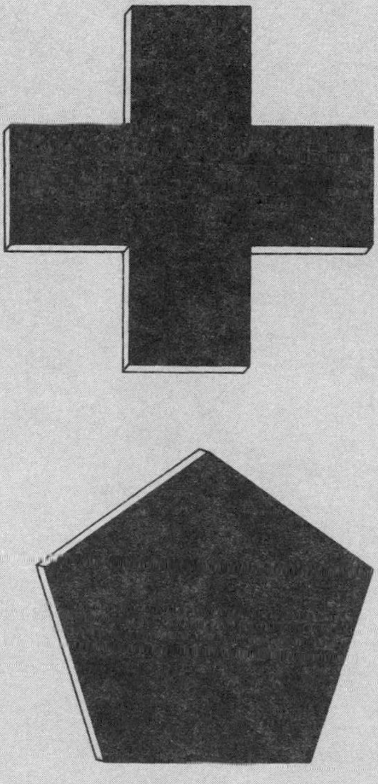

If you cut the cross at the top of the page into seven pieces, you can reassemble the pieces to make the regular pentagon shown. Where should you make the cuts?

197

a) Here we show John, Mary, and Paul going up the stairs. In how many different orders can the three children climb the stairs?

b) If Anne joined them, then how many different orders could there be?

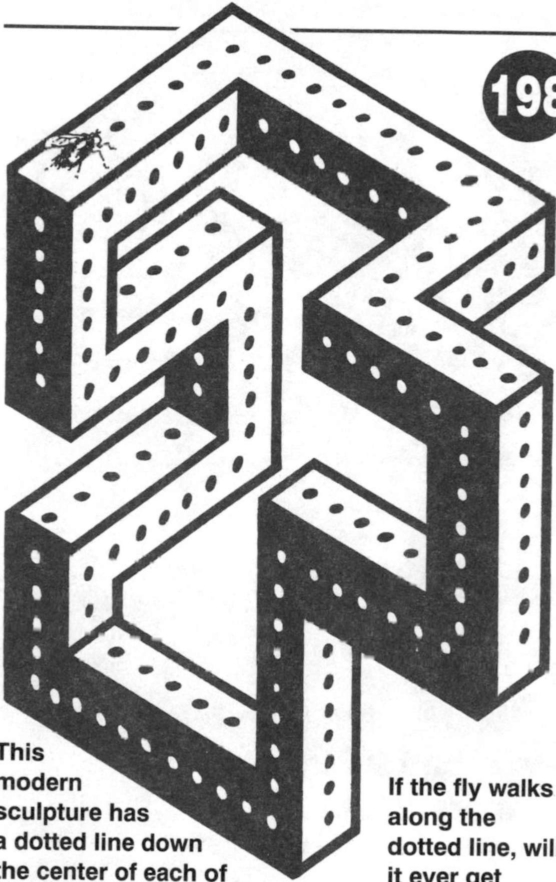

198

This modern sculpture has a dotted line down the center of each of its sides (including those you can't see).

If the fly walks along the dotted line, will it ever get back to its starting point?

199 **If 5 cats take 5 minutes to catch 5 mice, how many cats are needed to catch 100 mice in 100 minutes?**

200

If a phonograph record 12 inches across has an outer nonplaying margin 1 inch wide, and a nonplaying central area 4 inches in diameter, and there are an average of 90 grooves per inch, how far does the needle travel during one playing of the record?

201 To what question must you always answer, "Yes"?

202 There were 12 girls standing in a circle. Every other girl of the 12 had red hair. The 4 girls who had green eyes were standing evenly spaced around the circle. Three of the girls in the circle were sisters, and they were standing equidistant from each other. None of the other girls were related. Only one girl apart from the sisters had both red hair and green eyes. How many of the sisters had both?

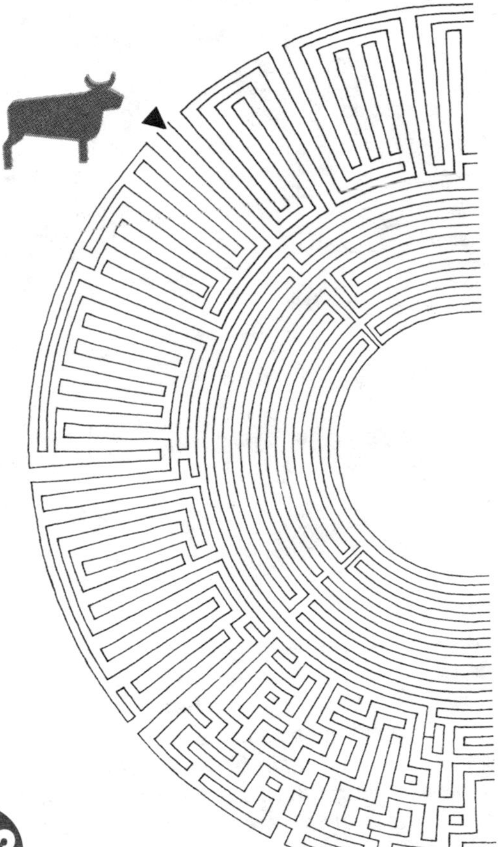

It's no easy matter for the bull to find his way to the ring in this stadium.

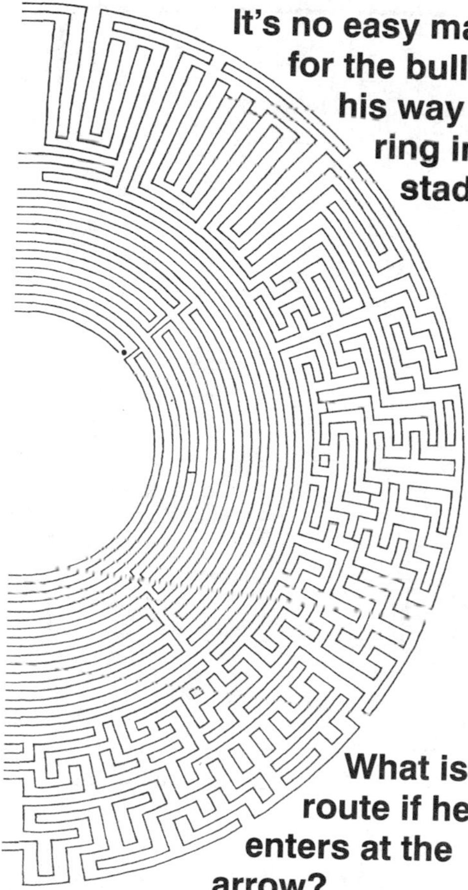

What is his route if he enters at the arrow?

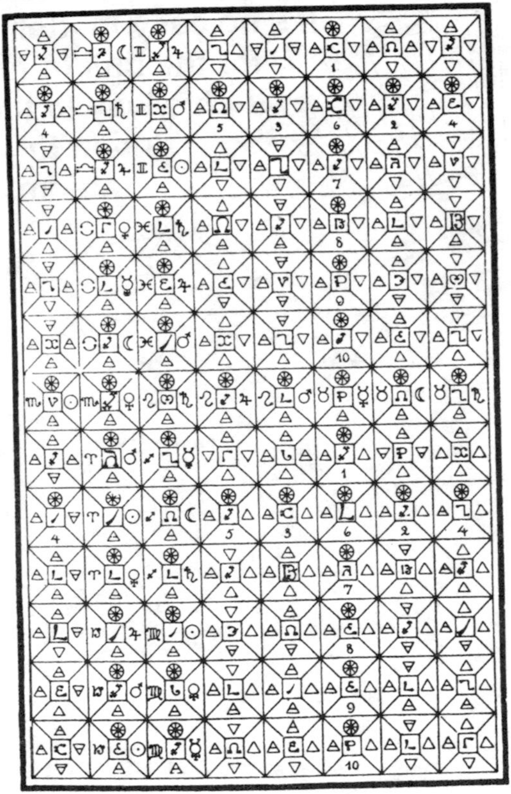

204 The astronaut transcribing this Martian inscription was

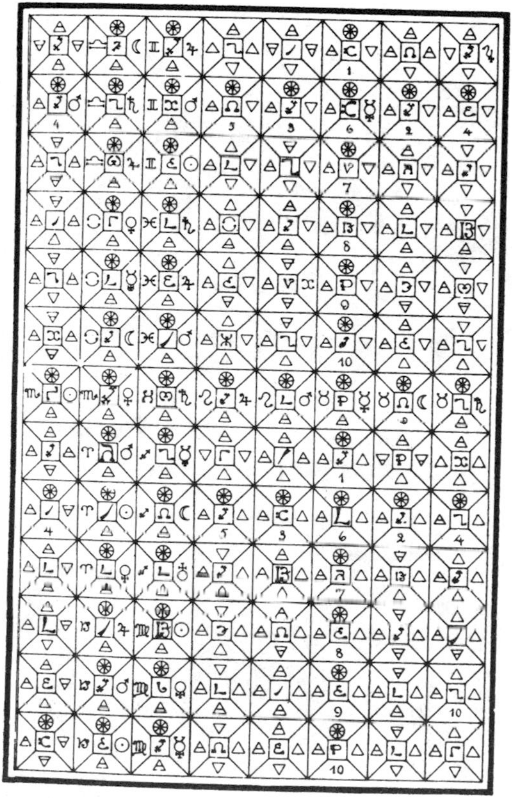

suffering from altitude sickness. Can you spot the 20 mistakes he made?

205 **Can you find 27 differences between these two pictures?**

206 In order to "decode" the trace from his deep-space radar scanner, the technician needs to find the points at which the horizontal lines come closest to each other. Can you help him?

207 Bruce was in deep trouble when his mother found the apple pie looking like this. Where is the missing slice?

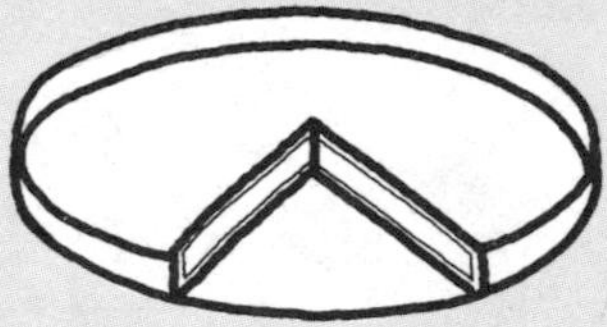

208 **Fred MacDermot enjoyed making complicated models, but when he came to this page in the instruction manual he took it straight back to the store and complained bitterly. Why?**

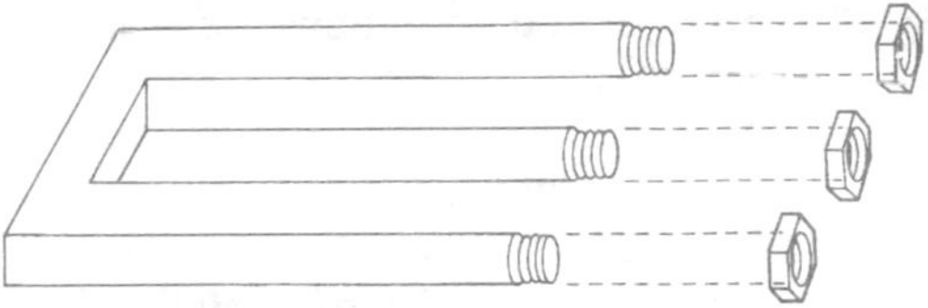

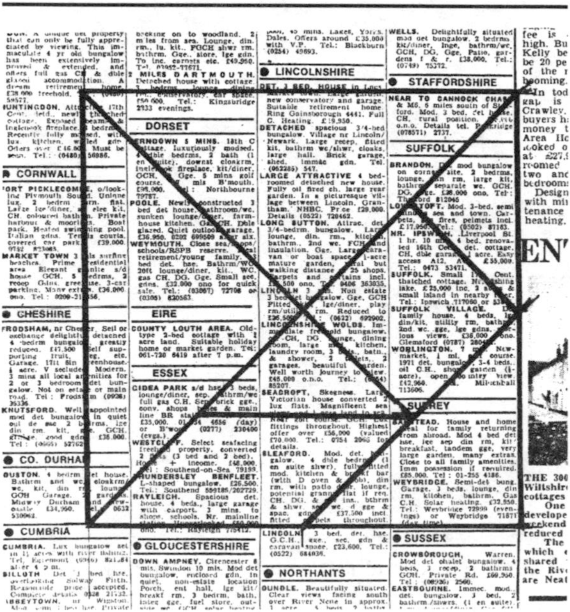

209 The tangram is a traditional Chinese puzzle. You can make your own by cutting a square of newspaper into sections, as shown. Each of the men shown here is made from all seven tangram pieces, but one of them appears to have a foot missing. Can you rearrange the pieces so that the second man has a foot to stand on?

DORSET
SUFFOLK
EIRE
COUNTY LOUTH AREA
ESSEX

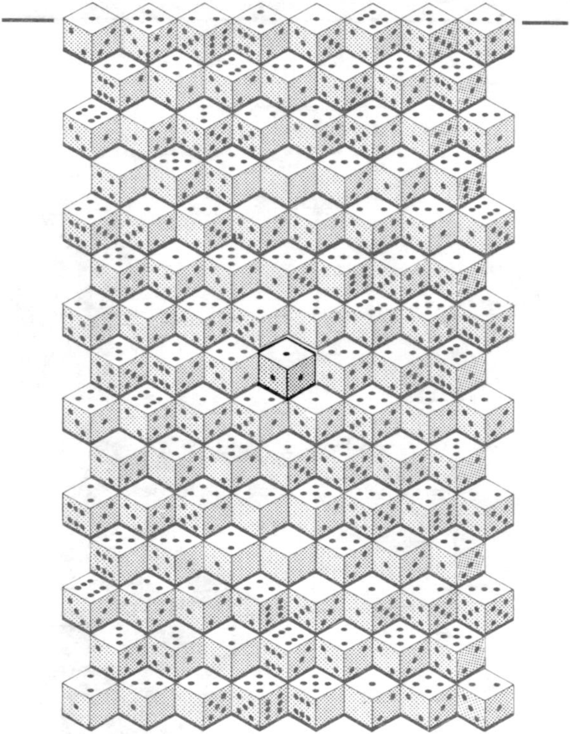

210 In this dice maze, you may move from one die to the next only if the numbers on adjacent faces are the same. However, once on a die, you may move to any of its other visible faces. From the central die, move to a die with three blank faces.

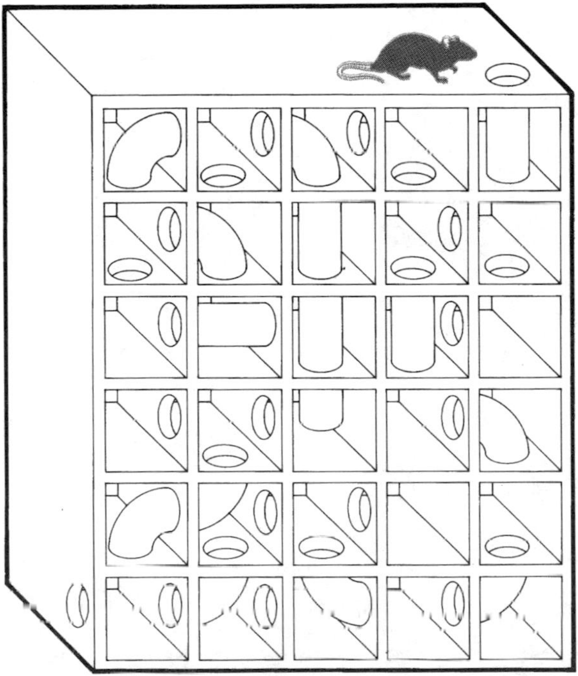

211

This rat is the subject of an intelligence test. Can he find the holes to climb through and the pipes to slide down to get out of the box at the bottom left-hand corner?

212 A small girl lived with her parents on the ninth floor of an apartment building. If she wanted to go out, she would take the elevator from the ninth floor to the first floor. But when she came home, she would only take the elevator to the sixth floor, and then walk up the rest of the way. Why did she do this?

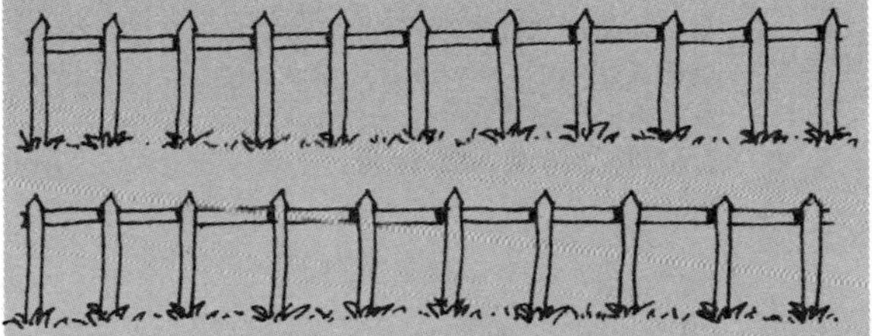

213 On her way to school, her friend counted 63 fence posts, each one yard apart. How long was the fence?

214 A hedgehog has two and so doos a guinea pig. Dogs and gerbils have one each, but rabbits and hamsters don't have any. Any what?

215

As part of their sales drive, the transport company announced that they were giving away 34 free season tickets for each of the six crosstown rapid transit subway routes. The figures show

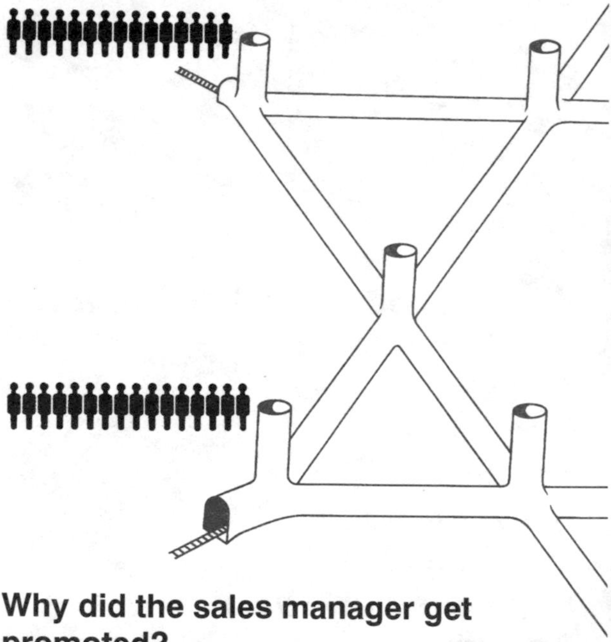

Why did the sales manager get promoted?

how many tickets were given to passengers at "end-of-line" stations. Can you distribute tickets among passengers at the six inner stations so that each line has 34 free-ticket holders?

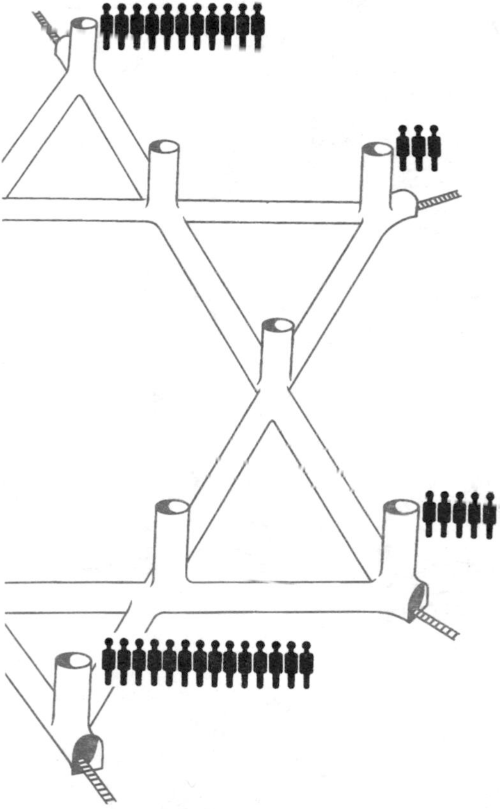

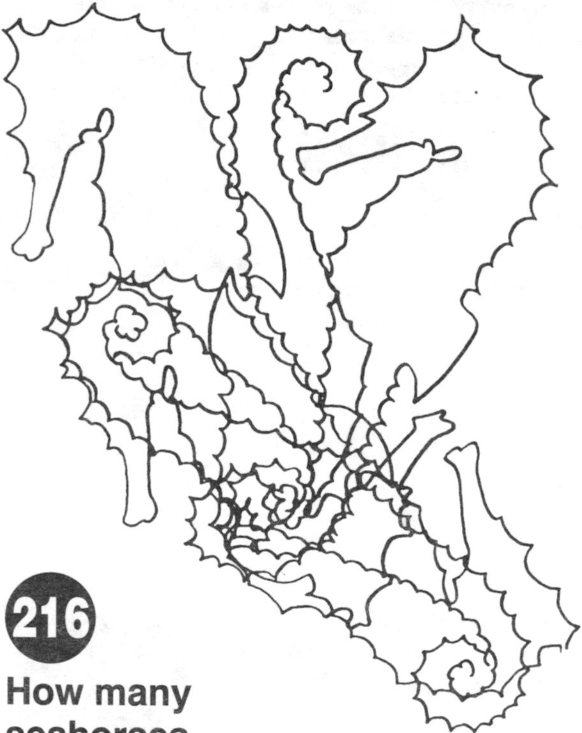

216

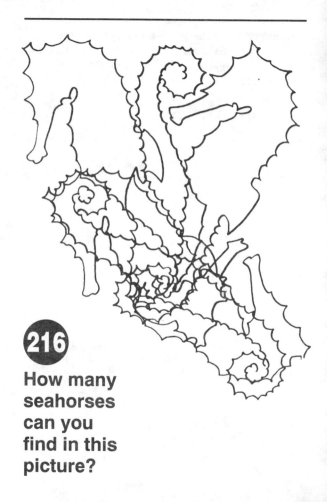

How many seahorses can you find in this picture?

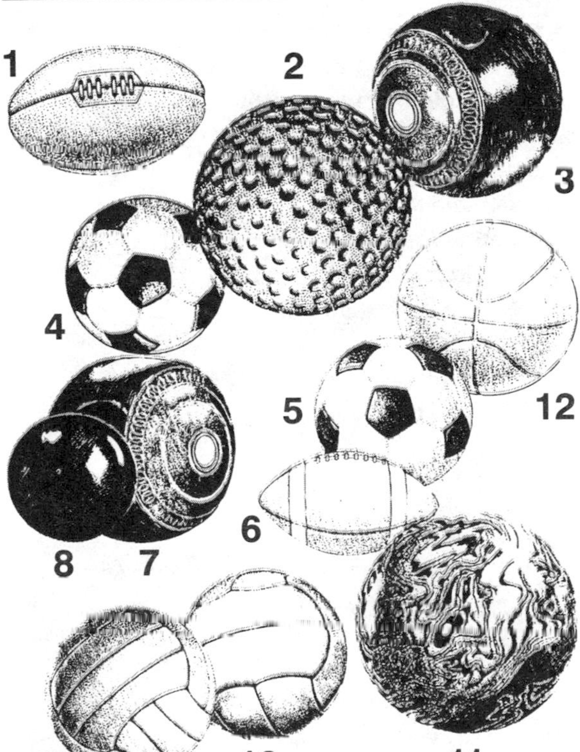

217 Which is the odd ball out?

218 The school board was most impressed. When told that his monthly salary would be **** rising to $3,000 after 6 months, the new teacher said, "What a fascinating figure. Divided by 10, the remainder is 9; divided by 9, the remainder is 8; and so on, down to a remainder of 1 when divided by 2." What is his starting salary?

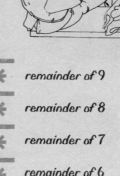

10) * * * * *remainder of 9*

9) * * * * *remainder of 8*

8) * * * * *remainder of 7*

7) * * * * *remainder of 6*

6) * * * * *remainder of 5*

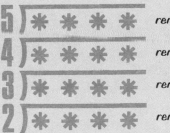

5)* * * * remainder of 4

4)* * * * remainder of 3

3)* * * * remainder of 2

2)* * * * remainder of 1

219 **In the 17th century, popular woodcuts were often copied. Unfortunately, the forgers were**

careless, and their work can be spotted easily. Turn the page and see if you can pick out the 21 errors.

bai aille
SOLIDARNOŚĆ

de fournoue

220

Which route should the confused motorist take to the parking lot?

221

These two Mayan gods are sworn enemies. If they meet, it will be a fight to the death. As they are gods, they do not get lost; nor do they hide from each other. Can they both come out alive?

222

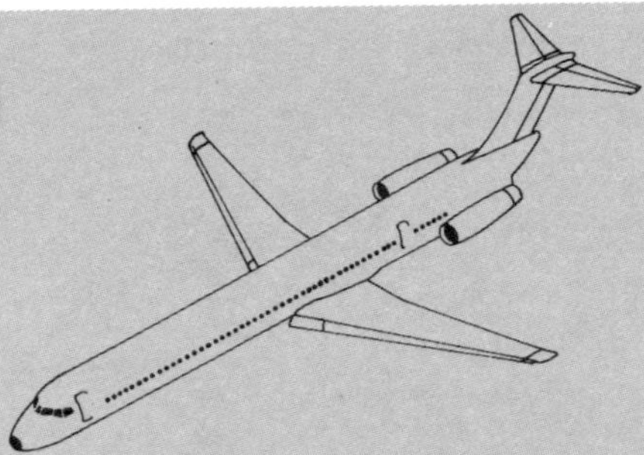

Amy, Beth, Jo, and Meg were all flying off on business. Amy's plane left from Heathrow airport, and Jo's from Schipol. Beth was going to Canada, but Amy was not going to Hong Kong. The person who caught a plane at Orly was going to Mexico, but the person on the plane that left Kennedy was not going to Australia. Who was going where, and from which airport?

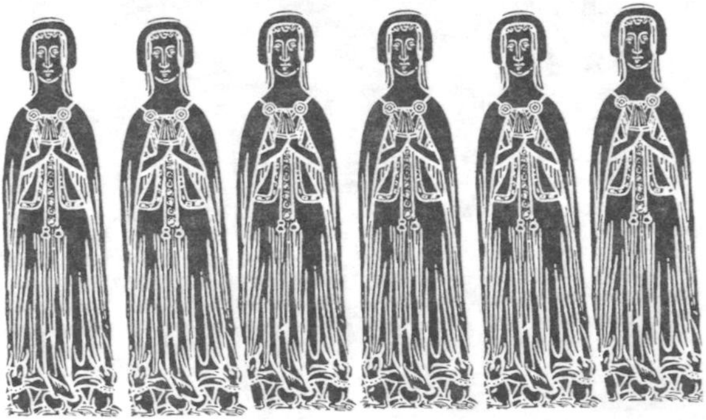

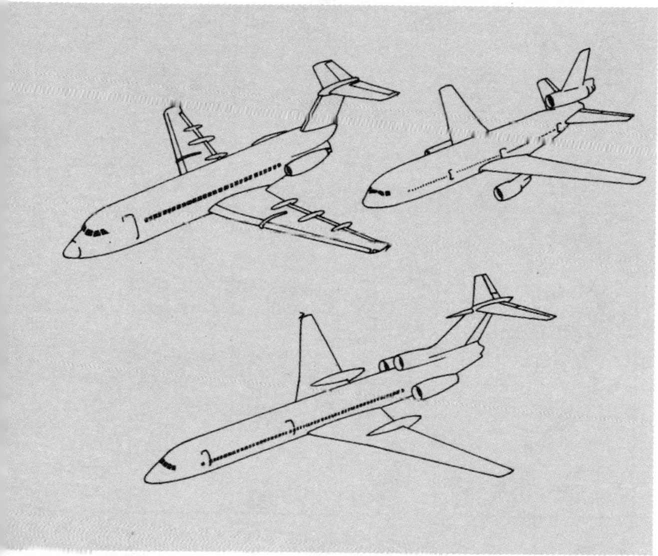

223

Here lie six persons, all long since dead;
All born legitimate, it is said;
And none of them did a relative wed;
Two sisters, with their two brothers;
Two maidens, with their two mothers;
Two mothers, with their two sons;
Two fathers, with their two daughters;
Two husbands, with their two wives;
Two grandmothers, with their two granddaughters.
How can this be?

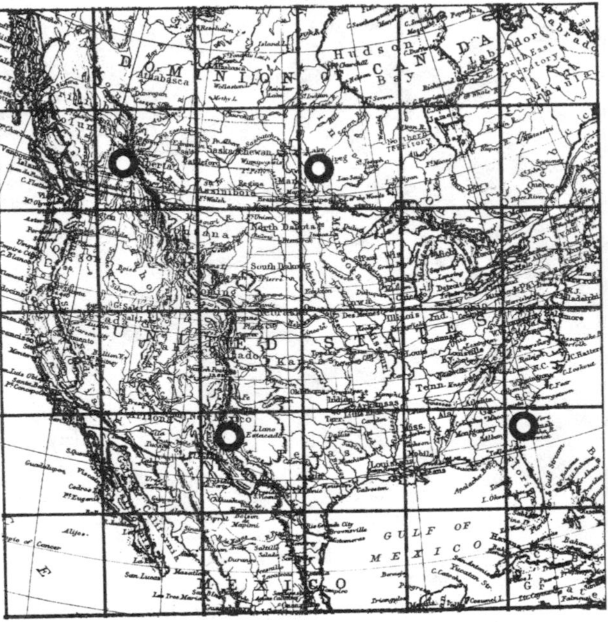

224 **Take a piece of newspaper or an unwanted map and mark it into 36 equal squares. Then mark four dots in the squares, as shown.**

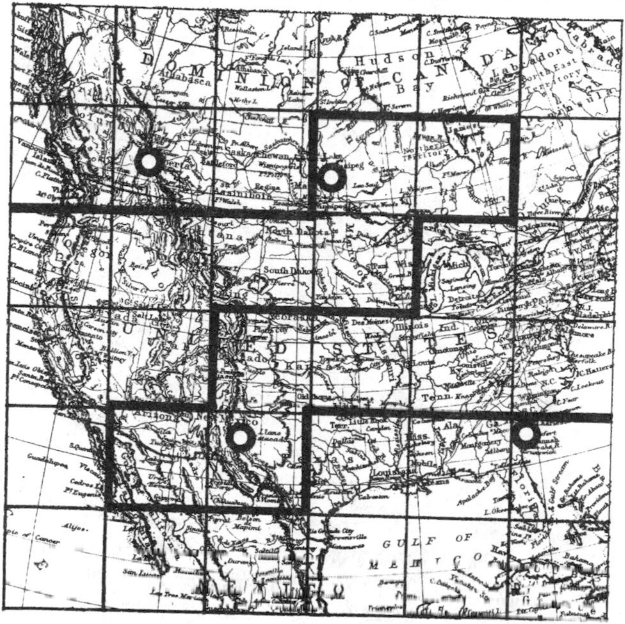

It's possible to cut the paper into two identical pieces, both the same shape and size, and each containing two dots. We've drawn one solution. Can you find another?

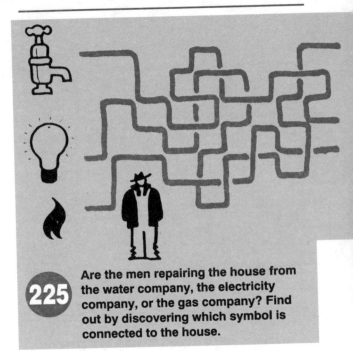

225 Are the men repairing the house from the water company, the electricity company, or the gas company? Find out by discovering which symbol is connected to the house.

226 Paul carried David with John holding David's legs. John offered to carry David with Paul holding David's legs. If each man is to have a turn being carried, in how many ways can they carry each other?

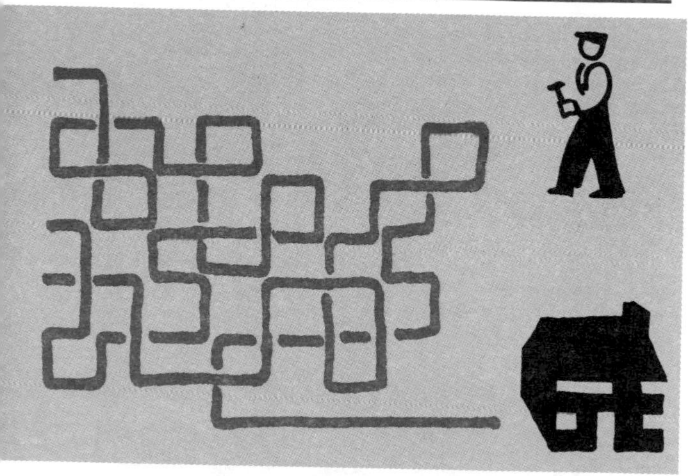

DAVID
JOHN
PAUL

227 **Mary tricked David with the question,**

"What gets lost every time you stand up?"

Do you know the answer?

228 **There are twelve differences in these two pictures. Can you spot them all?**

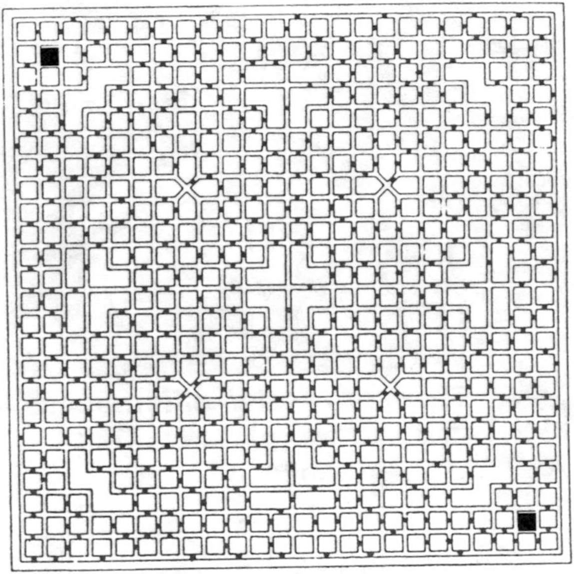

229 Find the route from one black square to the other.

230 **Find the route through the maze which collects the fewest number of dots.**

231

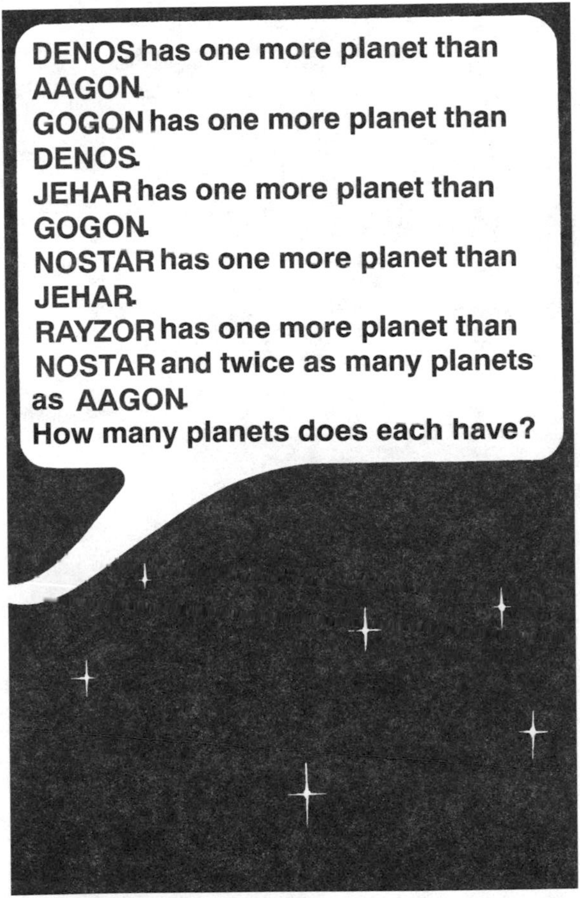
DENOS has one more planet than AAGON.
GOGON has one more planet than DENOS.
JEHAR has one more planet than GOGON.
NOSTAR has one more planet than JEHAR.
RAYZOR has one more planet than NOSTAR and twice as many planets as AAGON.
How many planets does each have?

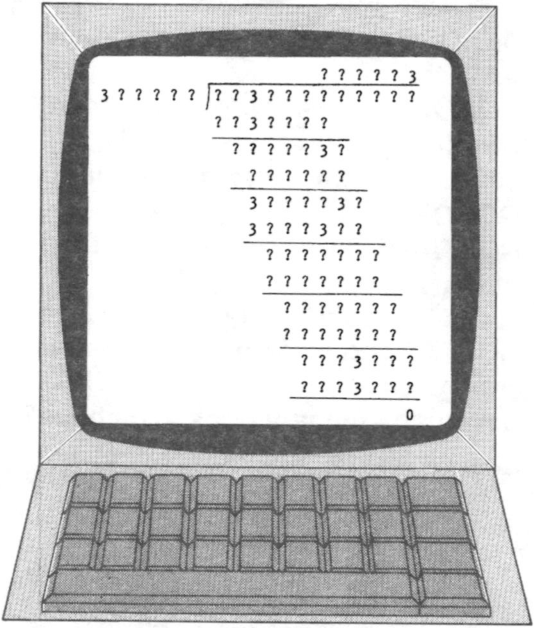

232 **A bug made the computer monitor display only the figure 3s in this long division. However, the operator remembered that the divisor and the quotient had the same numbers but in the reverse order. What was the full calculation?**

233 When the USS *Dolphin* set sail, there were as many men allotted to each lifeboat as there were lifeboats on the ship. During an engagement, the *Dolphin* was holed and began to sink: 10 lifeboats were smashed and 100 men lost, but the rest were saved as 10 extra men were packed into each of the remaining lifeboats. Given that a ship of this size would carry between 3,000 and 4,000 men, how many men were aboard when the *Dolphin* sailed?

234 **Can you make these five squares into three squares by removing three of the nails?**

235 Titus Scribner told his family that each month they would save twice as much as they had saved in the previous month. They would save $1 in the first month, $2 in the second month, $4 in the third month, and so on. How much money will they have saved at the end of a year?

236 A remarkable situation once arose at the beginning of a card game. When each of the players had been dealt one card, it was found that the cards

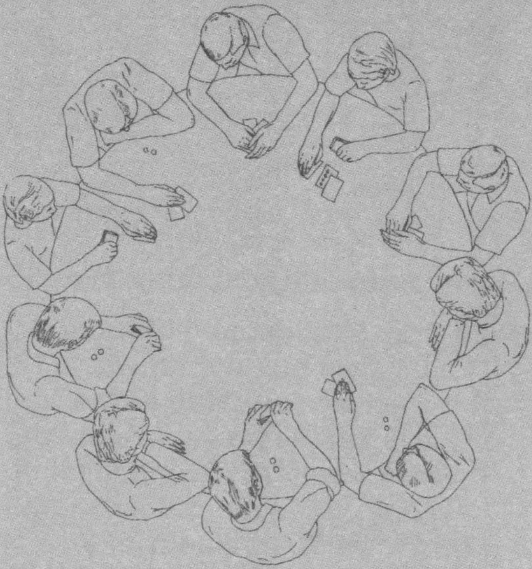

ranged from 1 to 10 in value, with no value repeated, and that the sum of any two adjacent players' cards was equal to that of the two players sitting directly opposite.

Can you work out the relative positions of the ten cards? For example:

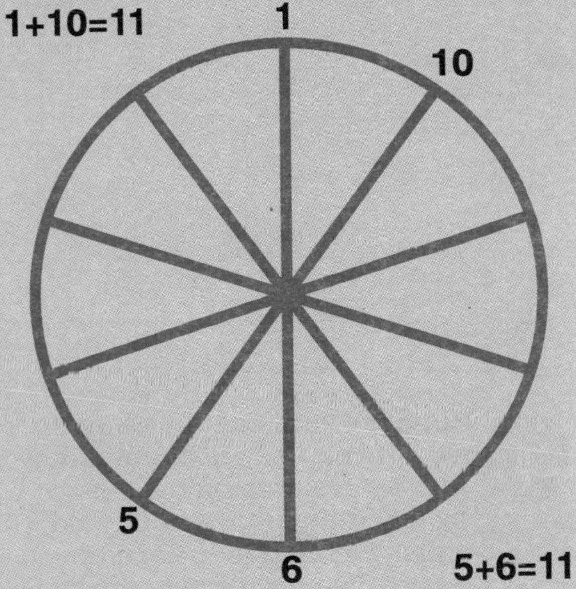

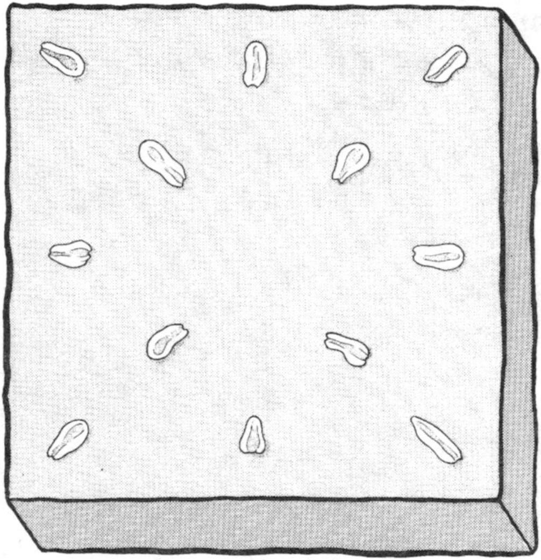

237 Suppose you and three friends were given this square of fudge with twelve nuts on the top on the condition that you divided it equally among you. Each of you were to have a piece of the same size and shape with three nuts on the top. How would you cut up the fudge?

238 These dates were torn off a calendar. Can you rearrange them, moving as few as possible, so that both rows add up to the same amount?

239

The printer mixed up the cartoon strip. Can you work out the proper order of the pictures?

4
5
6

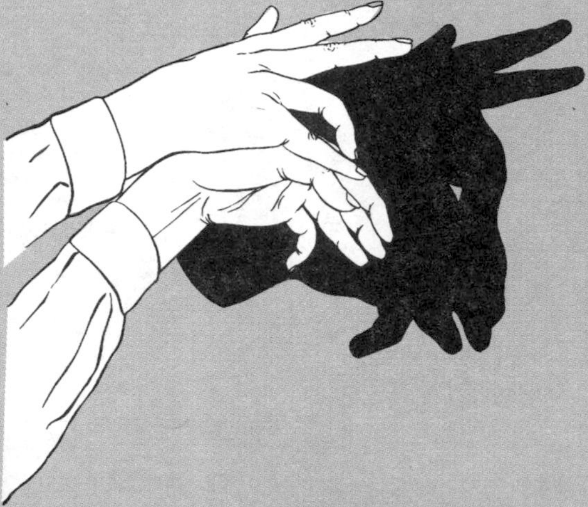

240 Try making animal shadows on your wall. We've shown you how to arrange your hands to make the goat. Can you work out how to make the rabbit, camel, and bear shadows shown on the opposite page?

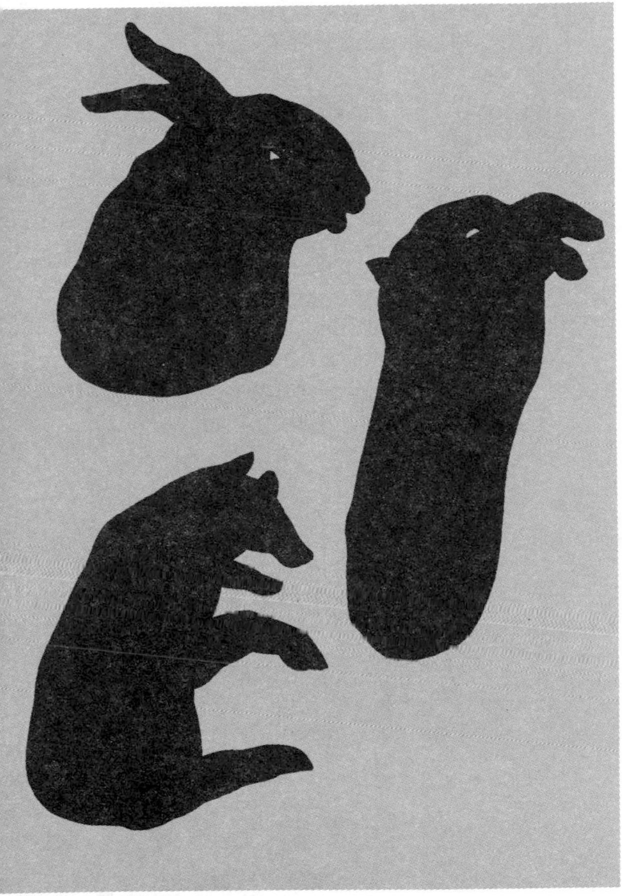

241

Which of these six famous men is the odd one out?

George Washington

Sherlock Holmes

Shakespeare

242

Match up the couples skating in the ice dancing championship.

Ludwig van Beethoven

Napoleon

Nero

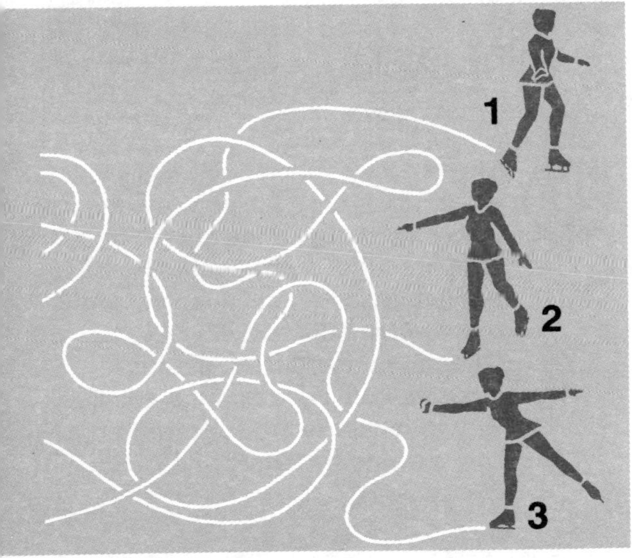

243 The grocer had ten customers, each wanting to buy a 2lb bag of sugar. A 20lb bag of sugar had been delivered that morning, but he had not yet divided it because he could only find the 5lb and 9lb weights. One of the customers, getting impatient, showed him the quickest way to measure the sugar with the two weights he already had. How did he do it?

244

All cats are greatly interested in the smell of fish. Some cats are overweight. Some overweight cats make good mouse chasers. Therefore:

a) All good mouse chasers smell fishy

b) Some overweight cats are interested in the smell of fish

c) Some good mouse chasers are greatly overweight

d) All cats become overweight through their interest in fish

True or false?

245

If you had 2 lizards in front of a lizard, and 2 lizards behind a lizard, and one lizard in the middle, how many lizards would you have?

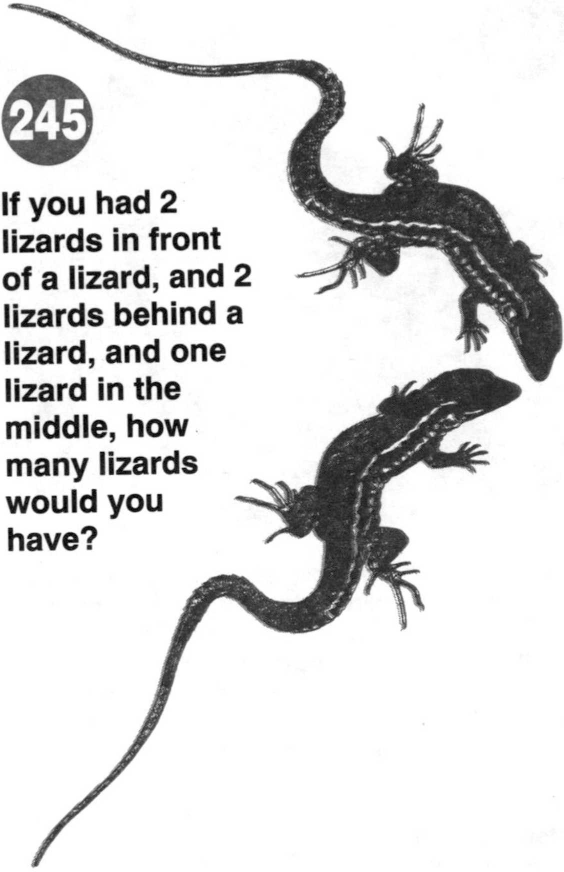

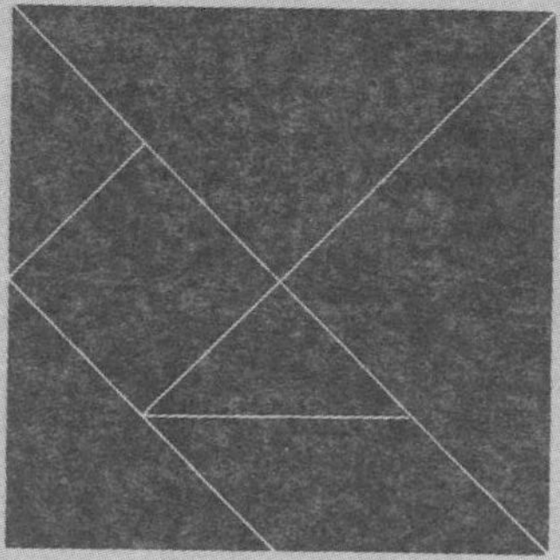

246 Cut a square of paper into seven pieces, as shown, in the diagram on the left. Can you rearrange the pieces to form each of the cats below? Each cat is made from all seven pieces.

247 As the first of the seven yachts crossed the finish line, the *Albatross* was half a length behind the *Barnacle*, and the *Cormorant* was half a length in front of the *Duck*. The *Duck* was in front of the *Albatross*, and the *Egret* had

more than three yachts behind her. The *Fulmar* finished a length in front of the *Duck*, and the *Gull* finished half a length in front of the *Egret*. There was at least half a length between each two yachts. Can you work out the order of finish?

248

Try doing this in your head without using pencil and paper.
If 513 people watched this magician, and one-third of them guessed how he did the trick, how many did not know?

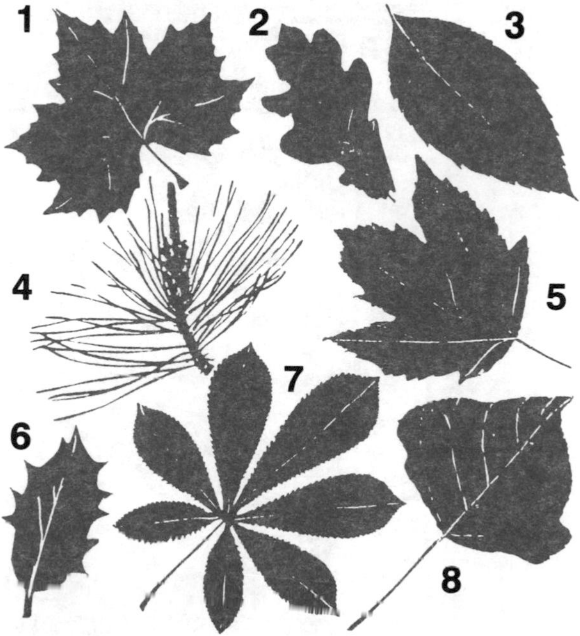

249

Rearrange the jumbled letters to find the names of the trees from which these leaves come.

1 PALEN
2 AKO
3 SAH
4 NIPE
5 MASCYROE
6 LOHYL
7 EOSRH TECSHUTN
8 ROLPAP

250 **Reassembling a mosaic is a mammoth task, particularly when the original plan (above) has been lost. The restorers**

had to rely on experience. Turn the page and see how many mistakes they made.

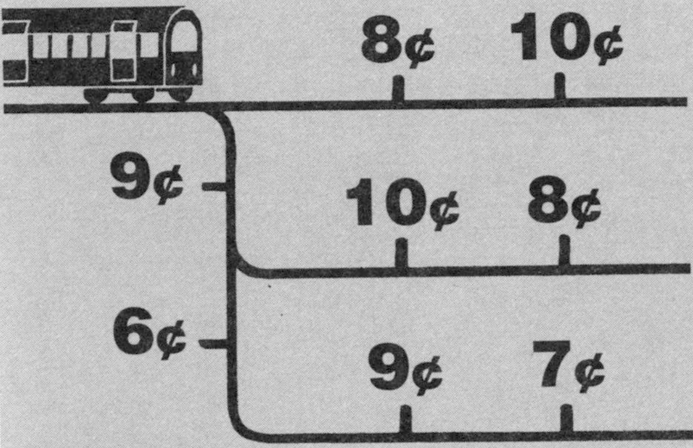

251 Which is the cheapest route home?

252 Jimmy left home at ten past one and waited a quarter of an hour for a bus, which then took 25 minutes to get to

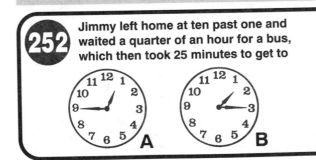

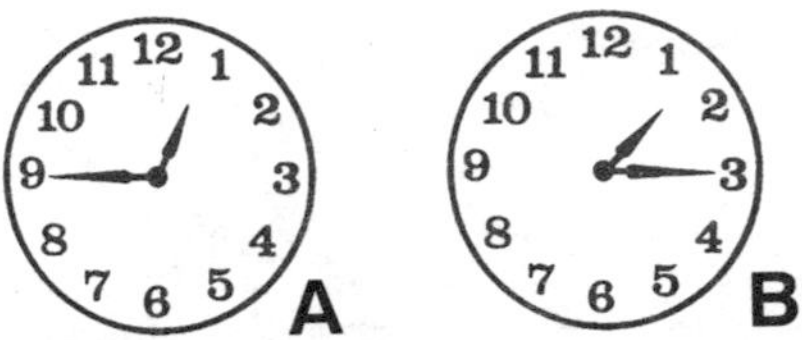

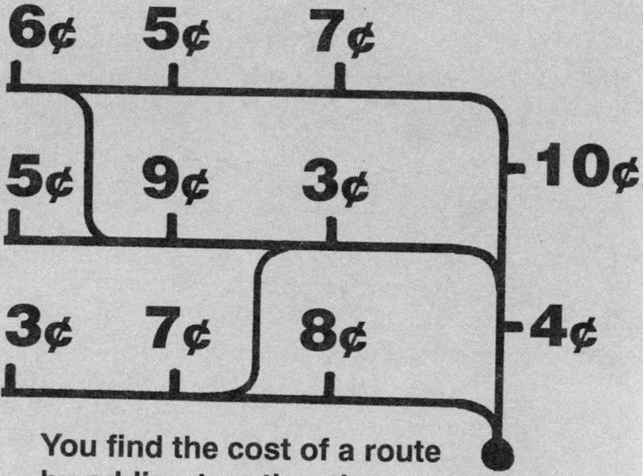

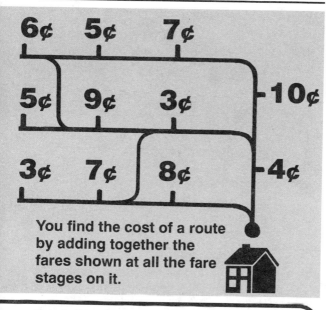

You find the cost of a route by adding together the fares shown at all the fare stages on it.

the station. As they arrived, Jimmy noticed that the station clock was 10 minutes slow. Which clock face shows the time on the station clock?

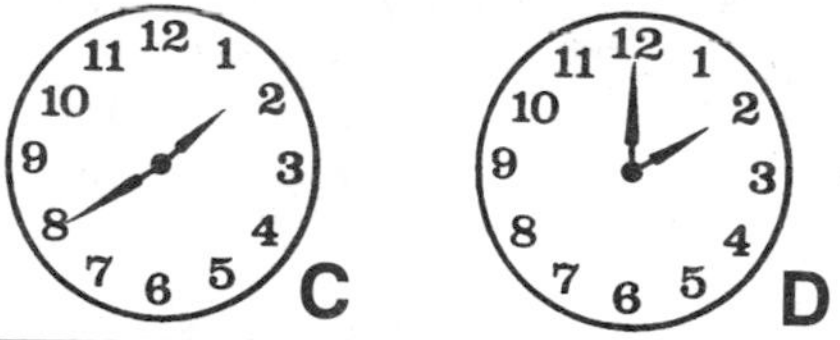

253

Four gamblers placed their bets on the order in which the first four horses in the Gold Trophy race would place. Gilbert had two of the four in the correct order: his list was 1st, Little Buttercup; 2nd, Nanki-Poo; 3rd, The Gondolier; and 4th, Pirate King. Sullivan's list read: 1st, Pirate King; 2nd, Little Buttercup; 3rd, Nanki-Poo; 4th, The Gondolier – he only had one horse placed correctly. Arthur had thought that Nanki-Poo and Pirate King would place next to each other, but he was wrong. William won the bet. What was his winning order?

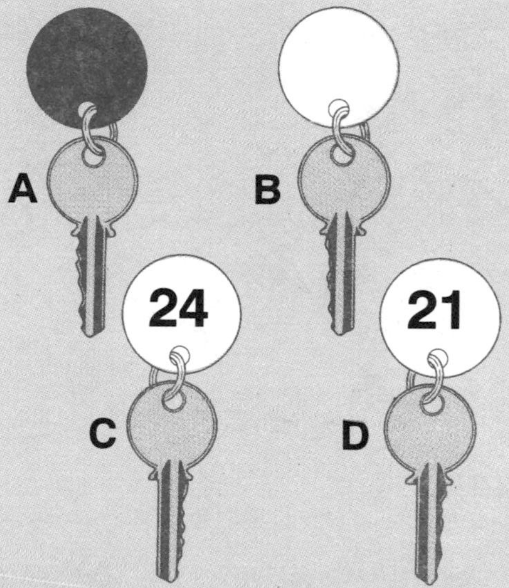

254 Each of the key rings belonging to the Grand Hotel is either black or white on one side and has either an odd or an even room number on the other side. If you saw four of the keys lying on the table, as shown above, which two of them would you pick up and turn over to find out if every black key ring had an odd number on its other side?

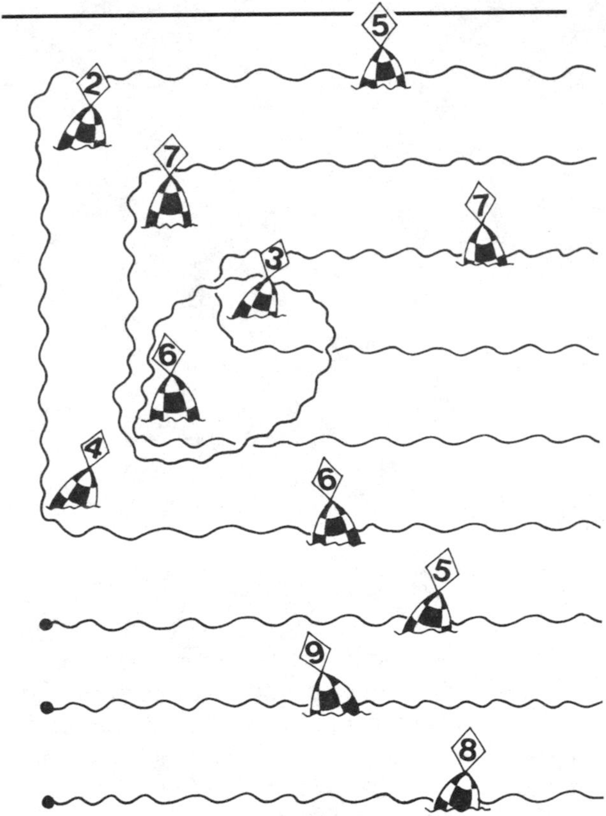

255 Add up the points every time a speedboat passes a buoy. Which boat has the highest score?

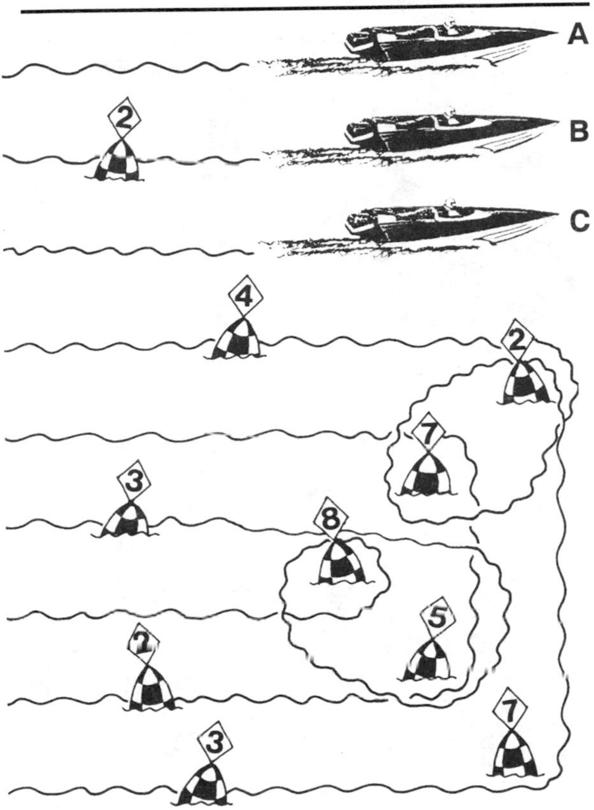
A
B
C
2
4
2
7
3
8
5
7
3

256

Which of the little men correctly completes the sequence of pictures on the right?

257

Which is the odd one out?

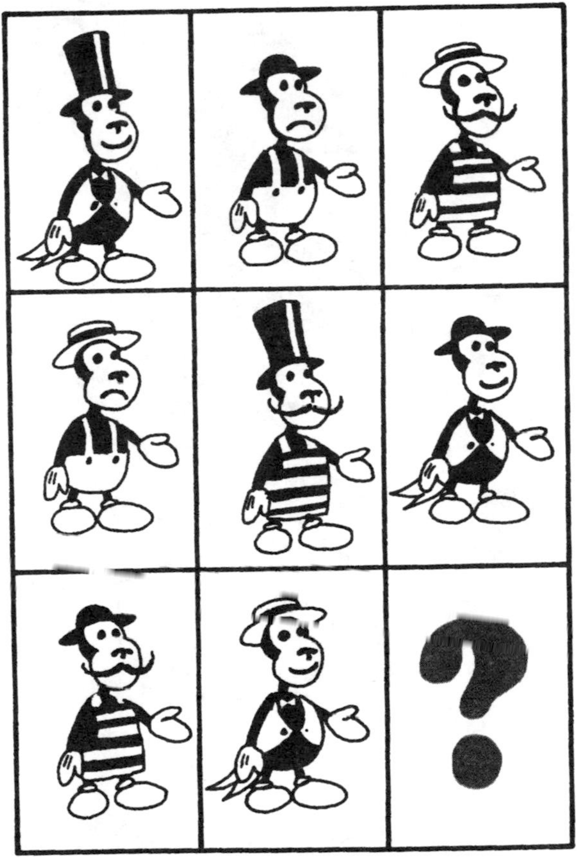

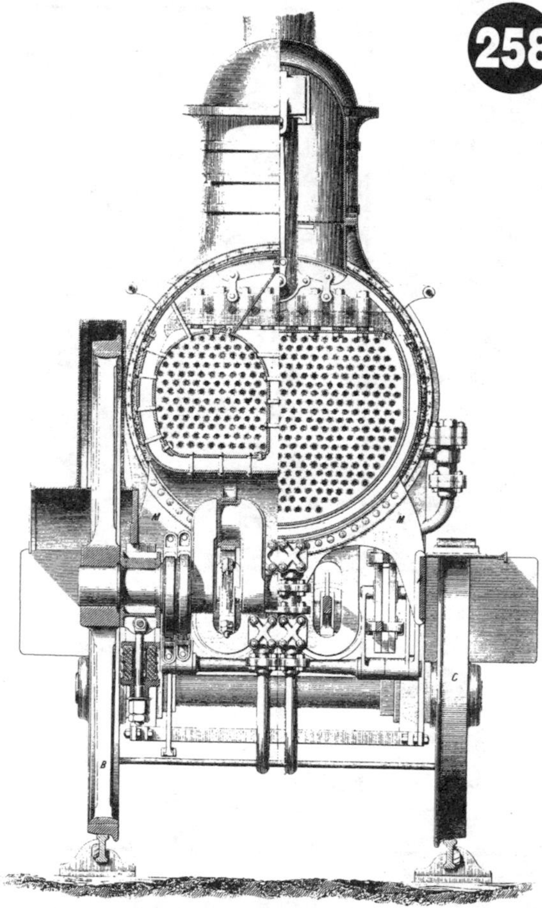
M
M
B
C

Patent inspectors need a keen eye for detail. How many differences can you find between these two 19th-century engineering drawings?

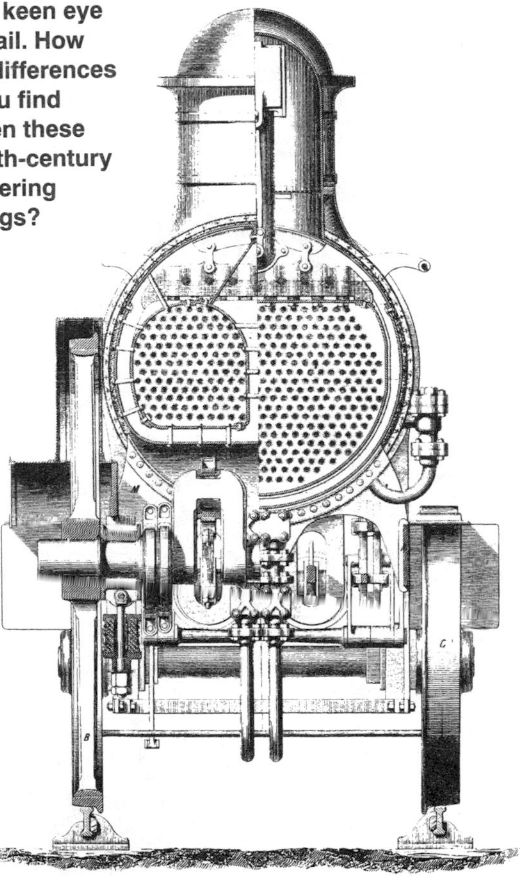

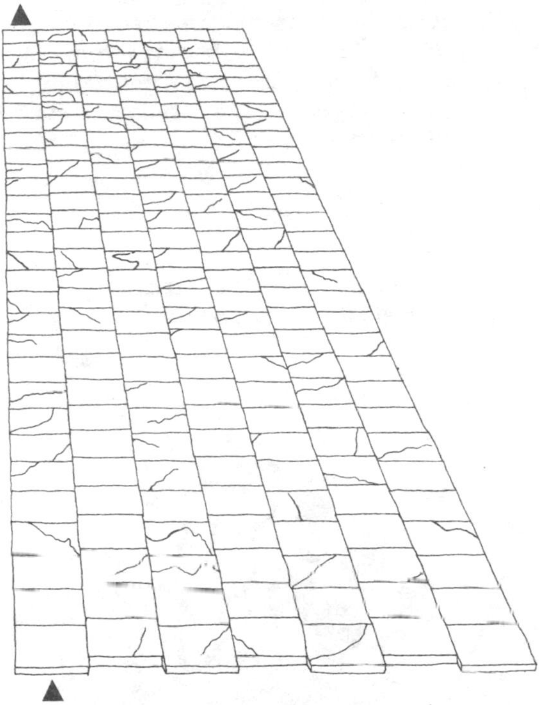

259 Step, tile by tile, from the middle tile at the bottom of the page to the middle tile at the top. Diagonal moves and stepping on cracked tiles are not allowed.

260 A number consisting of three different digits is subtracted from the number made up of the same digits in reverse order. The result consists of the same three digits in yet another order. What are the numbers?

261 Can you use the digits 1 to 9 once each to complete the sums on this supermarket checkout slip? One of the items costs three times as much as one of the others.

262

Complete the sequence.

212;179;146;113;??

263

Mark has twice as many marbles as Brian, and together they have 21. How many does Mark have?

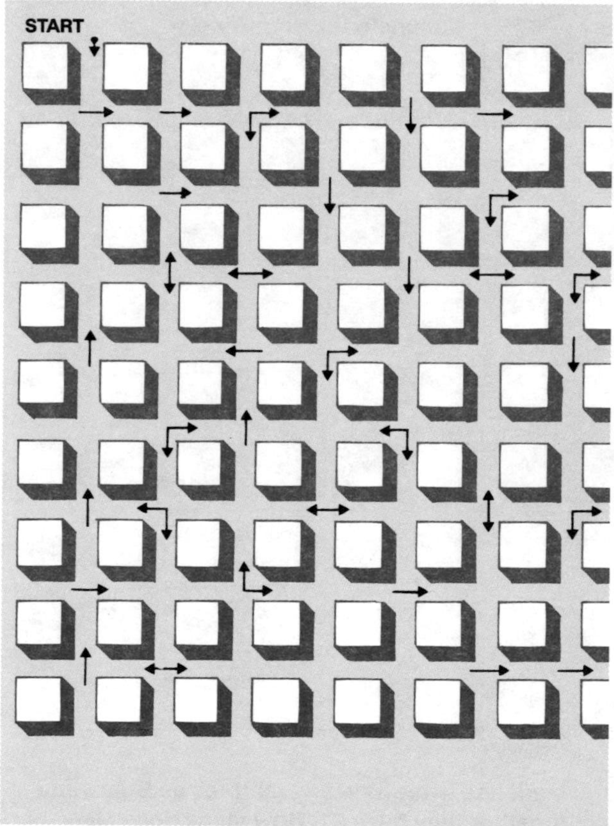

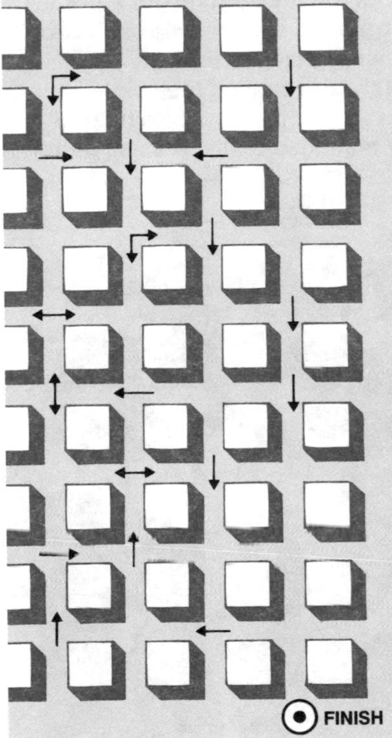

264

Follow the arrow pointing down from "start" and see if you can find the route to "finish." In this maze, you can only change direction when you meet an arrow, and then you MUST take the direction in which it is pointing. If you meet a double arrow, you may take either direction. You ARE allowed to cross your own path.

A costume ball in a castle had seemed a romantic idea – until the drawbridge got stuck in the up position, stranding eleven ladies and two gentlemen on the wrong side of the very deep moat that completely surrounded the castle. Everyone else had left, so there was no help to be had. Then they managed to find a small motor

boat, but it would only hold one lady at a time (they had all chosen to wear very full skirts) or both the gentlemen. How did they all manage to cross the moat safely without getting wet?

265

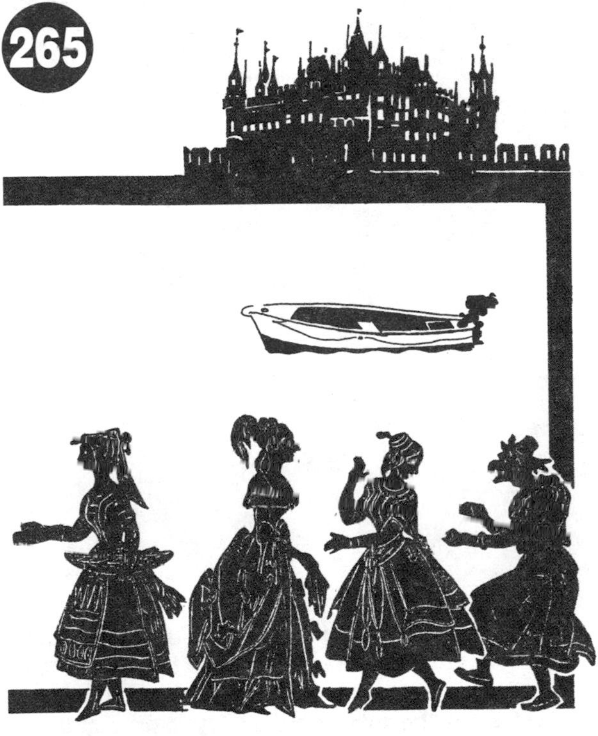

266

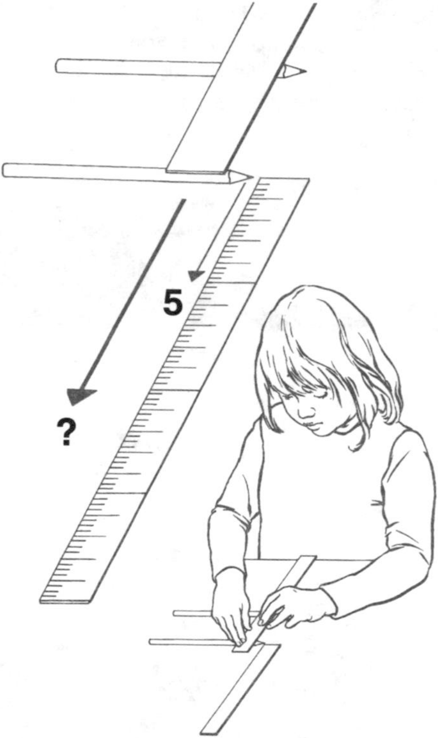

Rest a ruler on two round pencils. Now push the ruler forward (pressing down on it so that it does not slip) so that the pencils roll forward 5 inches. How far has the ruler moved? Try to predict the result before you make the model!

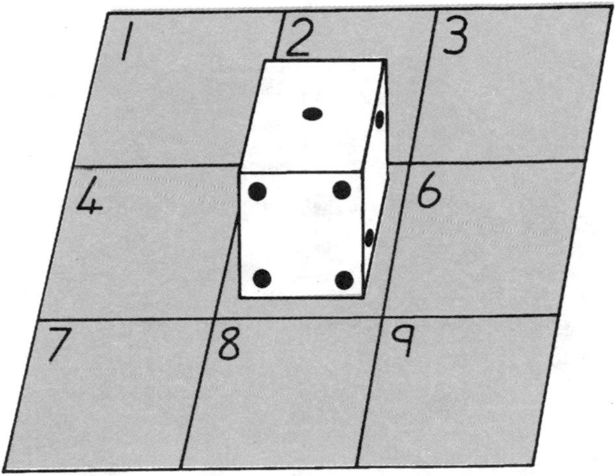

267

Can you roll this die so that it reaches the 7 square with its 6 spot uppermost in only six moves? On each move you may roll the die a quarter turn up, down, left, or right, but not diagonally.

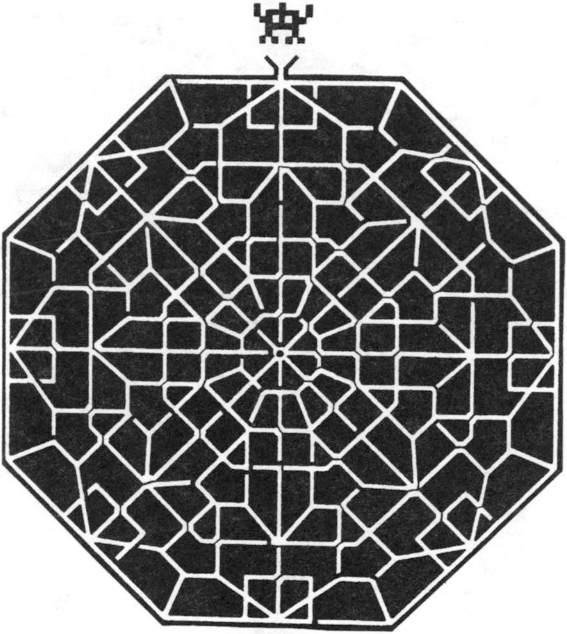

268

Which route should the space invader take to reach the center of the space maze?

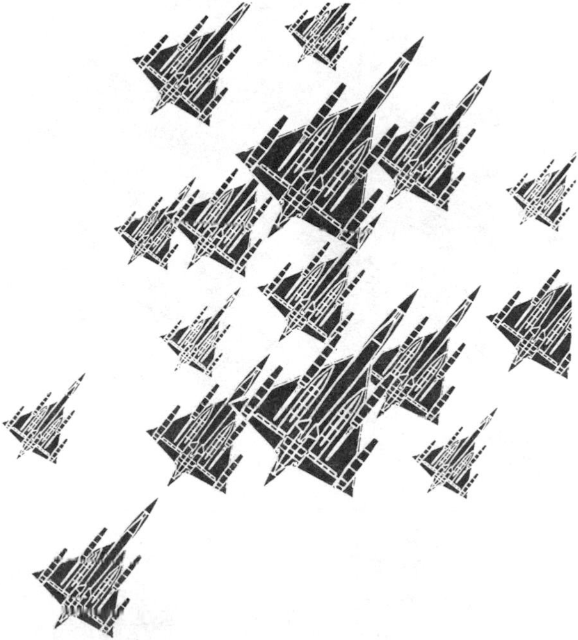

269 Captain Kroll had 16 fighters in his squadron until all but 10 of them were shot down. How many fighters has he got left?

270

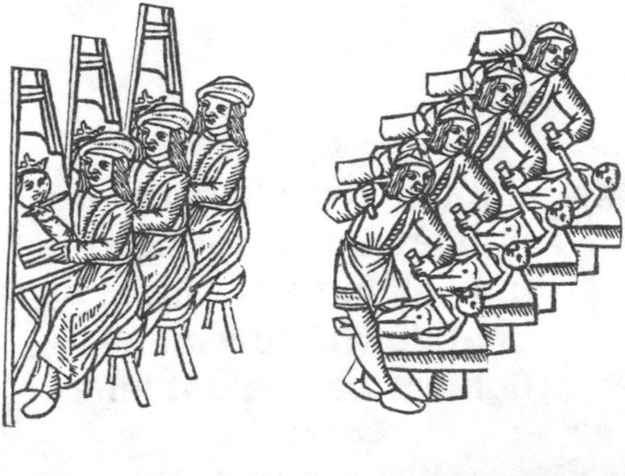

While building a medieval cathedral, it cost 37 guilders to hire 4 artists and 3 stonemasons or 33 guilders for 3 artists and 4 stonemasons. What would be the expense of just one of each?

271

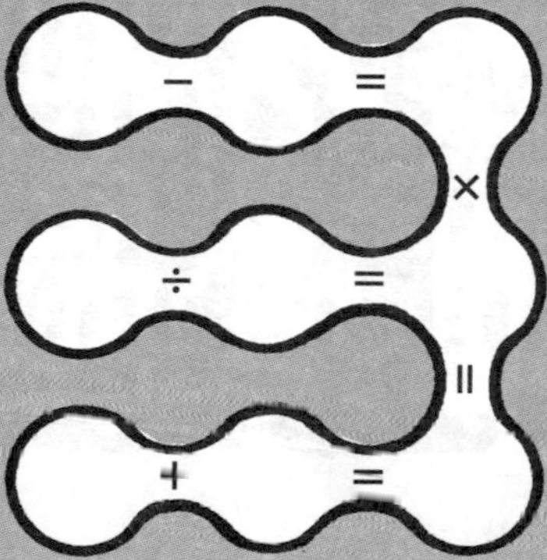

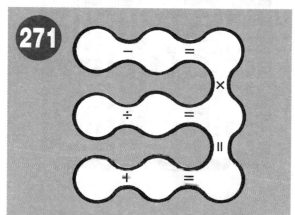

The solution to this puzzle requires the use, once only, of each of the numbers 1 through 9, and each of the four basic mathematical operations. The signs +, −, ×, and ÷ have already been inserted. Can you fill in the rest?

272 **The young Mayan in the bottom left-hand corner had to prove his ingenuity to his father by finding a path to the god. How did he do it?**

273

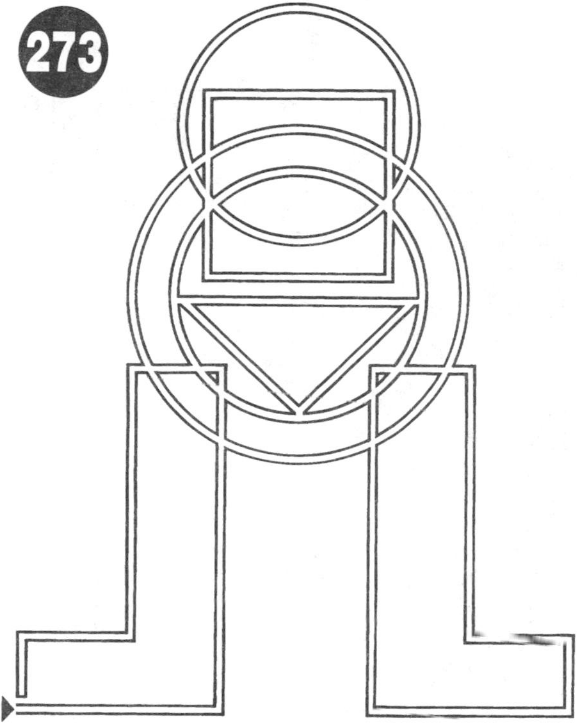

Before the robot can be fully operational, it has to be wired up. The engineer must run the wire through each channel in a continuous line without doubling up the wire. How does he do it?

274 An 18th-century American settler invented a new alphabet in which the reader could work out the sequence of letters from their shapes alone. Which of the six boxed shapes comes next in the sequence?

275 While the children were away at school their mother accidentally rearranged their toy car-race layout. The corner pieces are still in their correct positions, but can you quickly reorganize the six middle triangles to recreate a single continuous racetrack?

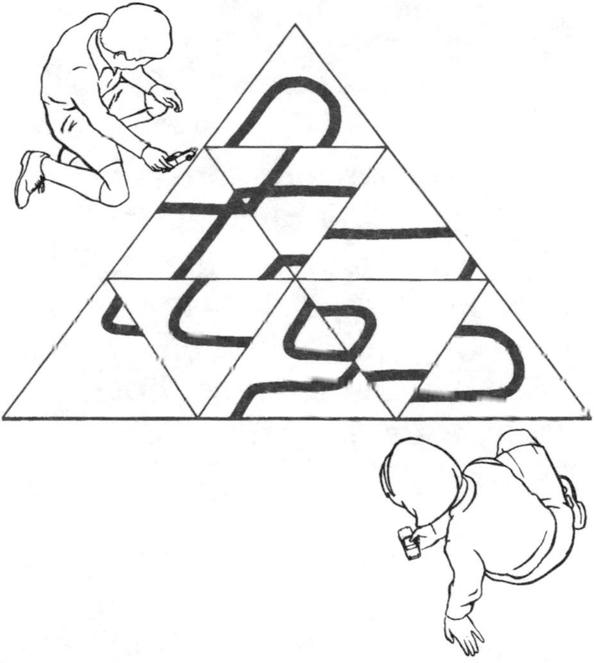

276 The rowboat crosses the river once every half hour. If it makes its first crossing at 7:30 in the morning and its last crossing at 8:00 in the evening, how many trips does it make?

277 Can you cut this key ring and its two attached keys from a single piece of stiff cardboard without any breaks or joints?

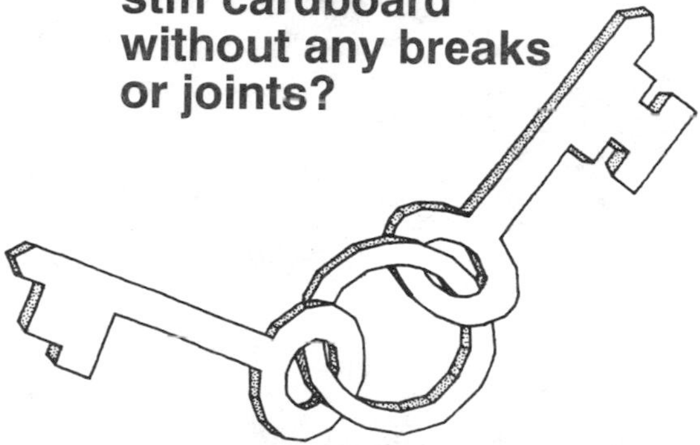

278 Can you write 5 odd figures that add up to make a total of 14? (Be careful – there is a catch.)

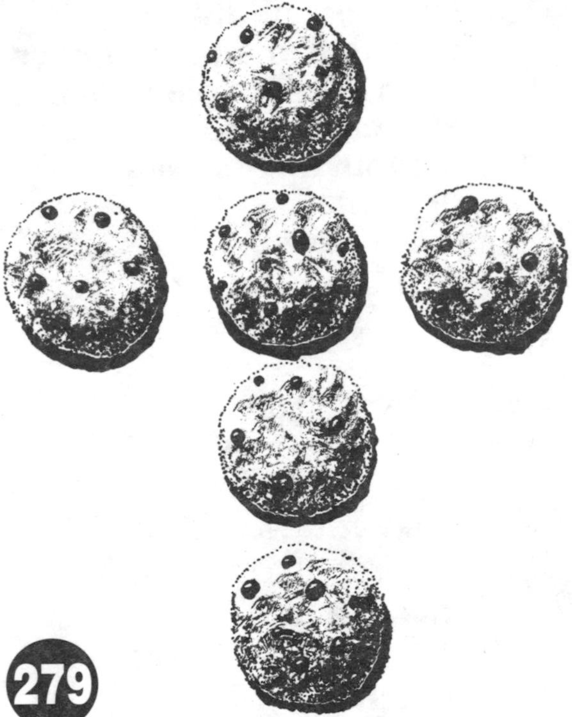

279

Can you rearrange these six chocolate chip cookies so that the cross has four cookies across and four going up and down?

280

This closed band has one twist in it – it's called a Möbius strip. Can you predict what you will get if you cut it along the dotted line?

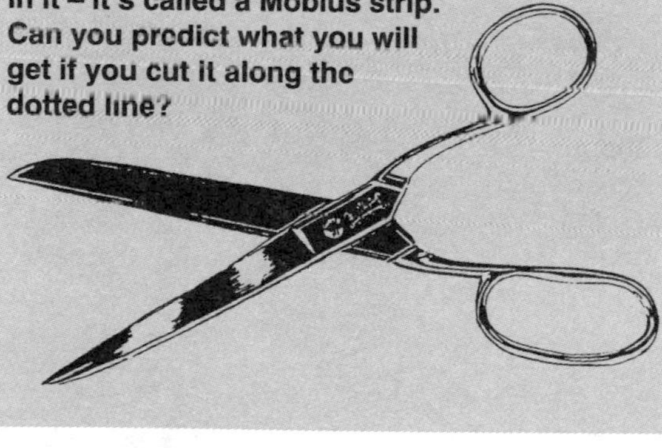

281

Shotgun Pete owned a lot of guns.

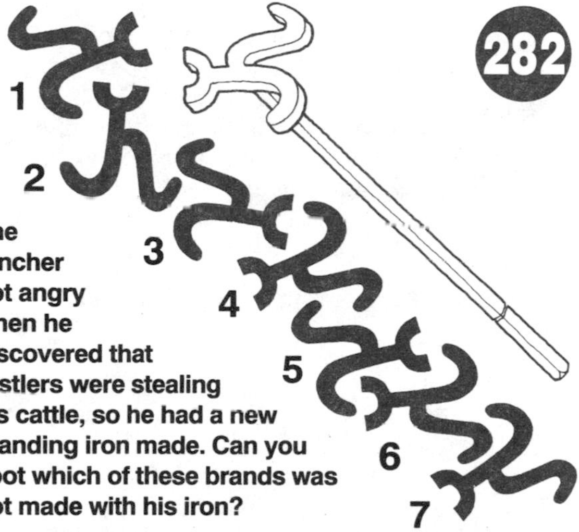

282

The rancher got angry when he discovered that rustlers were stealing his cattle, so he had a new branding iron made. Can you spot which of these brands was not made with his iron?

He left a quarter of them in Death Valley, gave one to each of the three passengers in the stagecoach, and kept half of them with him. How many guns did Pete own?

283 One of the men coming out of the cantina was overheard to say to the other, "There are two bandits in there, and one of them is the father of the other's son!" Can you explain how this could happen?

284 People have it – girls and ladies always, men and boys never, although Larry certainly had it first, and Bill had it twice. What is it?

285 Starting and finishing at the top, can you find your way around this Moorish mystery maze?

286 Find the driver's route from Buckingham Palace to the Houses of Parliament (right). Arrows show the direction of traffic in the one-way streets.

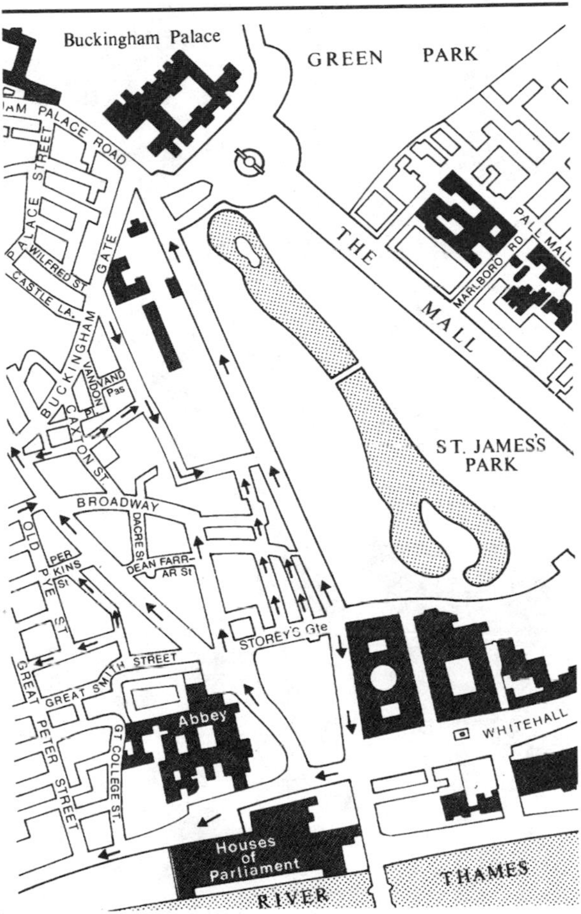
Buckingham Palace
GREEN PARK
PALACE ROAD
PALACE STREET
WILFRED ST
CASTLE LA.
BUCKINGHAM GATE
THE MALL
PALL MALL
MARLBORO RD
VANDON
VAND Pas
CAXTON ST
ST. JAMES'S PARK
BROADWAY
DACRE St
DEAN FARRAR St
PERKINS St
OLD PYE ST
STOREY'S Gte
GREAT SMITH STREET
GREAT PETER STREET
GT COLLEGE ST.
Abbey
WHITEHALL
Houses of Parliament
RIVER
THAMES

a	B	b	c	A	C	C	b
B	C	c	A	C	C	a	A
a	a	A	c	C	a	b	C
c	a	b	c	B	C	A	c
C	B	c	b	A	C	b	C
c	a	c	c	B	A	C	A
B	a	C	c	A	b	a	c
a	B	b	a	b	A	C	A
B	c	a	b	B	a	b	c
a	C	b	c	a	c	b	A

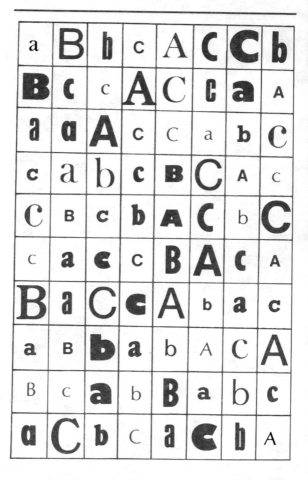

287 Start at the letter "A" in the bottom right-hand corner. Move to a "B," then to a "C," and continue in the sequence A-B-C-A-B-C. You may move vertically, horizontally, or diagonally. How many squares are there in the shortest route from the start to the "a" in the top left-hand corner?

288 The mayor says that he can cut a hole in his piece of paper large enough for him to climb through. He says he could do the same with a postcard! How does he do it?

289

The diver is working 20ft below the surface of the water. The gap between the water and the deck of his support barge accounts for one-eighth of the available length of air pipe, and two-thirds of the total length remains on the reel. What is his maximum working depth without a change of equipment?

290 How many units of pressure must I put in the third black balloon in order to maintain the same relationship within each group of balloons?

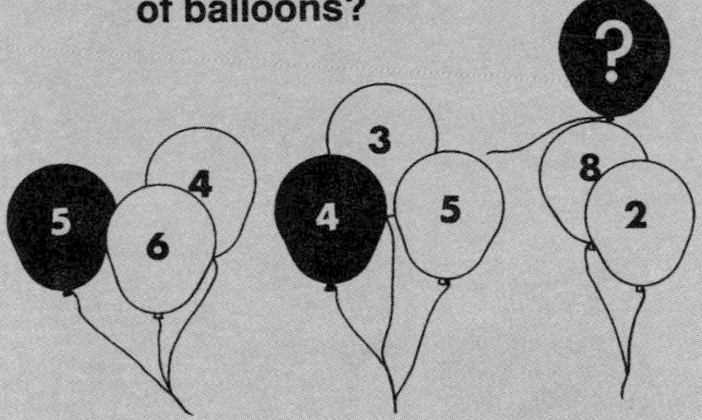

1 2 3 4 5 7 8 9

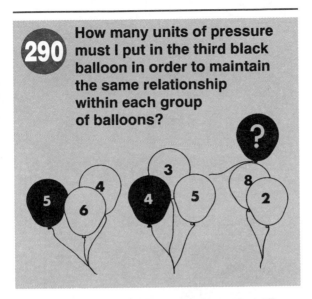

291 Can you arrange these figures into two separate groups, both of which add up to the same total? (And no, you can't turn the 9 upside down and call it a 6!)

292 The truck starts off with 100 boxes on its trailer. Another 25 boxes are added at its first stop; at its next stop, 45 boxes are taken away; at its last stop, 20 more are loaded on. How many boxes are left at the end of the journey?

293 "Look," said Clarissa, "all the odd numbers are printed in red."

"And all the even numbers are black," said Cynthia. What color is an odd number plus an even number?

294

The winning combination on this machine consists of the numbers 1, 3, 5, 7, 9 arranged in the form of a calculation: two 2-digit numbers multiplied and the remaining number then subtracted. The answer consists of the same digit repeated four times. Find the winning combination.

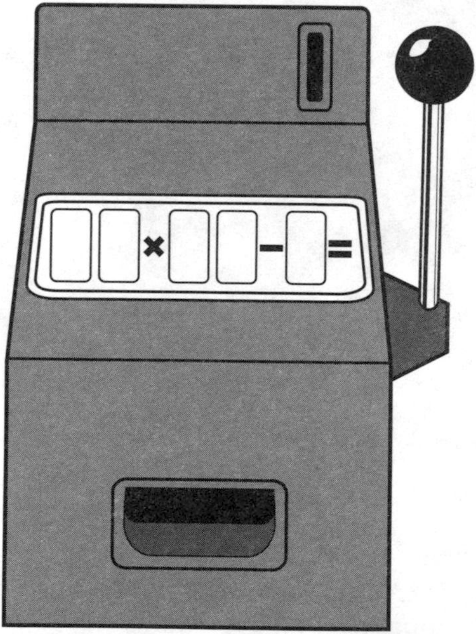

295 If two volumes are interchanged at each move, what would be the minimum number of moves required to return this set of books to its correct order on the shelf?

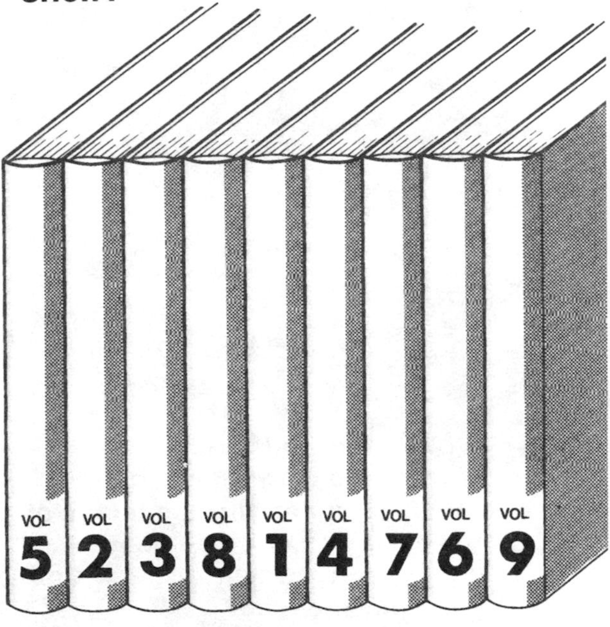

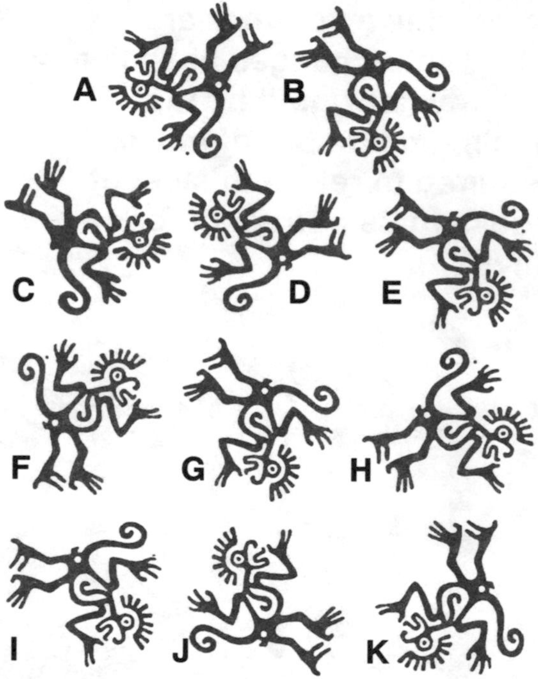

296 **A professor in Mexico discovered a hoard of gold rings, each bearing the image of a monkey. One, he decided immediately, was a forgery. Can you spot the fake?**

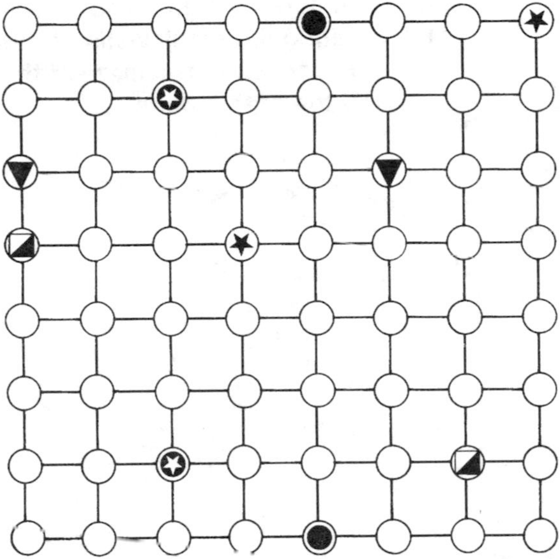

297 A robot was instructed to join each marked terminal to its matching twin using the connecting wires on the grid. No lines were to cross and no intermediate terminal could be used twice. Can you find the solution?

The museum curator found a novel way of decorating the blank walls of this corridor. Enter the maze at the top of this page . . .

298

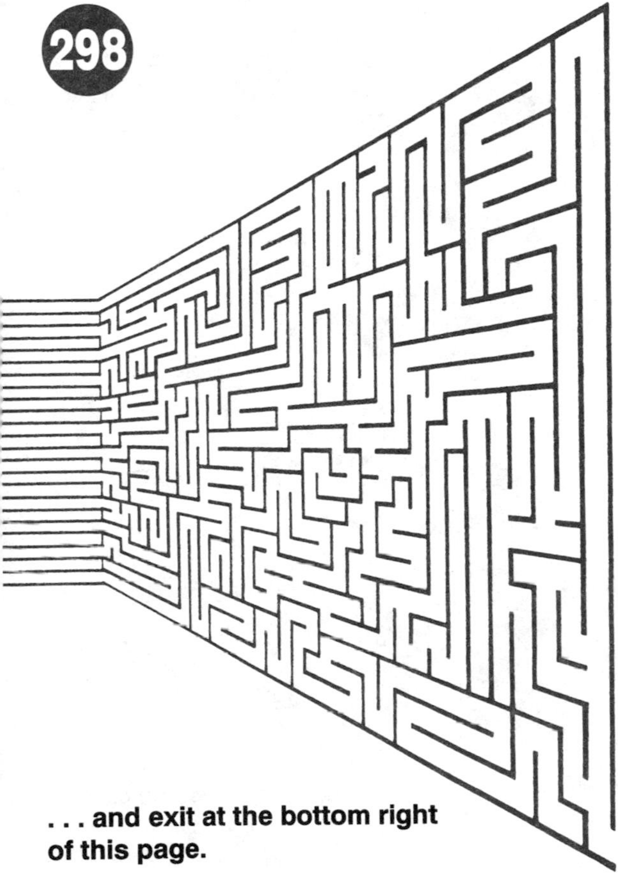

. . . and exit at the bottom right of this page.

299 Can you rearrange these playing cards so that no two cards of the same value or the same suit are in the same vertical, horizontal, or diagonal row of four?

300 You can only separate all three of these loops of string by cutting the middle loop – if you cut one of the end loops, the other two remain linked together. Can you retie the three loops to interlock so that they will all come apart whichever one is cut?

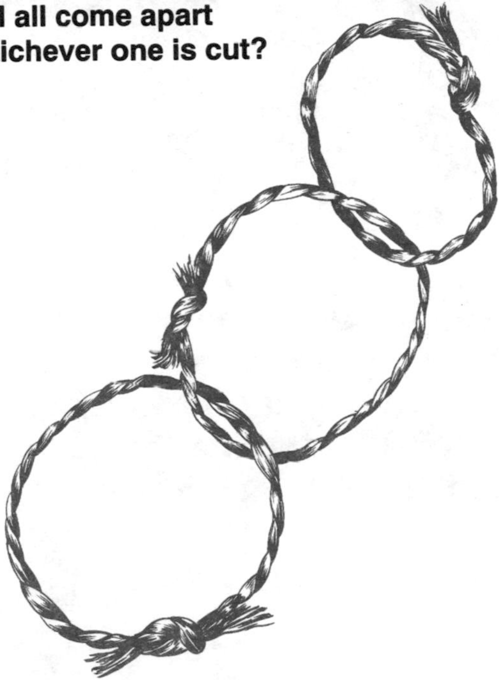

301

Three antique clocks were put up for auction. The first lost one minute in every 24 hours; the second lost one minute in every hour; and the third didn't go at all. Which clock would you buy if you chose the one that showed the correct time most often?

302

Some baseball players are amateurs. All amateurs play without financial reward, and many do so with great enthusiasm. Therefore:

a) Baseball players all play without any financial reward
b) All amateurs are enthusiastic baseball players
c) Some baseball players play with great enthusiasm

True or false?

303 **Can you find the earthworm's route to the surface?**

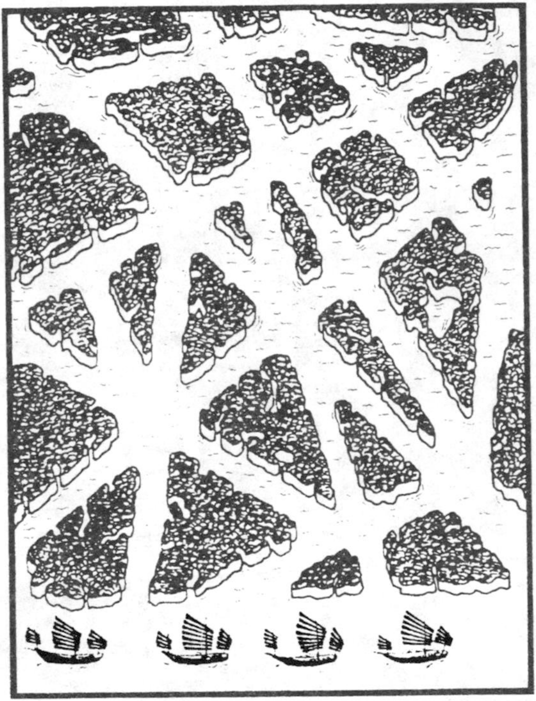

304 The Emperor of China realized that he needed only four boats for his men to be able to keep watch over all the channels between the Fu Chow Tong islands. Mark a cross at each of the four different points where the boats were stationed.

305

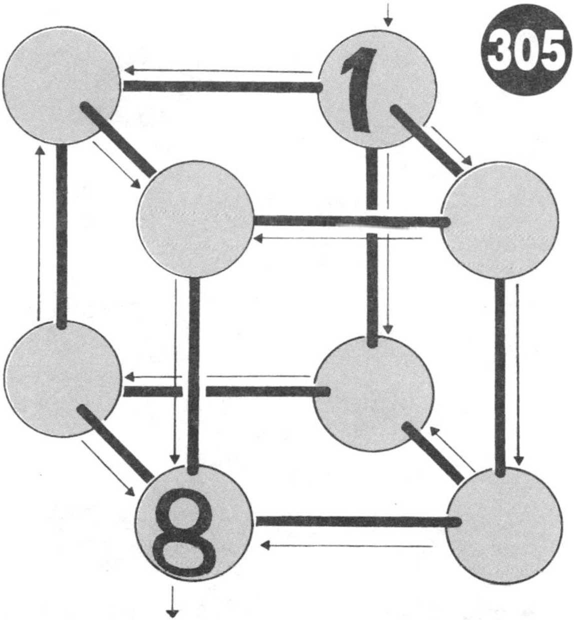

Merlin's magical model cube used to have a number in each corner. Taken in the order 1,2,3,4,5,6,7,8, they marked a vital spell path around the cube. Unfortunately, he has absent-mindedly erased all the numbers except the 1 and the 8, although he has left in the arrows that show all the possible spell directions. Can you replace the numbers for him in their correct corners?

306

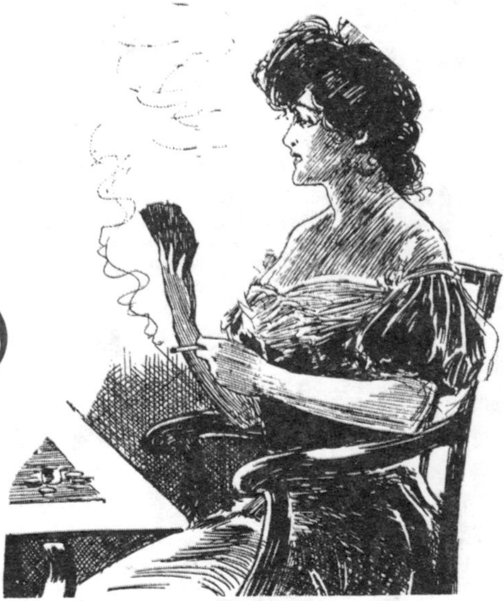

The fortune-teller had picked up six tarot cards: four from the suit of batons and two from the suit of cups. No two cards had the same number of pips. The pips on the cards from the suit of batons added up to three less than the total number of pips on the cards from the suit of cups. And one of the cards from the suit of cups had one-third of the total number of pips on all the cards. If there were no picture cards in her hand, which cards did the fortune-teller hold?

307

If two fathers and two sons went fishing, and each caught a fish and brought it home with him, why did they only have 3 fish?

308

With the sheriff closing in, Lucky Jim and his two henchmen have a few seconds to divide up the nine apparently identical gold nuggets they have stolen. Jim knows that one is heavier than the rest. Being smarter than the average outlaw, he locates it in a single weighing. How?

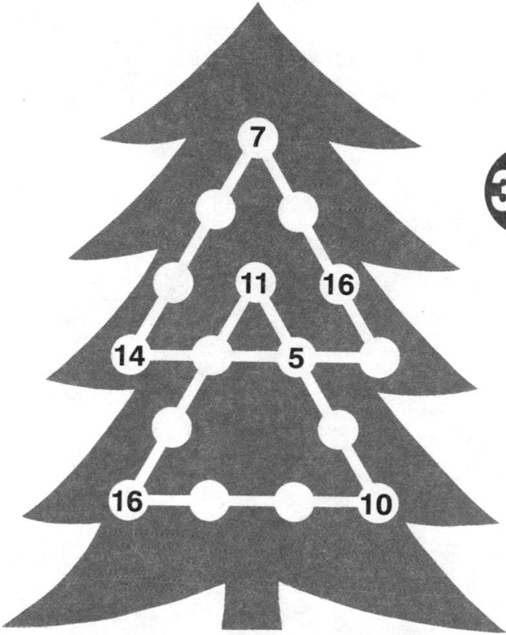

309

One of the tree lights flashes once a minute, another twice a minute, and so on up to sixteen times a minute. The total number of flashes per minute on each of the six lines is 34. Can you place the bulbs in their correct positions in the tree?

310 Can you match these athletes with their equipment?

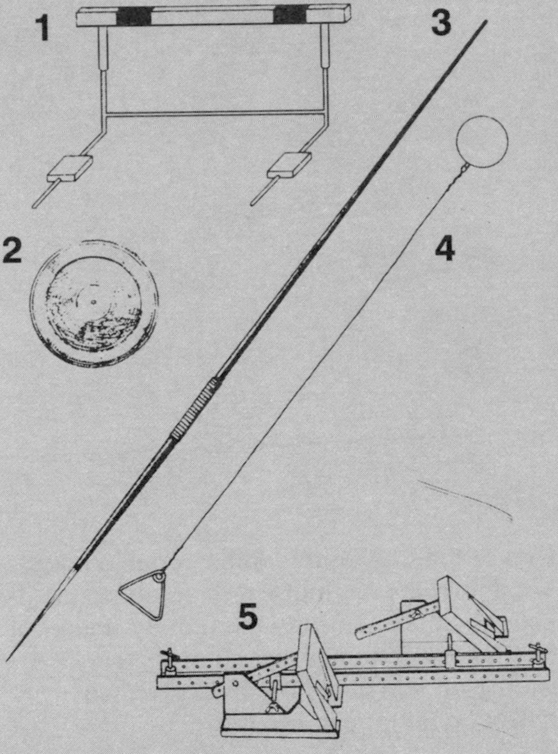

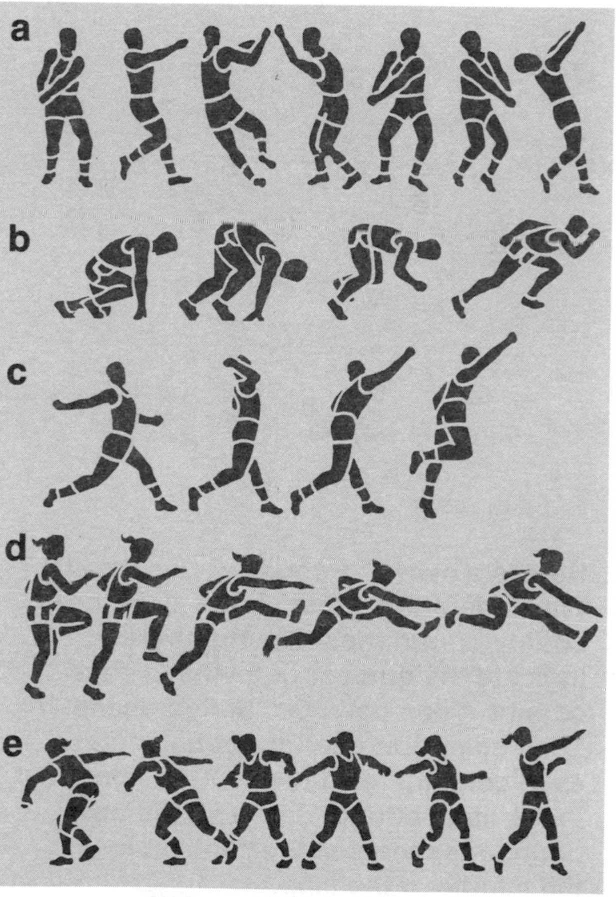
a
b
c
d
e

311

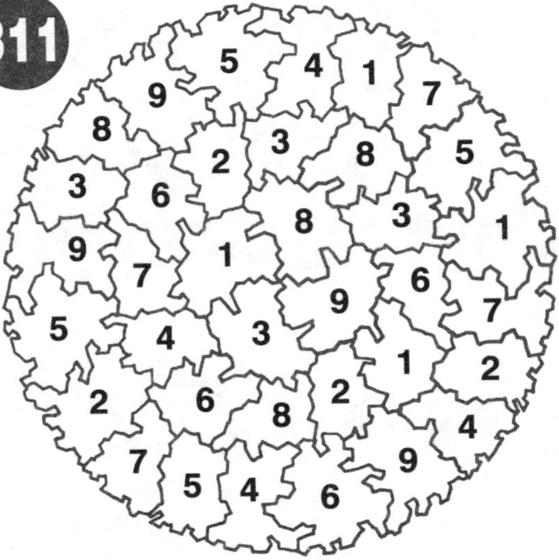

Here is a map of a country – we'll call it The Federation – that shows only the county boundaries. The numbers indicate the number of towns in each county. It has been decided to divide The Federation into four equal states, each containing 45 towns. Can you draw in the state boundaries? (All the new boundaries meet at the capital city in the middle of the map.)

312

A problem of mental arithmetic to solve in your head. Add seven to eight, multiply by nine, divide by three, subtract seventeen, divide by four.

313

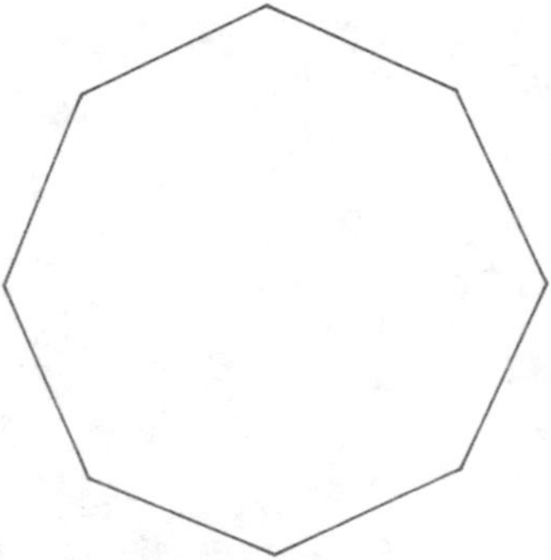

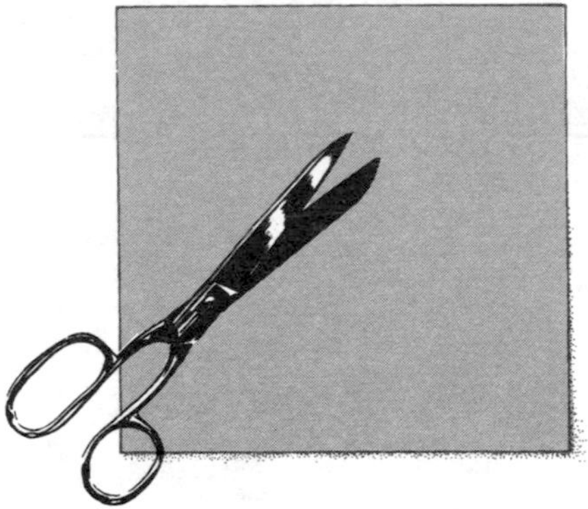

Anyone can construct a regular octagon with the help of pencils, rulers, compasses, and so on. But can you cut one out of a square of paper without using any of those things? You are allowed to fold the paper to make creases in it.

314

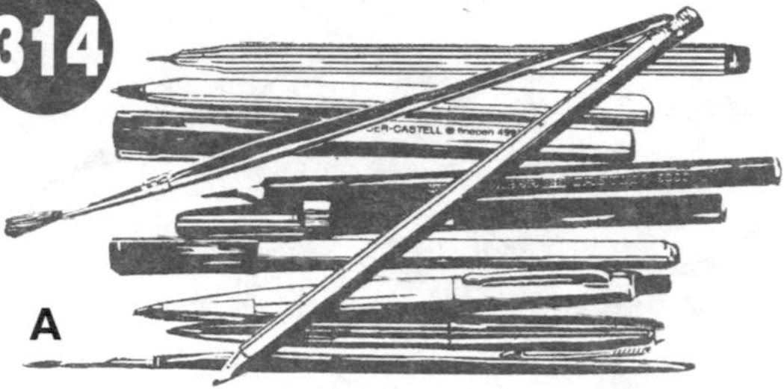

A

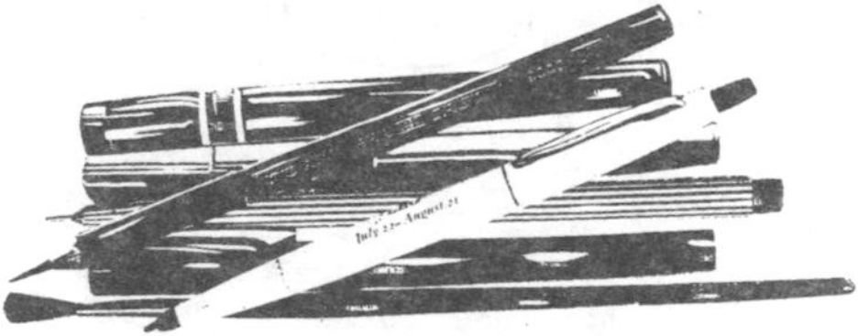

B

C

There are 11 objects in pile A, 7 in pile B, and 6 in pile C. Can you rearrange them so there are 8 in each pile? You may only add as many objects to a pile as it already contains, e.g., you could put 6 onto pile C, no more, no less. And you should be able to do it in three moves.

315

Use a dollar bill to make a bridge between two of the glasses. Then balance the third glass on the bill so that it stays there without any other support! All the glasses should stand straight up. You will find it easier to use a crisp new dollar.

316 This puzzle calls for 80 small objects – we've used pistachio nuts. You and an opponent are to take turns picking up nuts from the heap. The player picking up the last nut is the winner. You may both pick up any number of nuts between 1 and 9 inclusive when it is your turn, and you may vary the number picked up each time if you wish. There is a way of making sure that you always win this game. Can you discover what it is?

317

Three years ago, Mary was seven times as old as her sister Jane. Two years ago Mary was four times as old as Jane, and one year ago she was three times as old as Jane. How old are Mary and Jane?

318

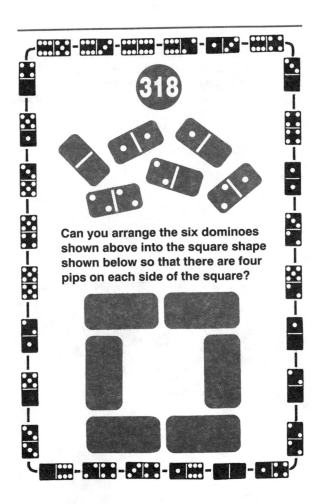

Can you arrange the six dominoes shown above into the square shape shown below so that there are four pips on each side of the square?

1

Here we see the bridge from above. The three interlocked rulers rest on the three empty glasses, and support the one full of water.

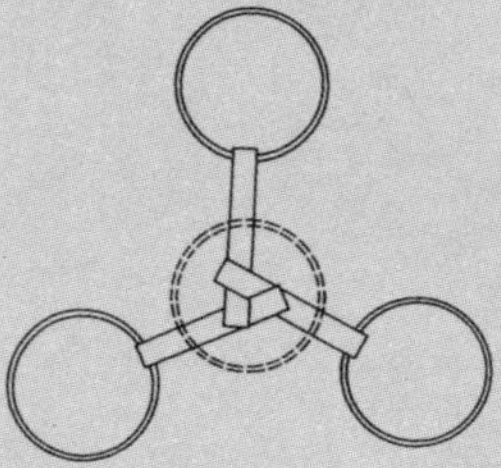

2

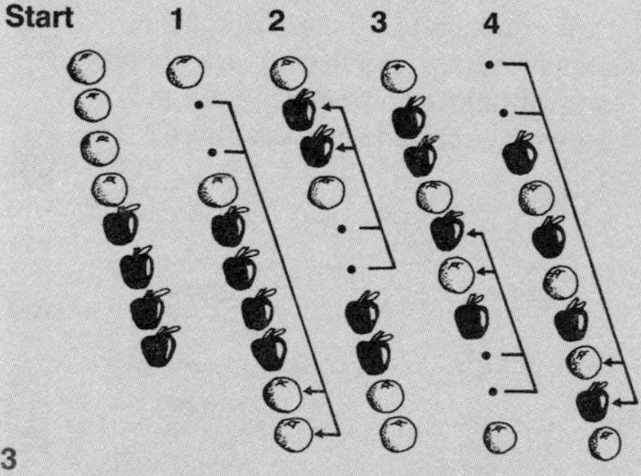

3

Eight – seven daughters and one son.

4

A.

5

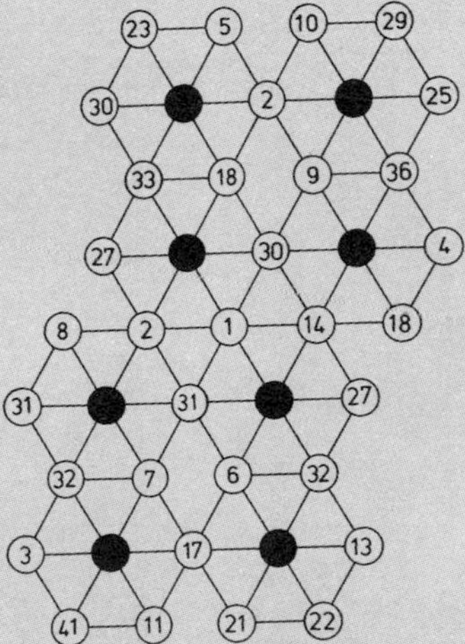

6

Arrange the matches as shown, to read one over the square root of one. The square root of one being one, the "fraction" now equals one.

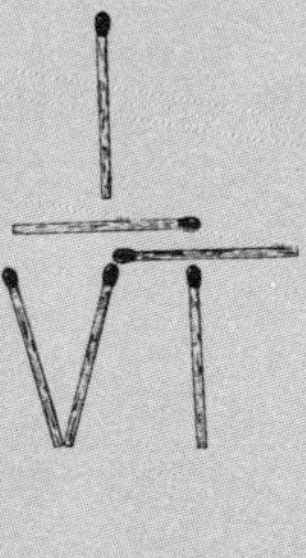

7

At 11.59 a.m.

8

One.

1 23 6 14 19 2 24 10 7
9 8 7 12 24 6 18 5 16
3 4 24 8 7 1 6 24 11
6 5 12 6 8 10 15 12 27
12 2 7 21 6 15 30 7
11 6 5 6 10 12 9 6 11
12 8 11 30 15 18 6 24 9
2 13 24 6 12 8 6 7 18
9 8 12 10 9 7 15 3 8

9

Three hours. If the project takes me 7 1/2 hours, then in 1 hour I can do 2/15 of it. Similarly, in 1 hour you can do 1/5 of it. Working together, in 1 hour we could do 2/15 + 1/5 = 1/3 of the project and so we could complete the project in exactly 3 hours.

10

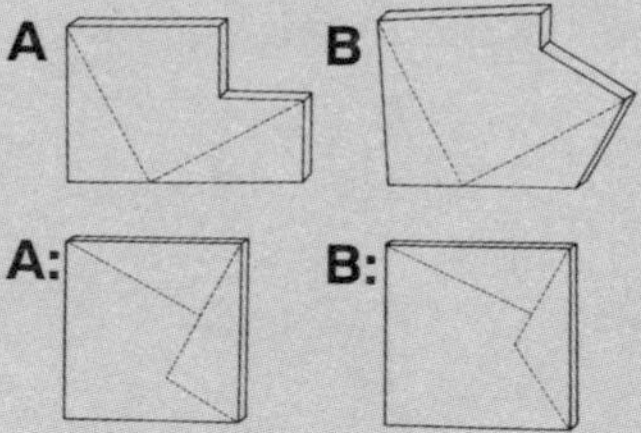

11

Twenty–seven, 25, 18, 16, and 14 nuts in bowls 1–5, respectively. The number in each bowl can be found by subtracting the sum of the other two pairs of bowls from 100. So 100–(52+34)=14, the number in the last bowl.

12
Four. Percy Street, a lawyer, married his client Charlotte (Mrs. Street), and they have a daughter, Primrose Hill, who is a widow. Her aunt is Alexandra Road, Mrs. Street's sister.

13
He should write (5+5)x(5+5)=100.

14
No. The object is an optical illusion – it is possible to draw it on paper but not to make it in three dimensions.

15
The referee. When two people are facing one another they are facing in opposite directions – and so the duellists would have been able to fire at each other.

16
He chose one of the slips of paper, and quickly tore it up and threw the pieces away. He then said to the trolls, "That was the fate I chose – let us see what is on the other slip. It says 'Dinner,'

so I must have chosen 'Freedom,' and you must release me."

17

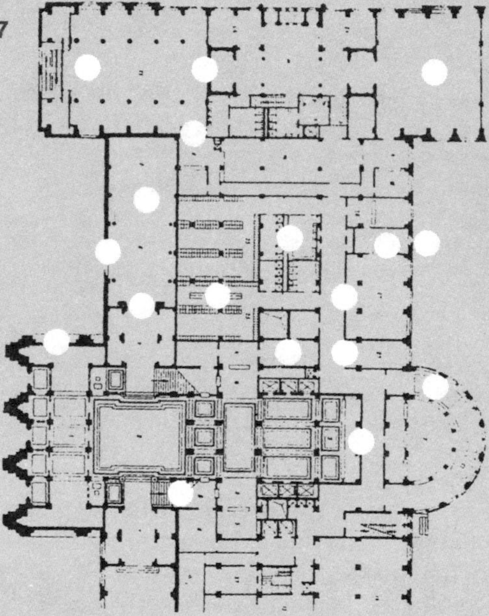

18

If Alan stole the bicycle, both Bill and Charlie were telling the truth. If Bill stole the bicycle, both Alan and Charlie were telling the truth. If Charlie stole the bicycle, only Bill was telling the truth. As only one of the three was telling the truth, Charlie must have been the thief.

19
He strung the tape between the survey posts, as shown here.

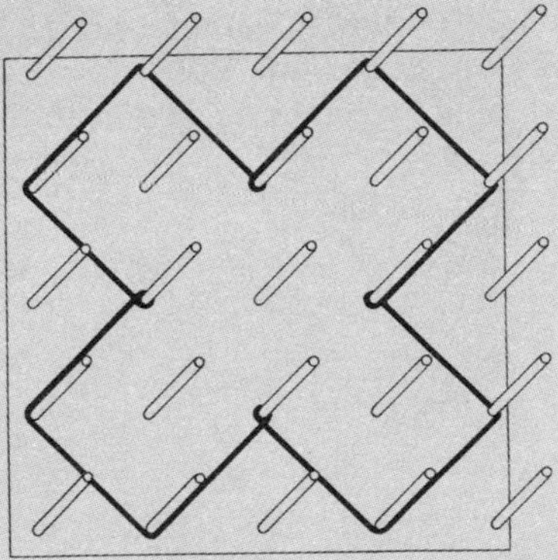

20
Neither. This is another "impossible" drawing. The steps are a visual trick: follow them with a finger and you can "walk" up or down stairs forever.

21
a) Three.
b) A woman carrying a broom.
c) A bucket.
d) Two.
e) Two.

22
This is written in code. (Hold the writing upside down in front of a mirror.)

23

The animals are: 1 Pig, 2 Peregrine falcon, 3 Gibbon, 4 Sea lion, 5 Tree frog, 6 Jerboa, 7 Galagon, 8 Piranha, 9 Siamese cat, 10 King crab, 11 Opossum, 12 Axolotl. Odd one out is the king crab, the only invertebrate.

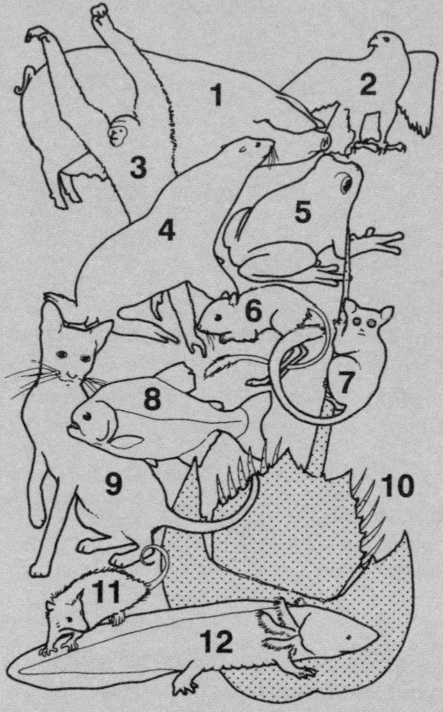

24
The total number of triangles is 50.

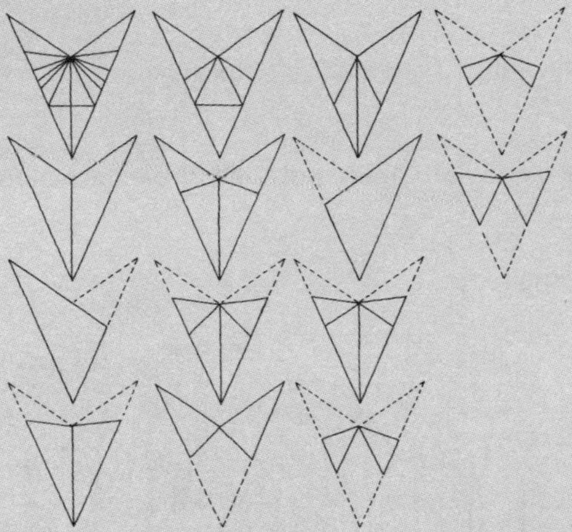

25
The match.

26
George Washington was unable to tell a lie and, therefore, had cut down the cherry tree. A tree that has been cut down cannot continue to produce cherries, so the fruit that Bart was eating could not have come from George Washington's tree. So Bart, unlike George Washington, was not telling the truth.

27
Forty-two books.

28
None – holes are always empty.

29
The blades are open, but the handles are closed.

30
Sunday.

31

32

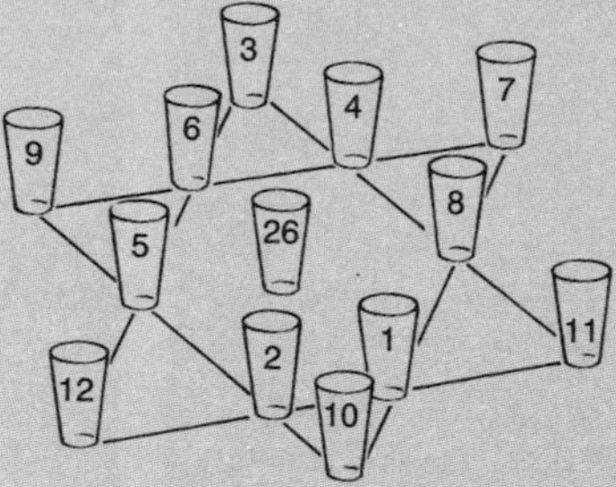

33
Eight pieces.

34

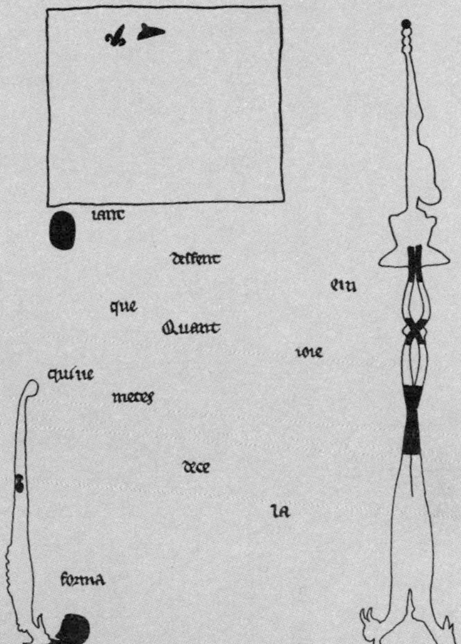

35

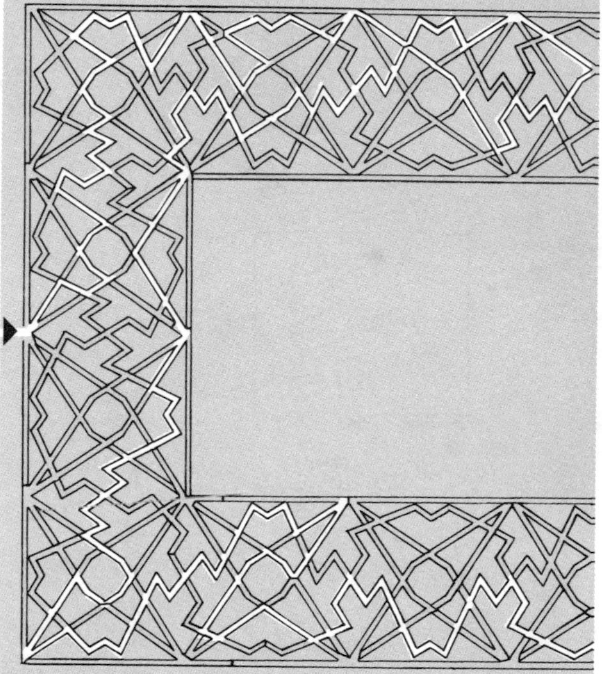

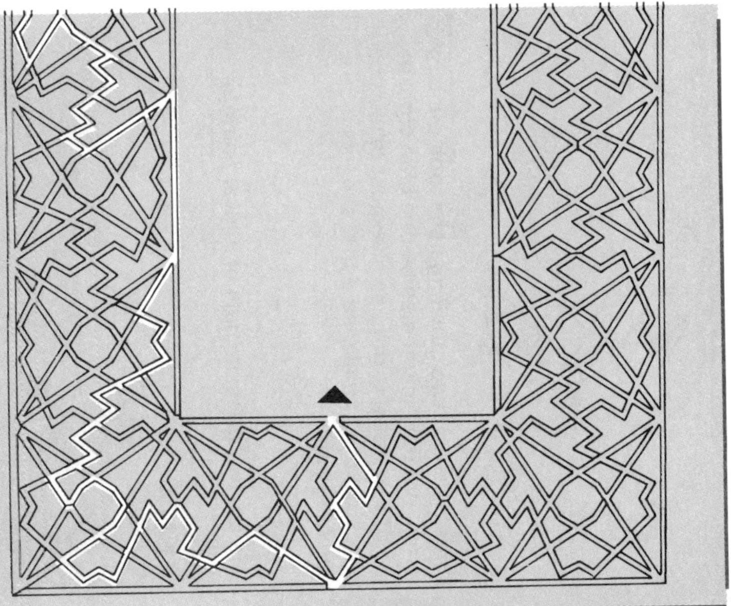

ANSWER 35

36

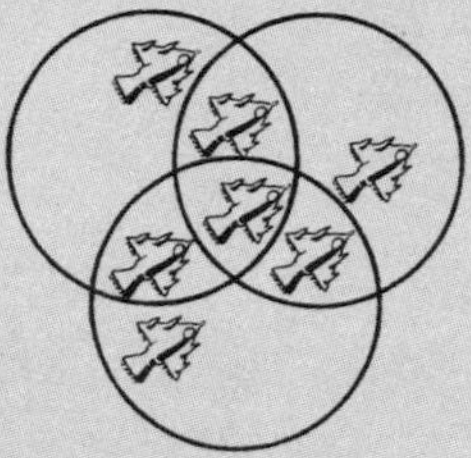

37

Three. The first two stockings she took out might match, but they might also be one blue stocking and one green stocking, so she must take out a third stocking to make sure that she has a matching pair.

38

Here are two possible sets of logical pairings:

hands/gloves
head/hat
cat/horse
horseshoe/nail
comb/tooth (combs have teeth)

38 (cont.)

tooth/nail (as in "fighting tooth and nail!")
hat/gloves
comb/head
horseshoe/black cat (occult symbols)
horse/hands (horses are measured in hands)

39

B is true; a and c are false.

40

41
Horus.

42

43
The cheetah took 72 leaps; the gazelle 108.

44
Black-topped bottles contain the square of the numerical contents of the preceding white-topped bottle. White-topped bottles contain half the quantity of the preceding black-topped bottle. Therefore the last bottle contains 512 pills.

42 (cont.)

45

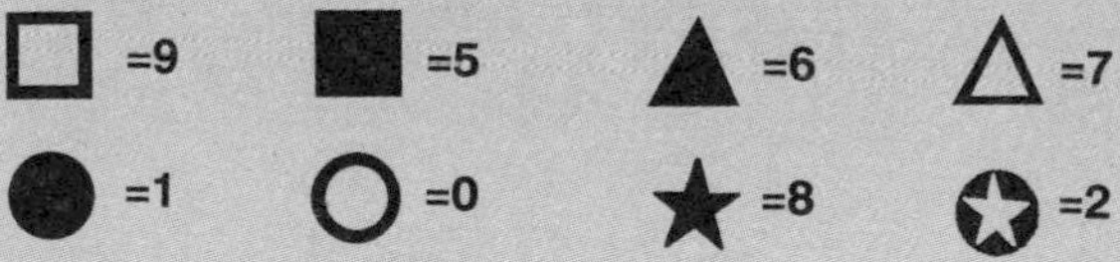

$$\begin{array}{r} 9567 \\ \underline{+1085} \\ \underline{10652} \end{array}$$

46

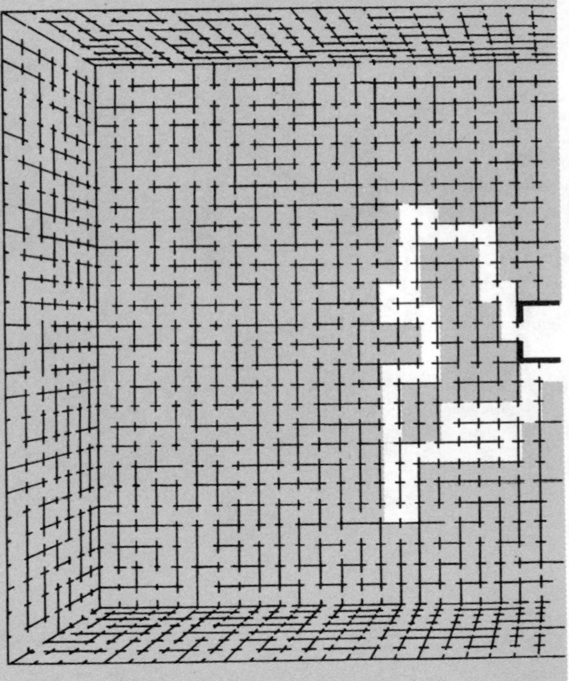

47

The figure contains 27 regular hexagons.

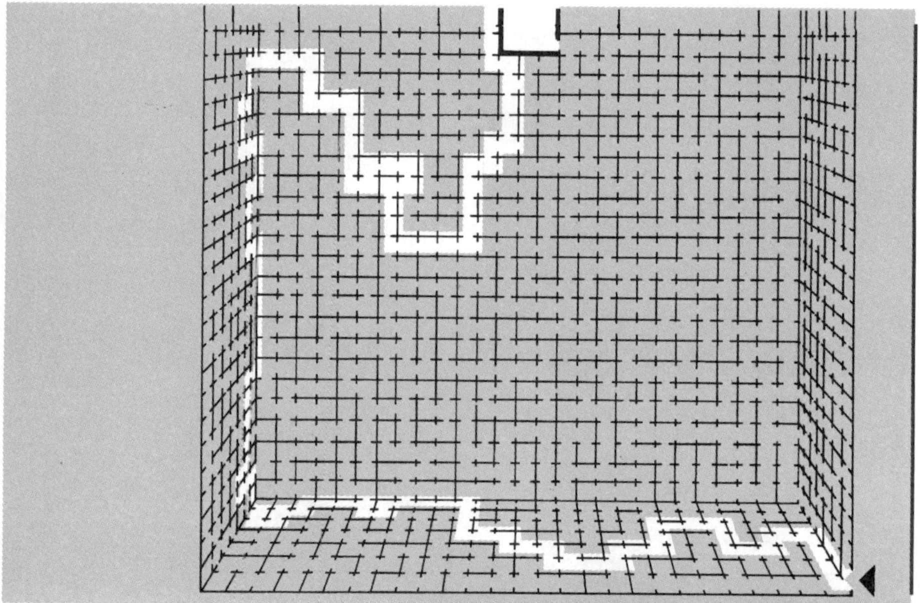

ANSWERS 46–47

48
There are twelve different ways of linking the points of a hexagon, as shown below.

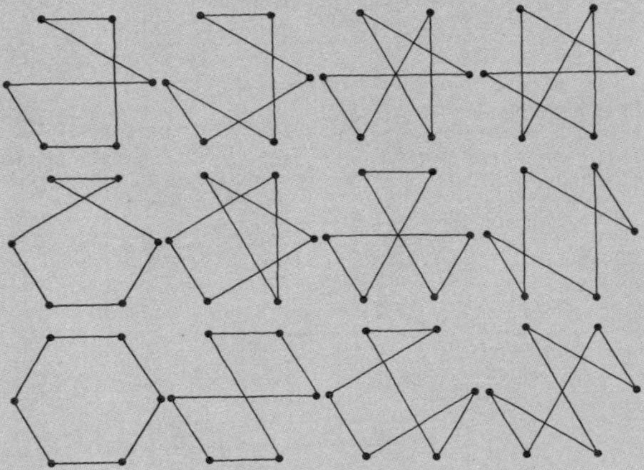

49
One hundred and six bricks.

50
Your feet from the floor.

51
Cube C.

52
No. 2. All the others show Timothy's hair parted on the left. No. 2 has a right-hand part.

53

B and c may both be true, but cannot both be false; a and b may both be false, but cannot both be true.

54

The window.

55

Take nine moves to make a stack of cards 1–5 on square B (with the 5 at the bottom, of course). With another seven moves, make a stack of 6–9 on C. Take five moves to stack 10–12 on D, and three moves to stack the 13 and 14 on E. Place the 15 on F. You then need three moves to place the 13 and 14 on the 15, five moves to place the 10, 11, and 12 on the 13, seven moves to place 6–9 on the 10, and nine moves to stack 1–5 on the 6, requiring a minimum of 49 moves.

56

We said "show" a six-sided figure, and this "shows," in perspective, a cube!

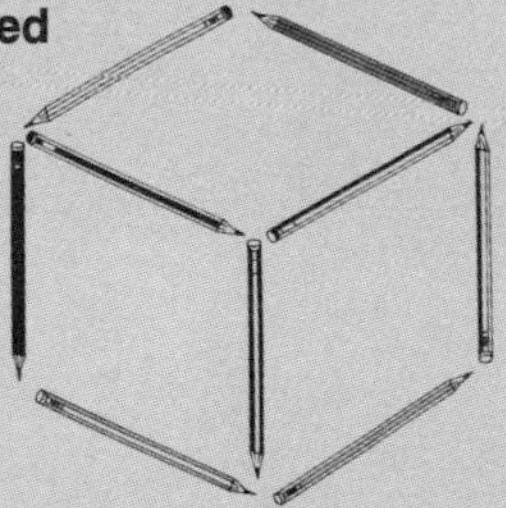

57

The point of this, and other similar puzzles, is that all the Chinamen disappear as the wheel is turned, and that 12 new figures are constructed from the parts.

58

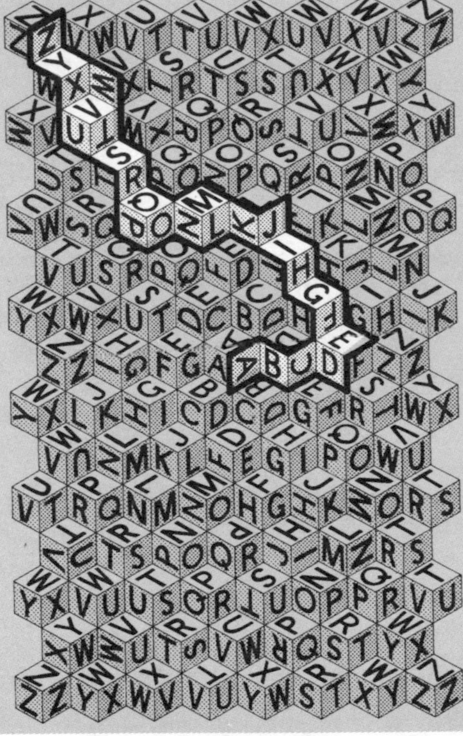

59 **Yes.**

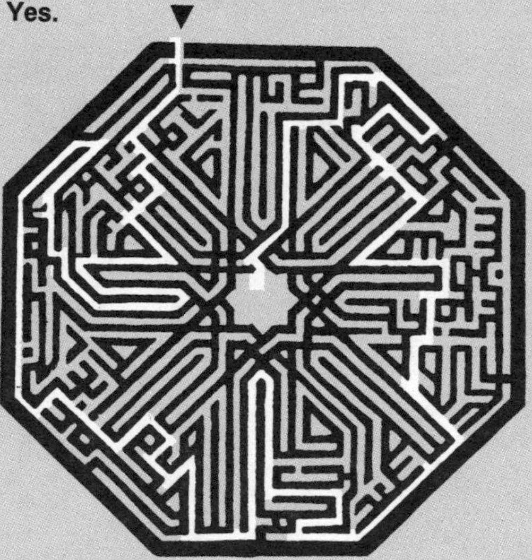

60

Each of the alarm combinations adds up to 26.

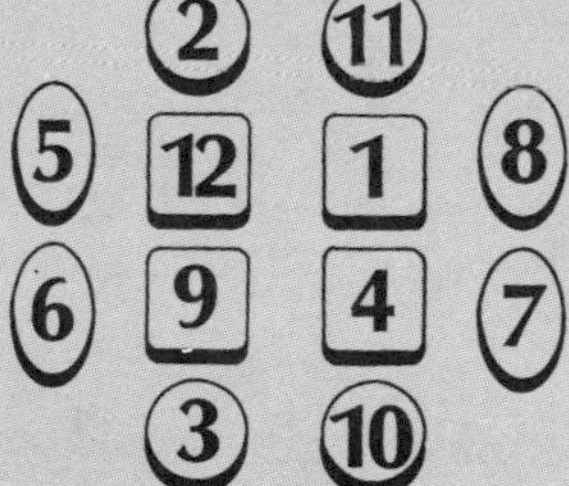

61.

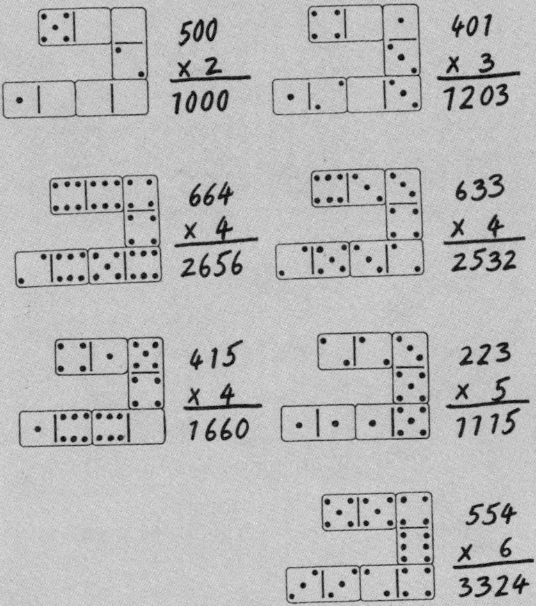

62

Rearrange the letters of BURNS ME THERE and they spell out the words THREE NUMBERS!

63

Only one; after that the cage would not be empty anymore!

64

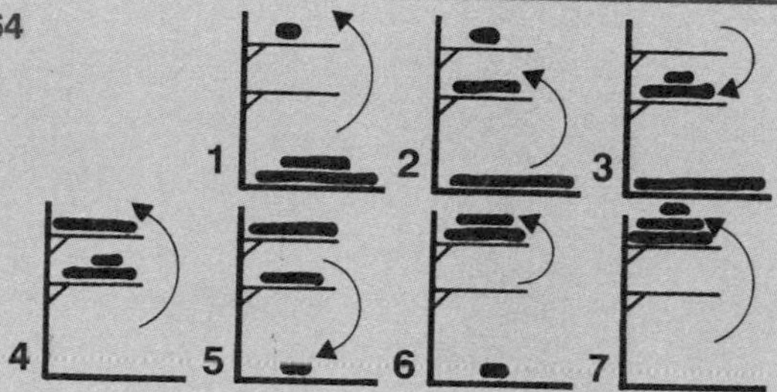

65

A is linked to D, and B is linked to C.

66

Start with the loading (a); double the load on each side (b); replace two piles of logs with three barrels (c); add three sacks to each side (d); replace each sack/barrel pair with a weight (e); remove two weights from each side (f).

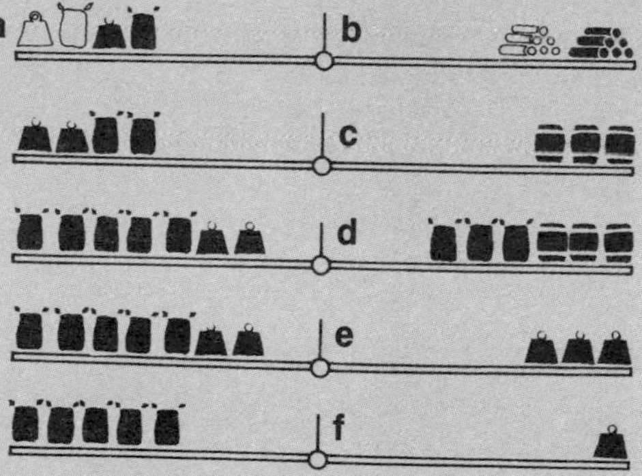

67

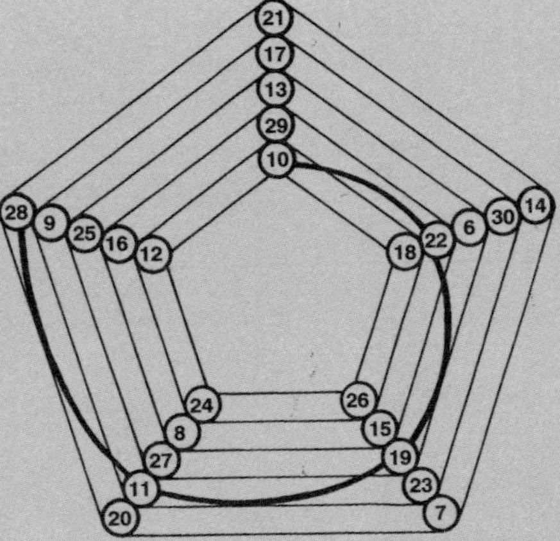

68
The total number of triangles is 35.

69

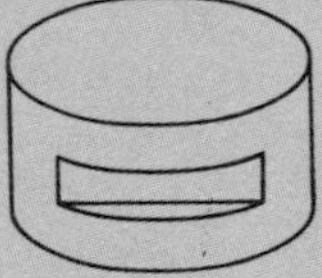

70
Yes.

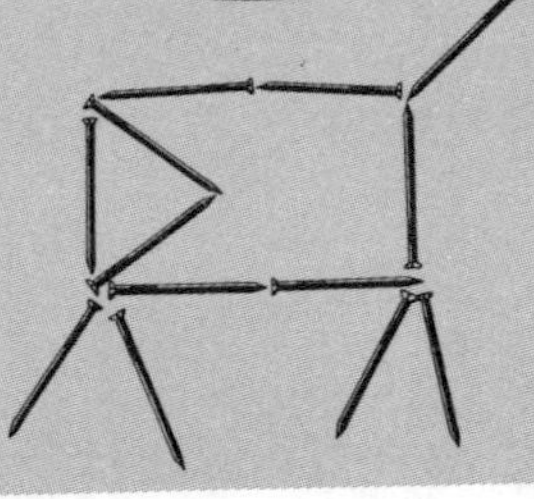

71

Loosen the loop and thread it back through the handles behind the rest of the double cord, as shown. When enough cord has been passed through the right handle, slip the scissors through the loop without twisting the cord. Pull gently on the scissors, and you'll release them from the cord.

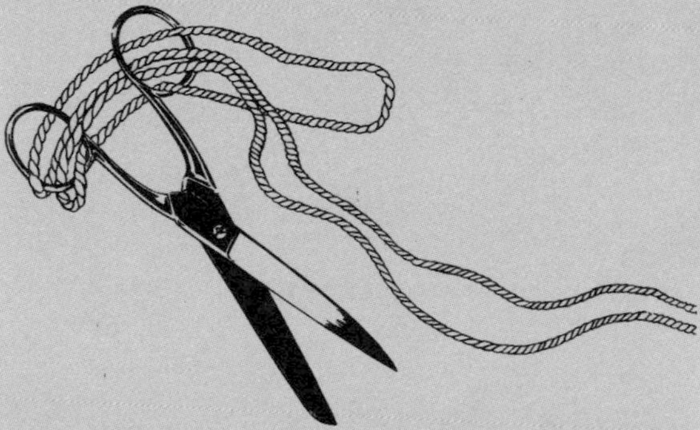

72

They filled the space below the hatch opening with large blocks of ice, and rested the crate on top, lining it up with the hatch opening. As the ice melted in the heat, the crate was slowly lowered into the hold.

73

Only c is true; a, b, and d are false.

74

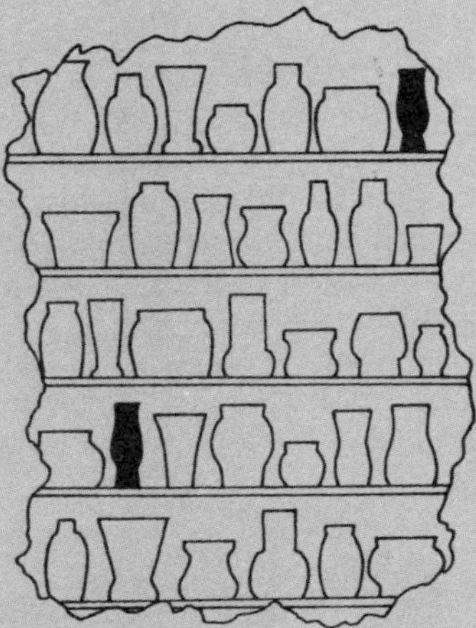

75

The total was 40 red apples and 32 green apples.

76

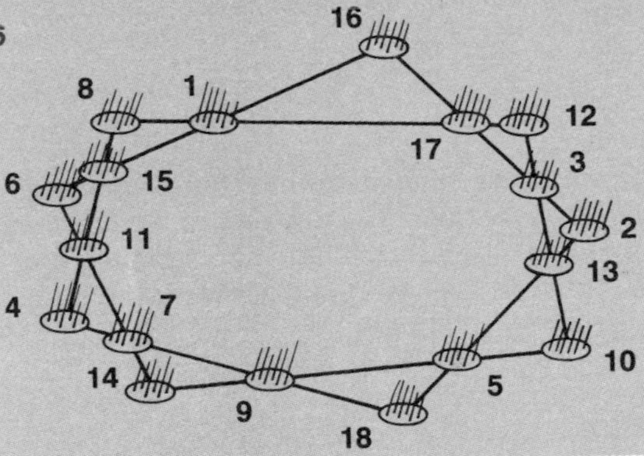

77
B, D, A, E, C.

B

D

A

E

C

78

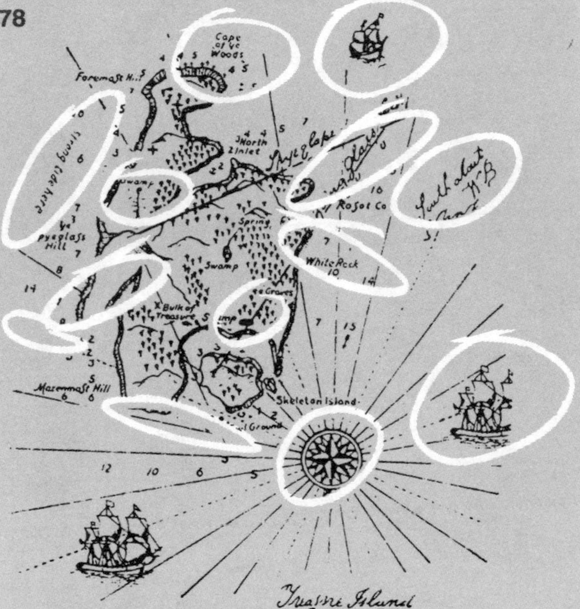

79

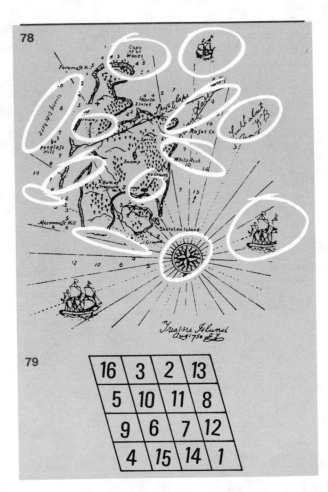

16	3	2	13
5	10	11	8
9	6	7	12
4	15	14	1

80

Forty-seven: each man's number is 43 less than that of the man running on his right.

81

82

Hold the sheet of paper face down with the A and B in your left hand and the D and E in your right hand (1). Fold in half, right to left (2), then bottom to top (3). Tuck squares D and E in between squares C and F (4), and finally fold squares A and B under the whole packet. Turn it over so that A is face up on the top.

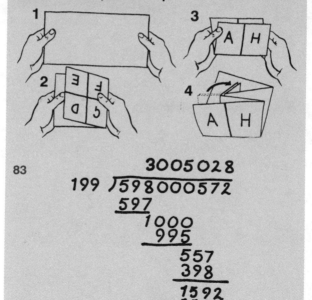

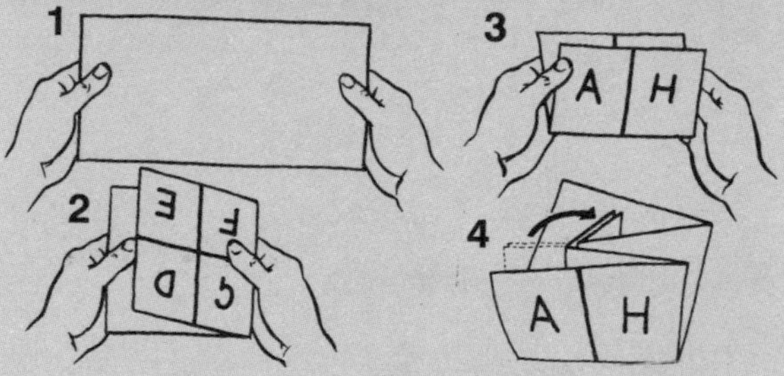

83

```
         3005028
199 )598000572
     597
       1000
        995
          557
          398
          1592
          1592
             0
```

84
Twenty-eight days. At the end of the 28th day, it reached the top of the pole, and once on top, of course, it did not slip back down.

85
Twenty-four ways.

86
"As many as you wish, Sir. The number of soldiers does not make any difference to the speed at which they march."

87

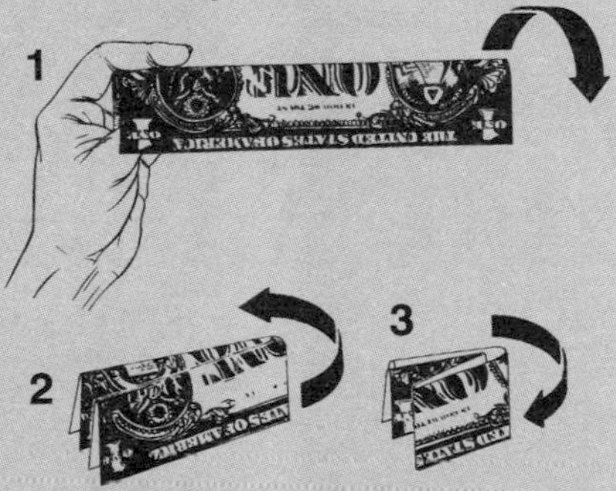

The illustration shows you how to fold the dollar bill. Notice that the second fold is made by folding the right half of the bill backward, and the third fold is made by folding it forward. If when you unfold the bill you open both these folds from the front, the person will be standing on his or her head.

88

Cover half the maze with a sheet of paper, as shown, and then count the number of lines from the middle of the maze to the outside. If the number is even, the ant can crawl out; if odd, he must cross a line. This solution works for all closed mazes of this type.

89

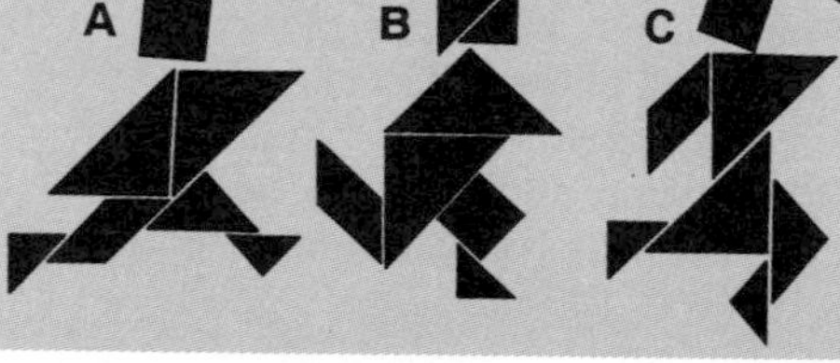

89 (cont.)

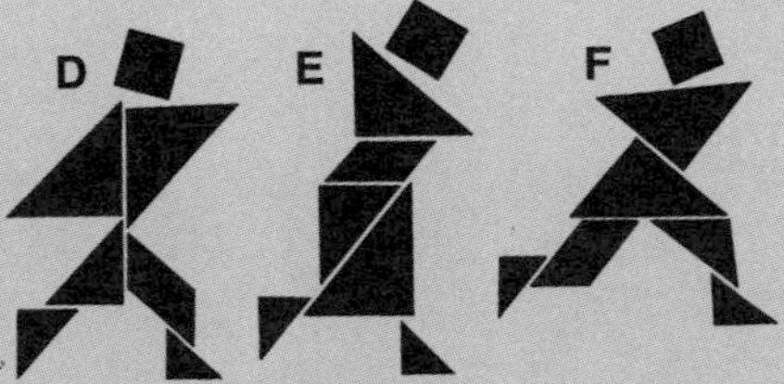

90
Yes.

91
The soldier had had a dream, so he must have been asleep. And as soldiers on sentry duty should never fall asleep, he deserved his punishment.

92
Brandy.

93

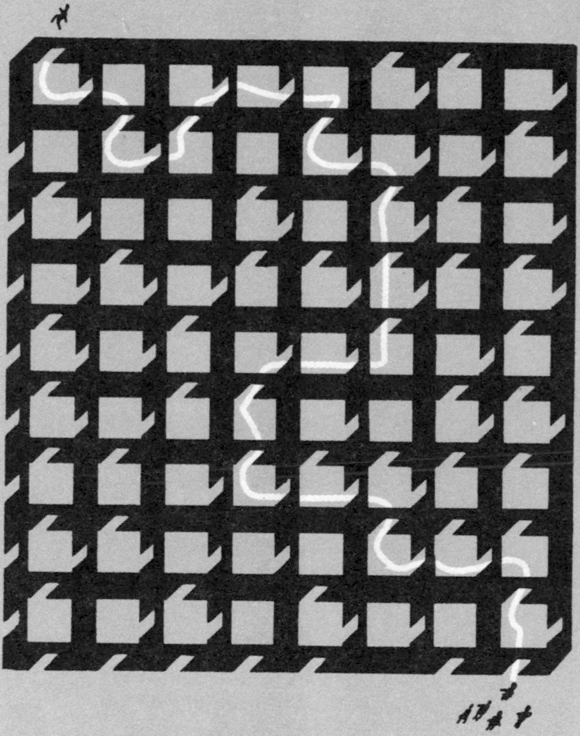

94

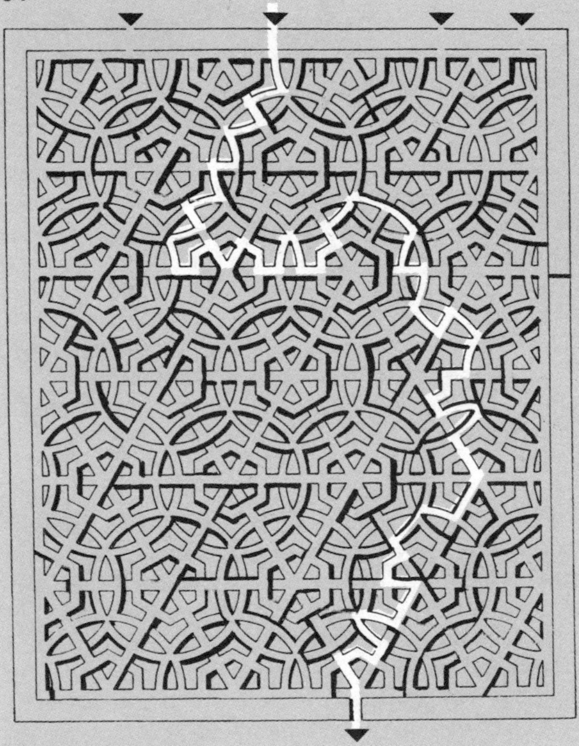

95
The figure in the lower left of the illustration is a griffin, which is an imaginary creature. All the others really existed.

96
Ask her a question with an answer that you can verify at once, e.g. “Is the sun shining?” – or a nonsense question, e.g. “What sort of bird is an elephant?”

97
Six nights. He can make 5 new candles from the 25 candle ends, and when they have burned down, he can make a 6th candle from the 5 ends that are left.

98
He could be born in the month of June in a town called May: there are three towns called May in the USA – in Idaho, Texas, and Oklahoma.
If the boy’s mother was divorced or widowed, she could have decided to marry again. If this happened when the boy was grown up, and he had become a priest or other official able to conduct civil marriages, he could have performed the wedding ceremony – and so married his mother!

99

It doesn't matter which of the tanks he attacks, because they are exactly the same size. The illusion is created by the size of the surrounding satellite tanks.

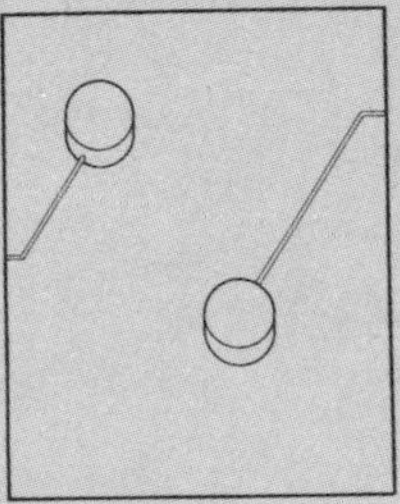

100

Building a got the contract. It contains 80 apartments; building b contains only 79.

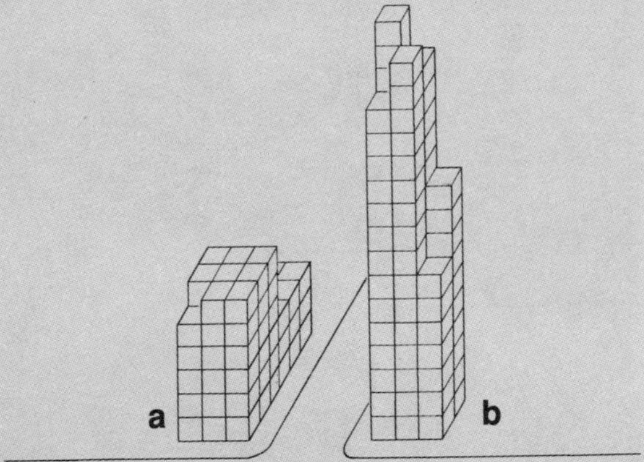

101

102

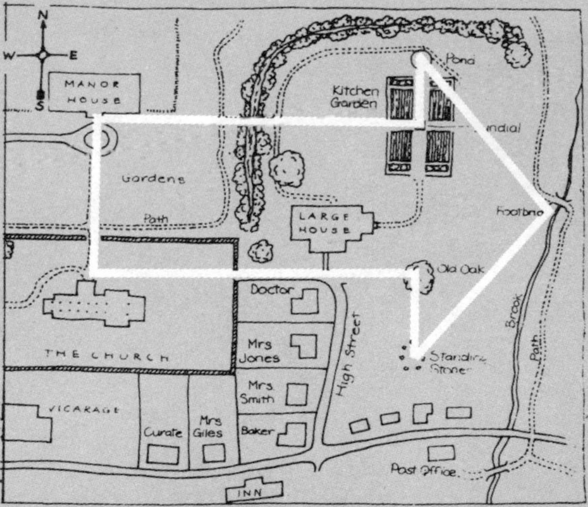
N
W
E
S
MANOR HOUSE
Pond
Kitchen Garden
Gardens
Path
LARGE HOUSE
Old Oak
Doctor
Mrs Jones
Mrs Smith
Baker
High Street
Brook
Path
THE CHURCH
VICARAGE
Curate
Mrs Giles
Post Office
INN

103

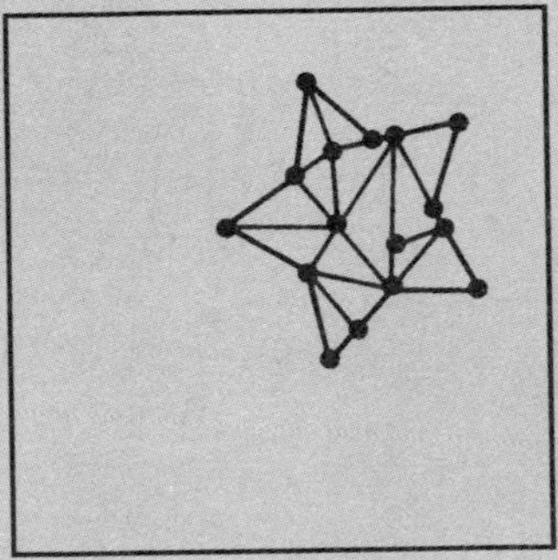

104

There were 190 passengers altogether on the first two journeys, and 225 passengers altogether on the fourth and fifth journeys, making a total of 415 passengers. So on the third journey there were 500–415=85 passengers.

105

They kept ducks.

106

B.

107

No. 2. Did you spot that No. 6 is upside down?

108

109

Two minutes. It takes one minute for the front of the train to travel from the beginning of the forest to the end of the forest, and another minute for the end of the train to travel the same distance. (The train travels 1 mile in a minute because it is moving at 60 miles an hour.)

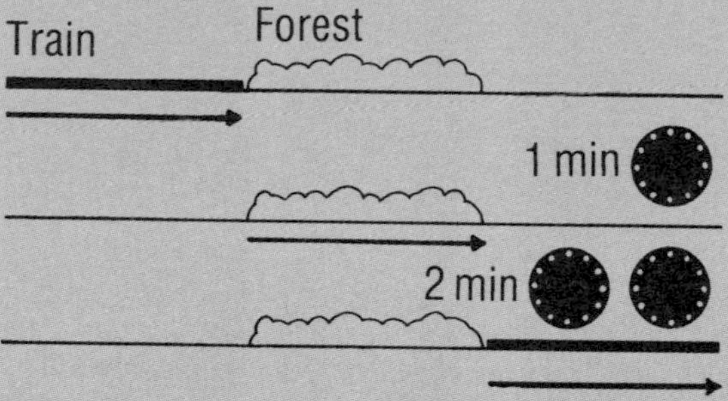

110
There were 6 ship's cats.

111
Surprisingly, eleven is the smallest number of square farms that can be carved from the plot. The commissar's solution is shown below.

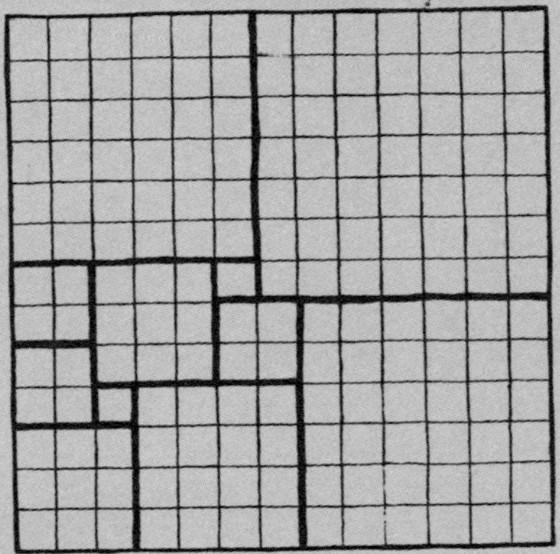

112
Make a triangular pyramid.

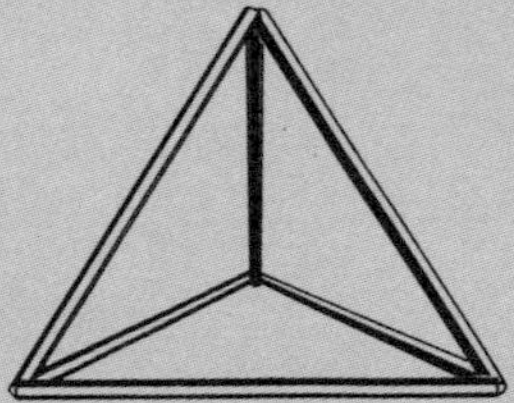

113

A, b, c, and e can be used as repeating tiles; d is the odd one out.

a 

b 

114

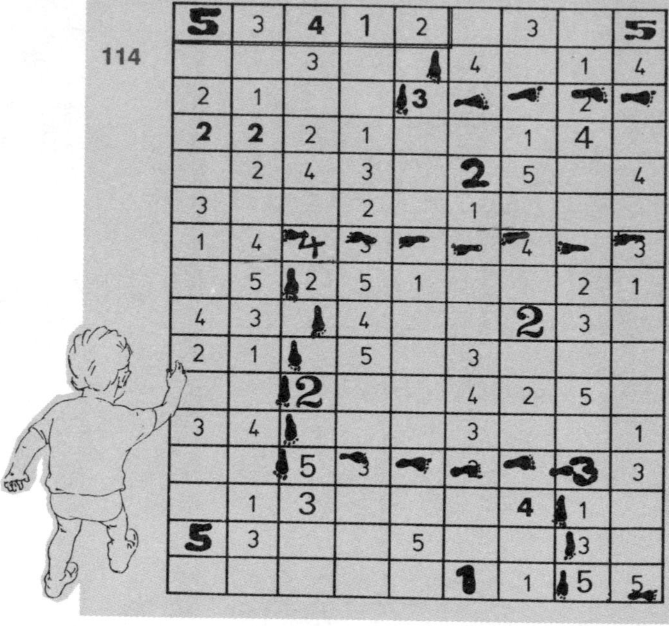

113 (cont.)

c 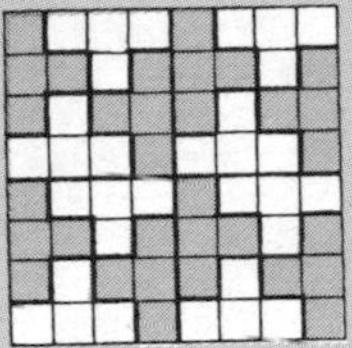

e 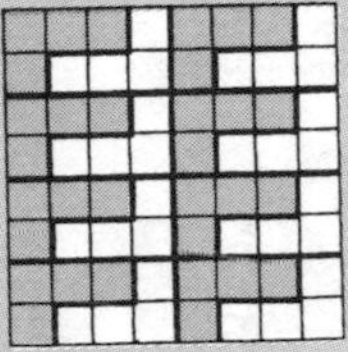

114 (cont.)

2		4	2	3	3		1
	3		1	5		2	
3		2	3			5	
5					2		2
	2	5	4	3		1	
1						3	
3	4		5	2		1	4
		3	2	1			2
	2						
1	5		4		1		3
3	3	1					
		4		3		2	4
	1		4				2
5			4		4		
		3	1				
4			1	4	2		

115

C, E, D, A, B.

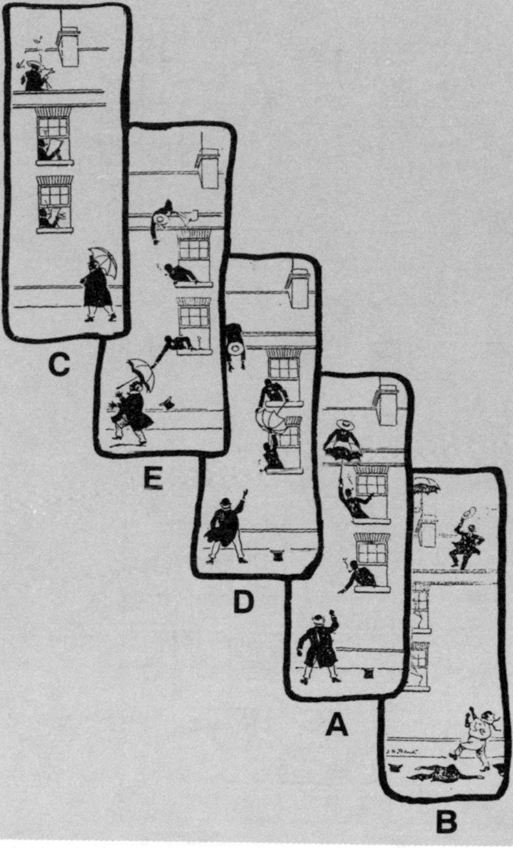

116

Ingrid's alphabet ...

1) E.

2) D, J, K, M, U, X, Y.

3) The W is an E on its side, and the Z is an N on its side.

Siegfried's alphabet ...

1) N.

2) G, J, K, M, X, Y.

3) The U is a C on its side, the Z is an N on its side, and the S is used twice.

117

A cow costs $7 and a horse costs $3.

118

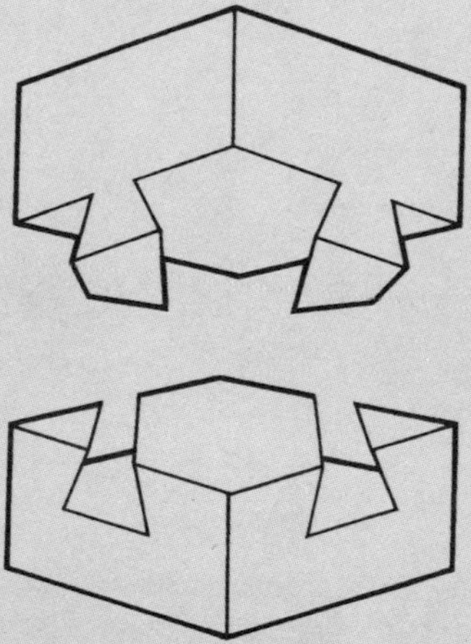

119

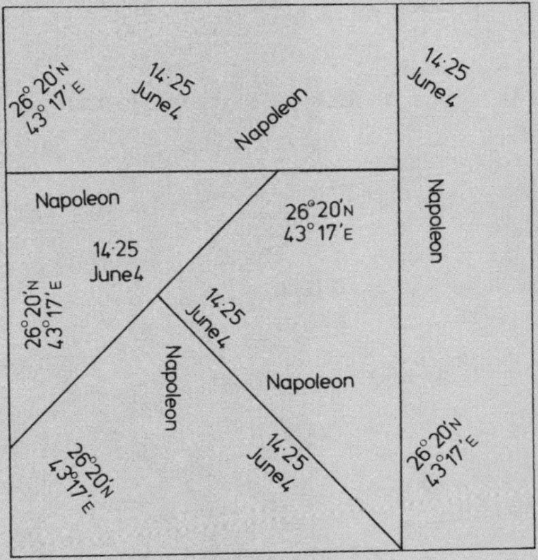

120

First row 4, second row 3, third row 6, and last row 8.

121

The 59th day – work it out backwards!

122

At this stage of the contest, Alf has scored 9, Bert has scored 16, and Colin has scored 12.

123

124

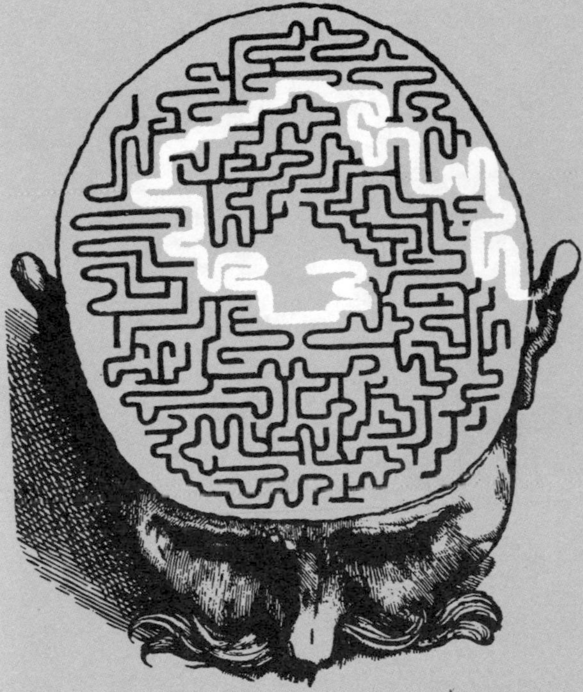

125

Mount Everest was always the highest mountain in the world – it was there before it was discovered!

126

127

Pyramid: jump from 18–20, 10–12, 17–29, 16–28, 28–30, 30–18, 21–23, 27–13, 13–11, 11–25, 26–24, 24–22, 22–8, 8–10, 5–17.

Traditional solitaire: 5–17, 12–10, 3–11, 18–6, 30–18, 27–25, 24–26, 13–27, 27–25, 9–11, 7–9, 22–24, 24–26, 26–12, 12–10, 10–8, 1–3, 3–11, 11–25, 31–23, 16–28, 33–31, 31–23, 21–7, 7–9, 4–16, 16–28, 28–30, 30–18, 18–16, 15–17.

128

	R				N							
	E					O	S	S	A	C	I	P
	W					R	E			N		
	O					E		L	I			
C	H	A	P	L	I	N		E	O			
	N		G				T			P		
	E	K		A		S					A	
	S	E	N		N	O	B	R	A	G		N
	I	N		I		D						
	E	N	E		W		H					
		E		K		R		I				
		D			C		A					
		Y				I		D				
							D					

129
A kitten.

130
Your name.

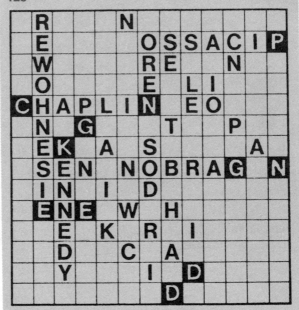

131

Whether the lights are red, blue, or green is irrelevant. The object is a perfectly symmetrical solid figure with twelve faces, and so can only be a regular dodecahedron. Each face is thus a regular pentagon.

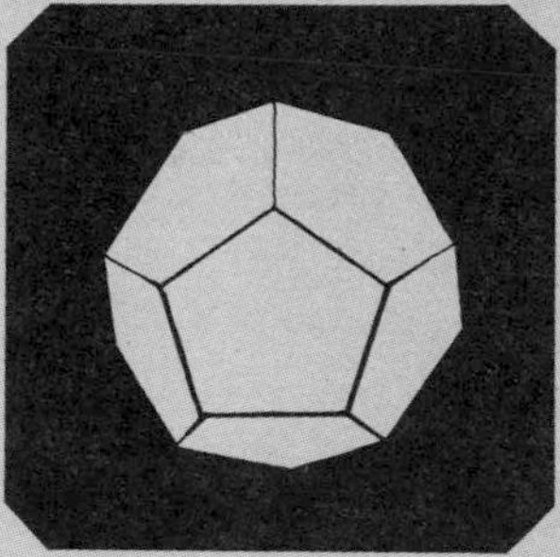

132

He asked, "Has there been a mistake or is the repeat of the yellow deliberate?" The full scheme is illustrated below.

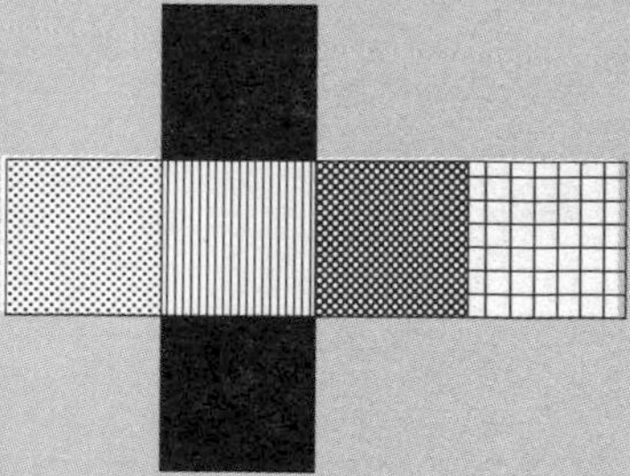

133

He made 10 errors and, therefore, scores 15.

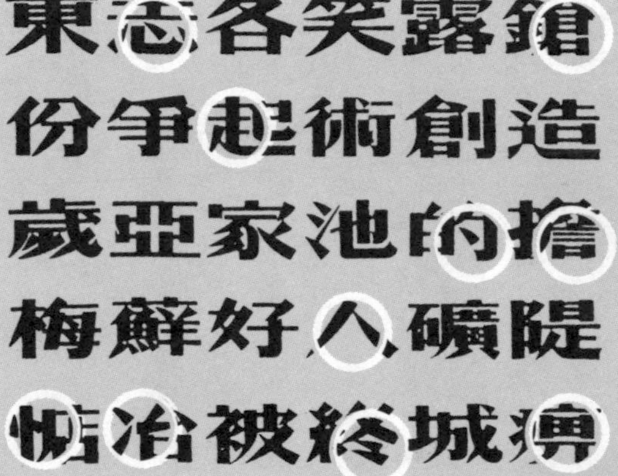

134

16	11	14	19	5
1	17	6	18	23
24	22	13	4	2
3	8	20	9	25
21	7	12	15	10

135

Be careful not to write the number as 11,111 when it should be 12,111. This number is divisible by 3 because the sum of its digits is divisible by 3.

136

Eight cats (14 dogs and 10 people). We know that 5d + 3p = 100 and that d is greater than p. The only solutions to this equation are d = 17 and p = 5, or d = 14 and p = 10. As we also know that d+p must be divisible by 3 the second solution must be the correct one.

137

There are many possible solutions, but the one shown here is the only one that can be written with as few as four signs.

98–76+54+3+21=100

138

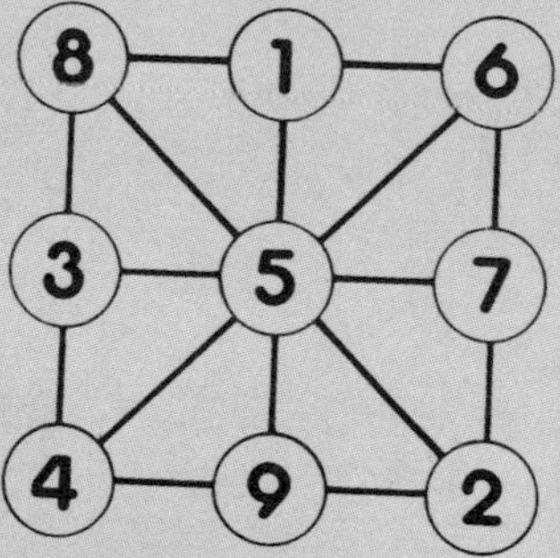

139

Three – one duck, one chicken, and one goose.

140

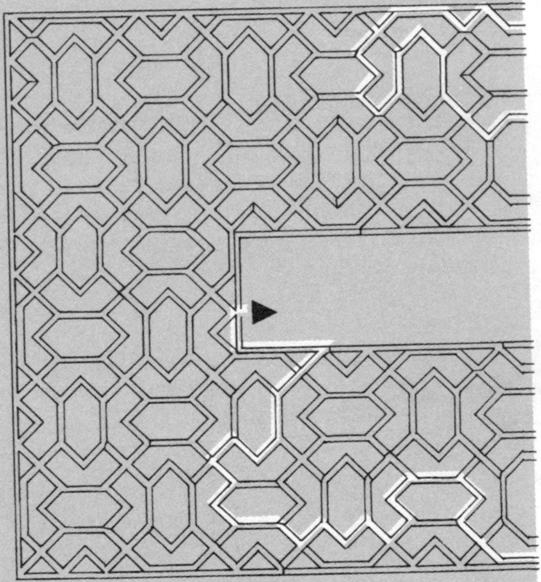

141

Place one of your fingers firmly on coin B to prevent it from moving. With your other hand, slide coin A away and then back again firmly

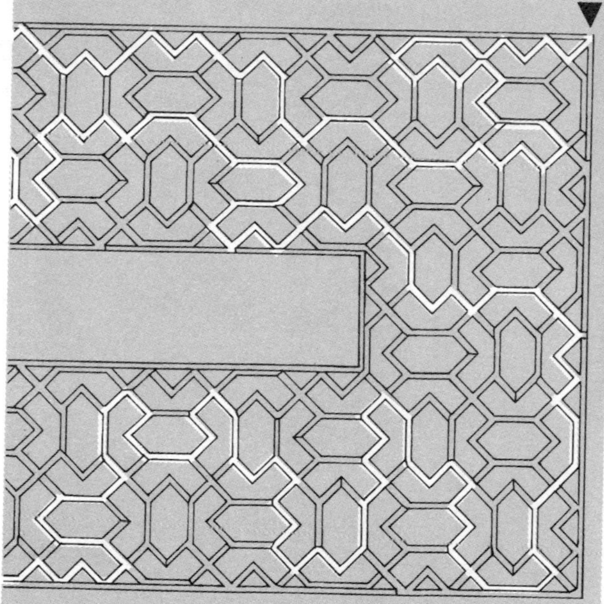

against coin B. This will force coin C away, and coin A can be moved into the gap.

142

Here is one possible solution. Four coins are stacked as shown, with the fifth held on its edge so that it is touching the other four.

143

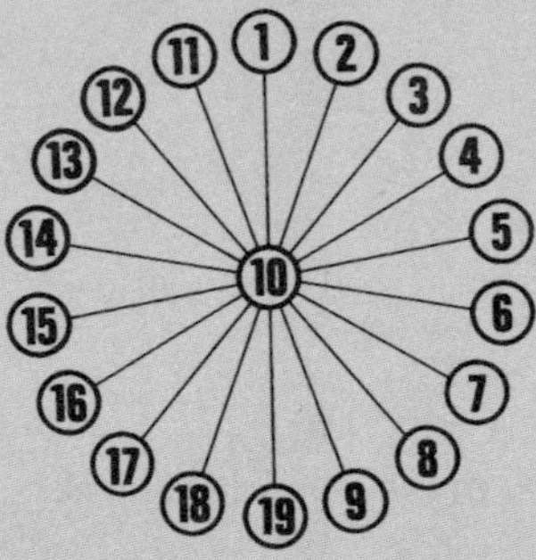

144

The numbers are 27, 13, 30, and 49.

145

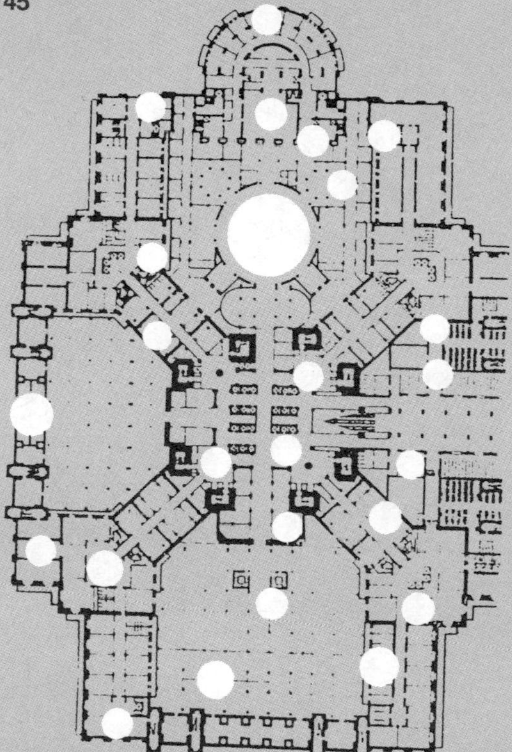

146

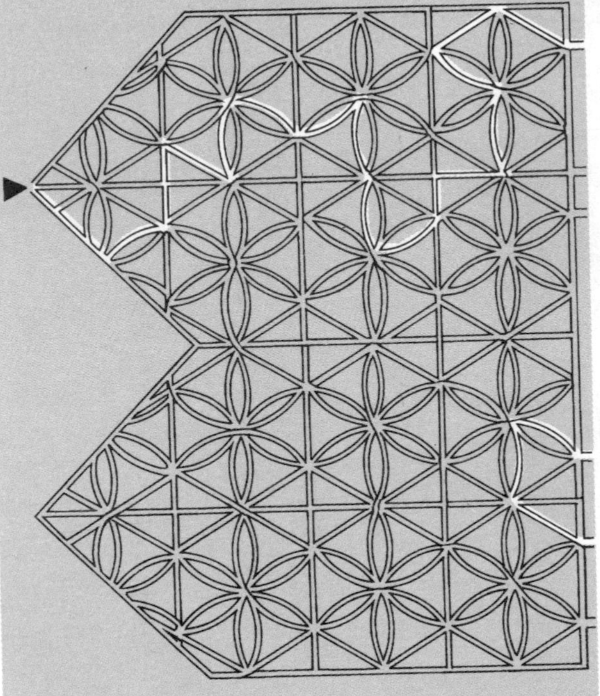

ANSWER 146

147

Three women are wearing dresses and hats. Another three are wearing jeans and are hatless. Only one is wearing jeans and a hat, so she is the odd one out.

148

Seven. He sold four loaves to the first woman, two to the second, and one to the third.

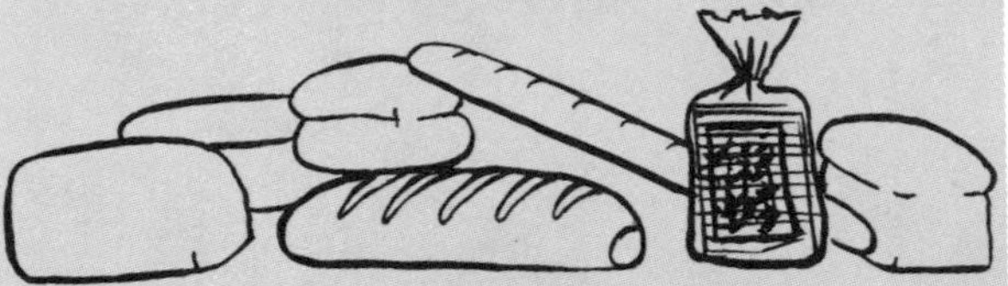

149
Sergeant Snodsip painted the letter "e" the wrong way around.

150
No. 7. Barkov is left-handed; all the time reflections hold their guns in their right hands.

151
He filled the 30-ounce jug and emptied it into the 50-ounce jug. Then he refilled the 30-ounce jug and poured it carefully into the 50-ounce jug until that was full. This left 10 ounces in the 30-ounce jug, which he sold to his customer.

152

Yes. In the 30 days of September, the finishing order could have been:
for the first 10 days, Ruth, Debbie, David;
for the second 10 days, Debbie, David, Ruth;
for the last 10 days, David, Ruth, Debbie.
So Ruth finished before Debbie 20 days out of 30; Debbie finished before David 20 days out of the 30; and David finished before Ruth 20 days out of the 30.

153

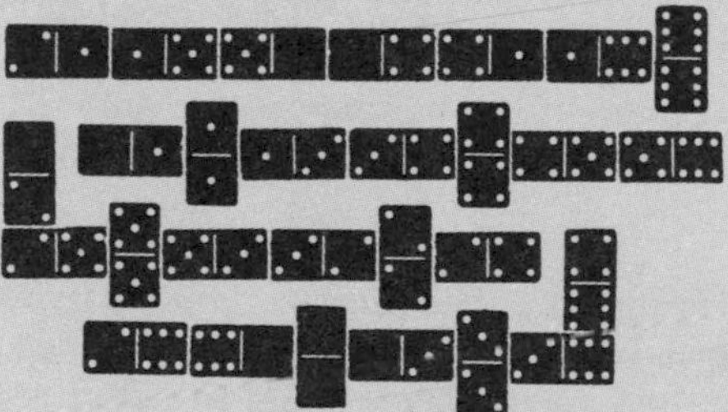

154

155

89	06	91	60	18
90	68	19	86	01
16	81	0	98	69
08	99	66	11	80
61	10	88	09	96

156

The man. All the others are seen from the side.

157

He bought 13 plates with the figure 1 on them – the numbers 1, 10, 11, 12, 13, 14, 15, 16, 17, 18, 19, 21, and 31 all contain the figure 1. (Although 11 is made up of two figure 1s, it is still only one plate.)

158

Five. The values of the arms slanting upward are added, and those of the arms slanting downward subtracted to give the value of the upright.

159

Twenty-one yards.

160

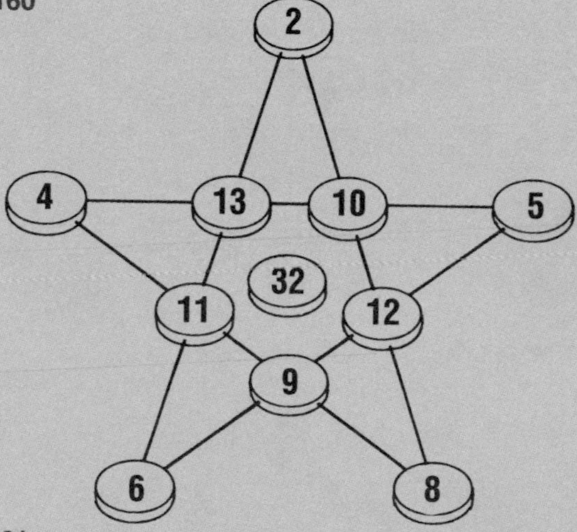

161

Twenty-three (she was 13 when he was 39).

162

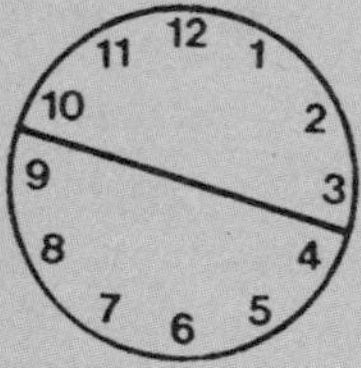

163

A million seconds is 11 days, 13 hours, 46 minutes, and 40 seconds – so she has had her new watch battery for more than a week.

164
H.

165
Cut the three parts of the puzzle from a folded sheet of paper (1). Unfold the small rectangle and slip it over the large rectangle, which is still folded (2). Tuck the keys over the front half of the large rectangle (3), then slide the small rectangle over the top of the keys and open out the large rectangle. Try asking your friends to take the keys off the key ring without making a tear!

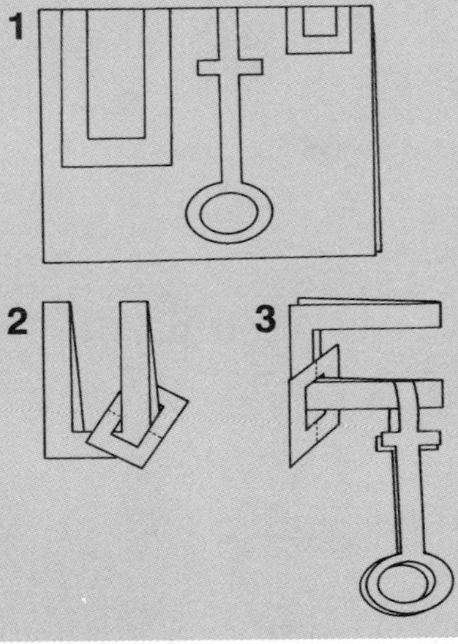

166

167

Sixty ways (15 ways from each M).

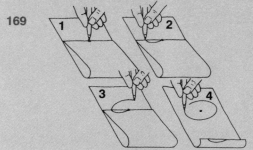

168

Shoe number 6.

169

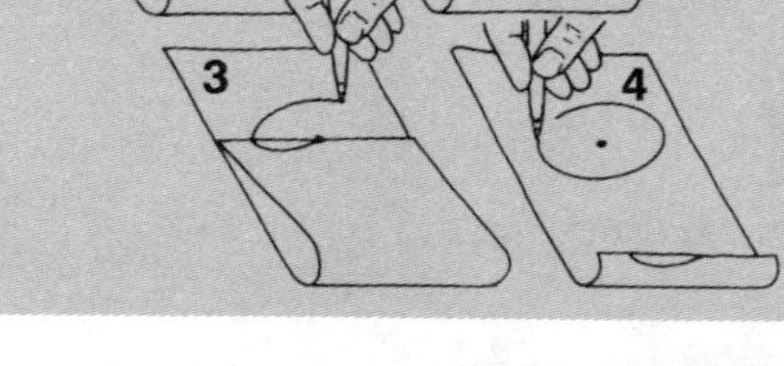

170

Take your friend's string in your left hand and slip it under the string tied around your right wrist, as shown here, making a loop on the other side. Put your right hand through this new loop, tug the string, and it will slip back through the string around your wrist – and you're free!

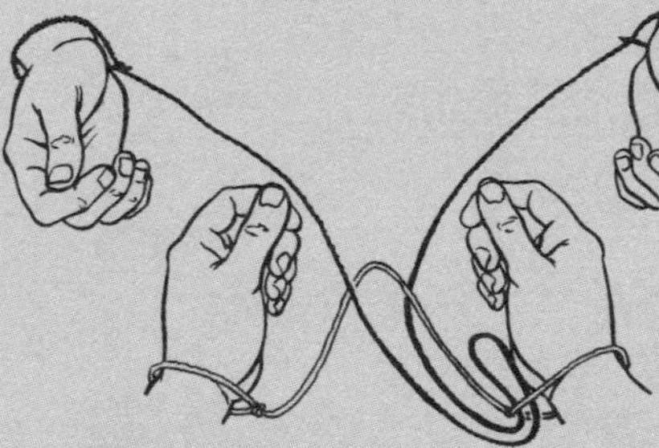

171

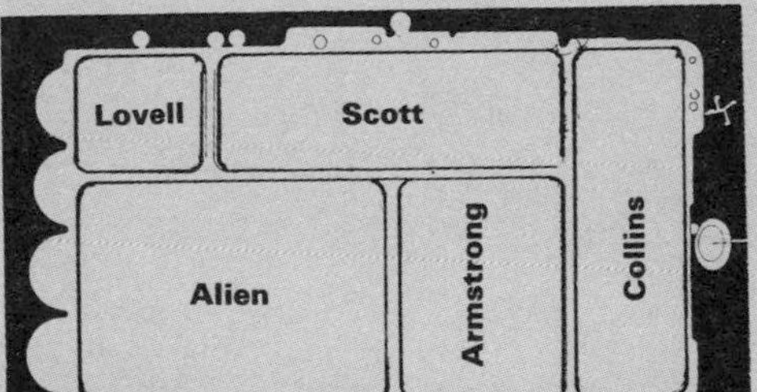

Armstrong is the captain.

172

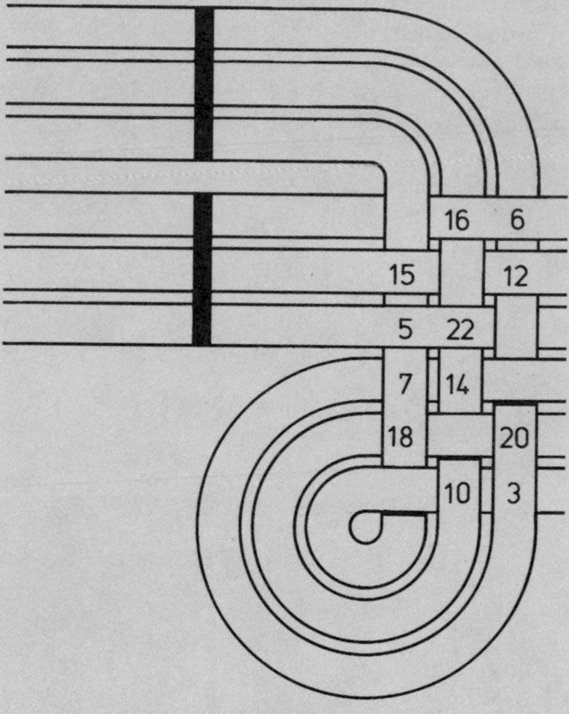

ANSWER 172

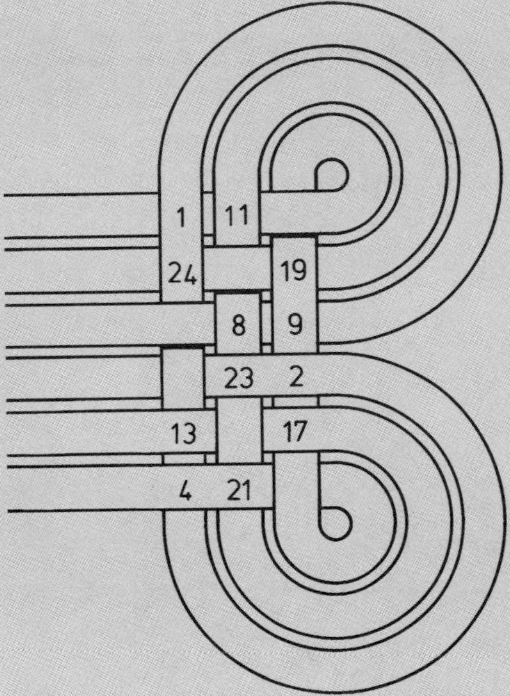

173
Ten trips.

174
Hold a mirror over the puzzle, and the answer is clear.

175

176
His card was black.
Since all three players raised their hands, there were two possibilities: two black cards and one red card, or three black cards. The successful player realized that if the first solution was right, the other two players would both see one red and one black card and instantly deduce that the third card would be black. Since this instant solution did not occur, each one of his opponents saw two black cards, so all three cards were black.

177

178
False.

179
He has drawn 14.

180

Black dots indicate paths which are blocked off in one maze but are open in the other.

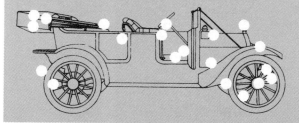

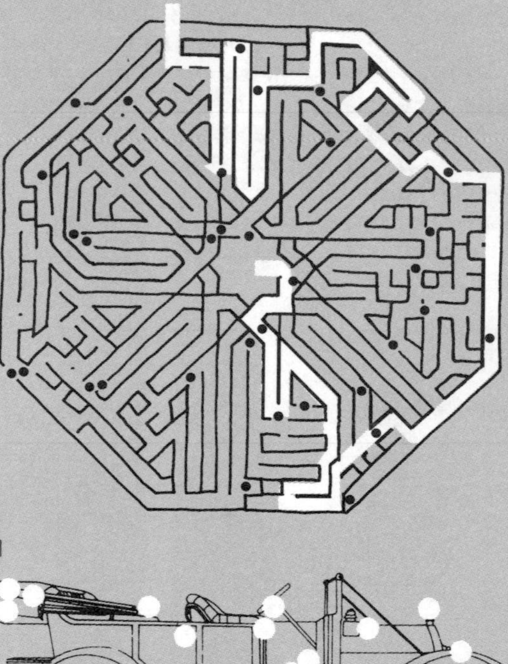

181

182

183

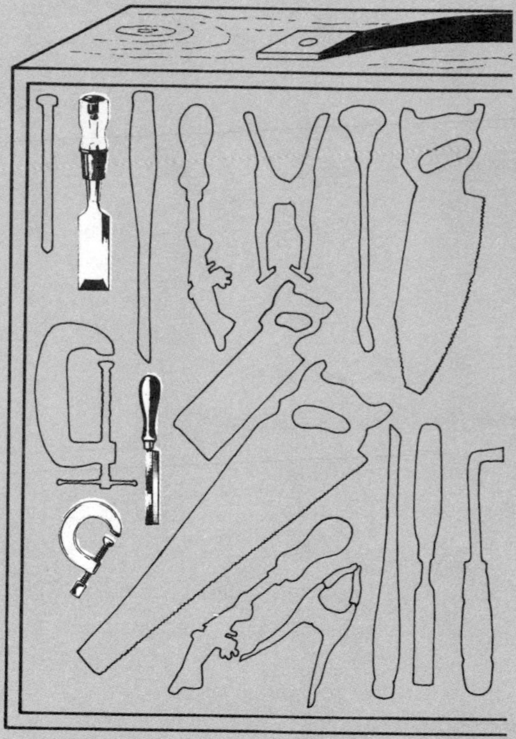

ANSWER 183

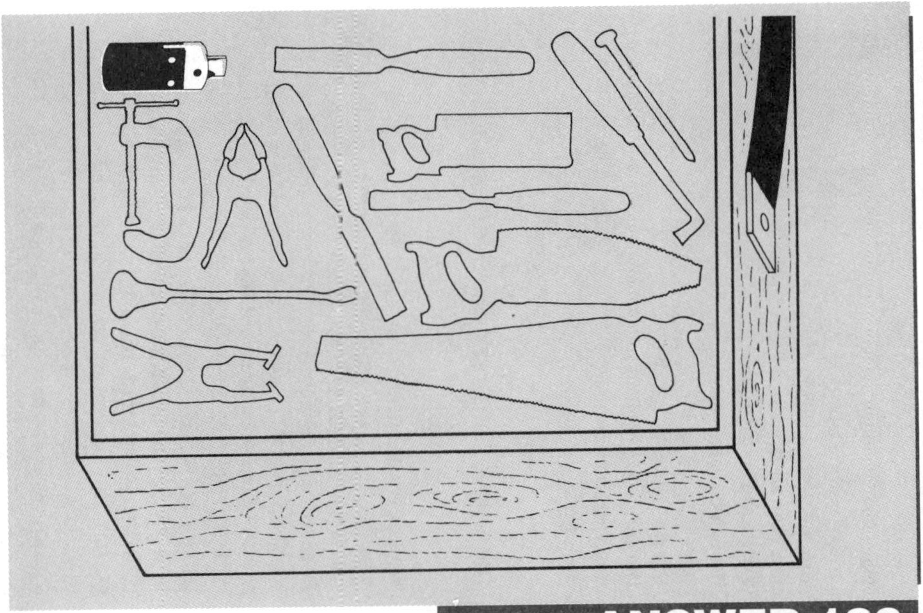

184

Fold the card as shown, and bring the strip made by the two slits through the circular hole. You can now gently slide one of the cherries through the loop, and so separate them from the card.

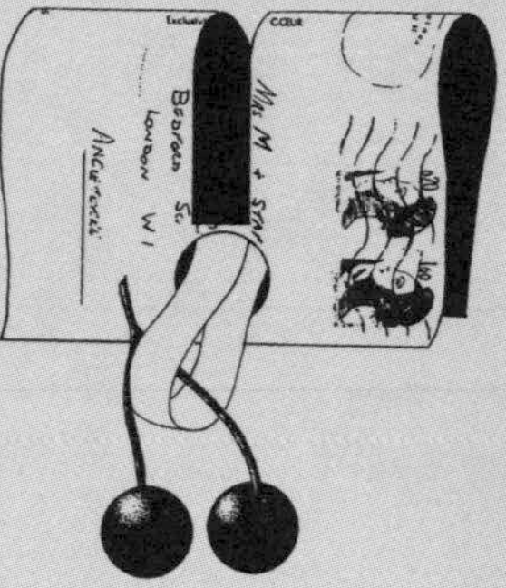

185

The words, "the Greek alphabet," have 16 letters!

186

We know Cleopatra's present to herself was a new barge. There are only two women on the barge, and as Charmian wasn't reading the *Pharaonic Times* and drinking asses' milk, it must have been Cleopatra. Caesarion was not drinking water, nor could he be drinking asses' milk (Cleopatra), beer (Mark Antony), or wine (Ahenobarbus). So he must have been drinking fruit juice, and Charmian must have been drinking water, and, therefore, he gave his mother the baboons. We know he was reading the *Daily Sphinx.* Cleopatra's present from Mark Antony wasn't her new robe, but it was

something she could wear, so it must have been the string of pearls – therefore, Mark Antony was not reading the *Ptolemaic Post*. A man was reading the *Heliopolis Gazette* and had given Cleopatra the trees – this must be Ahenobarbus, as we now know which gifts had come from Caesarion and Mark Antony. So Charmian's present must have been the new robe, and she must be the reader of the *Ptolemaic Post*. Which leaves Mark Antony reading the *Nile Street Journal*.

187

The missing number is 18. (Each number is doubled, then 10 is subtracted to produce the next number.)

188

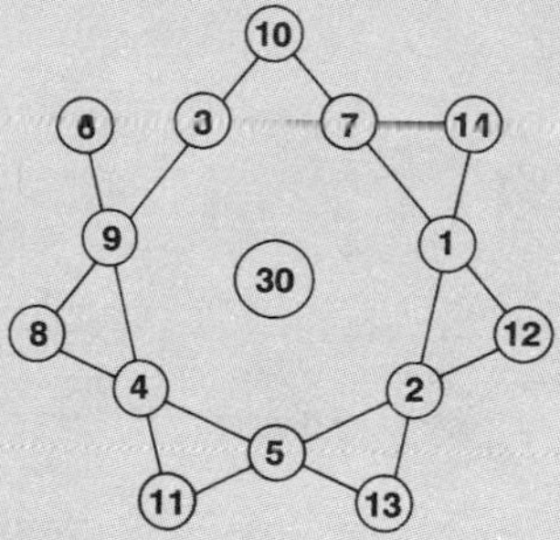

189

The answer is 9876543210, and thus every row is composed of all the digits from 0 to 9, in a different order each time.

190

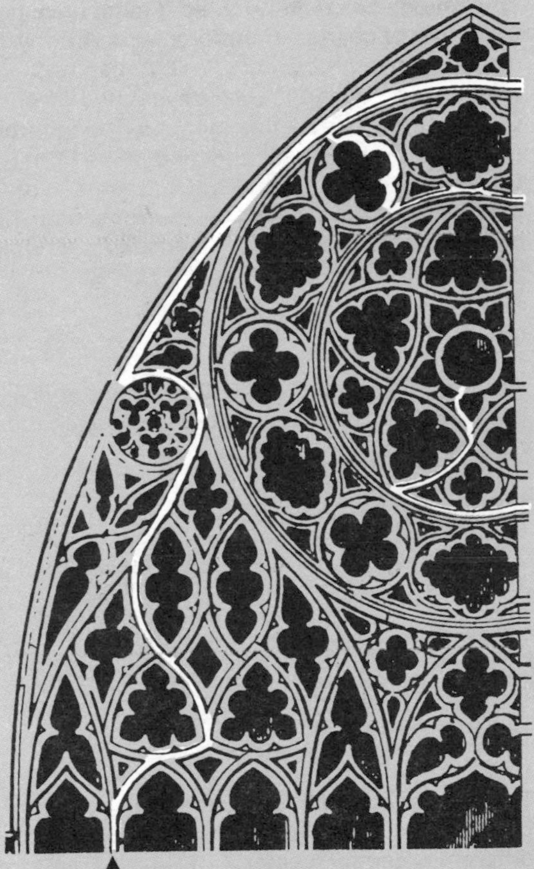

ANSWER 190

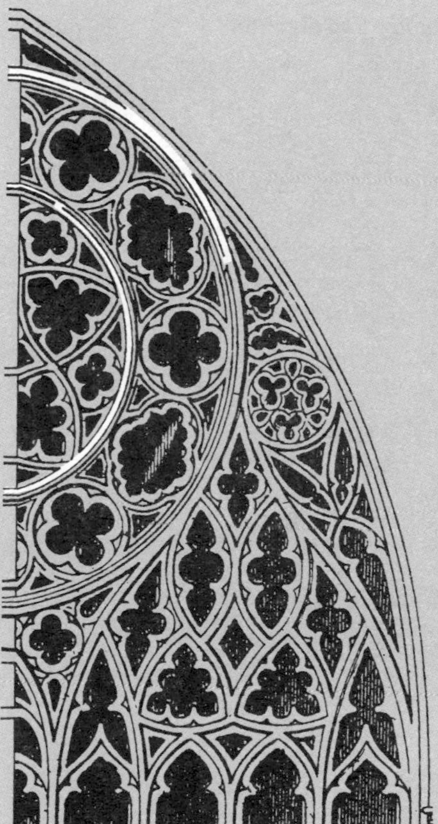

191

The numbers are 146 and 668.

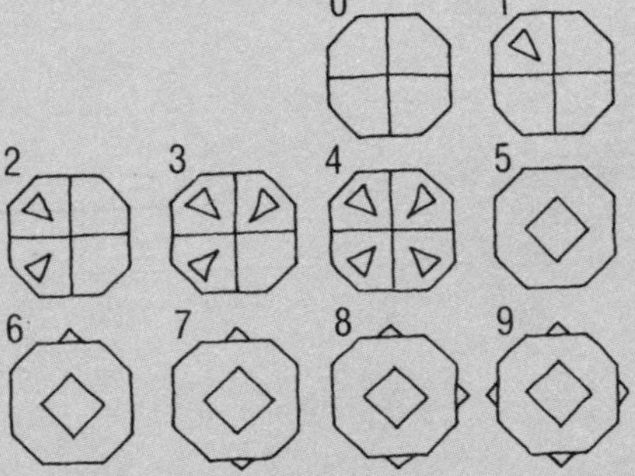

192

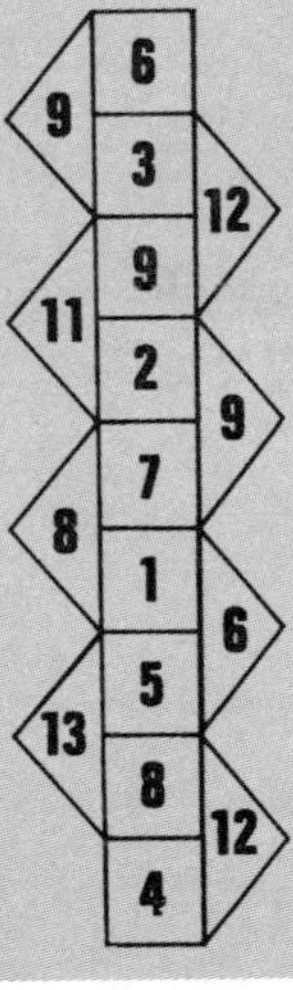

193

She took one letter from the In and Out drawer. If the letter she took out was stamped In, then that drawer must contain all In letters (because all the labels have been switched). Therefore, the drawer marked Out will actually contain the mixture of In and Out letters, and the drawer marked In will contain only letters stamped Out. If the letter she took out had been stamped Out, the In and Out drawer would have contained only Out letters, the drawer marked In would have contained the mixture of In and Out letters, and the drawer marked Out would have contained only letters marked In.

194

The two shorter sides of the triangular sails total 14ft – the same as the longest side. So there were no triangular sails at all, and only the square sails were worth bidding on.

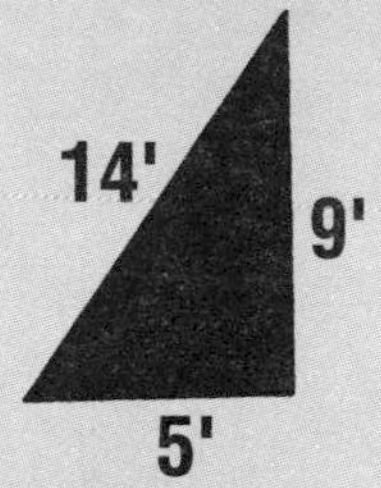

195

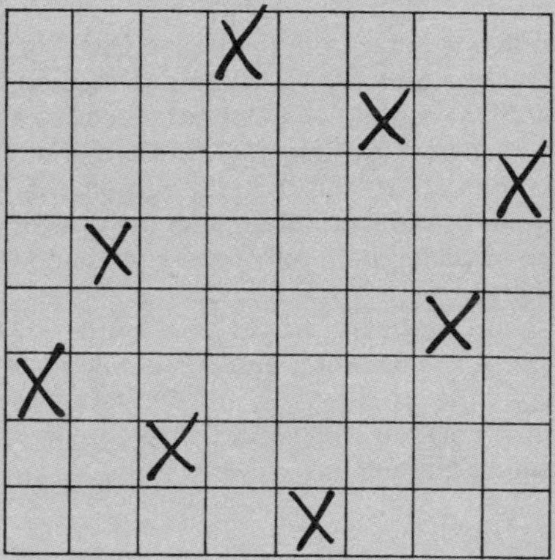

196

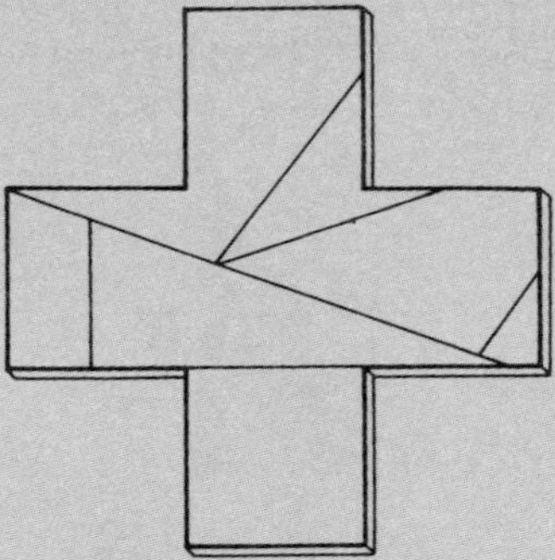

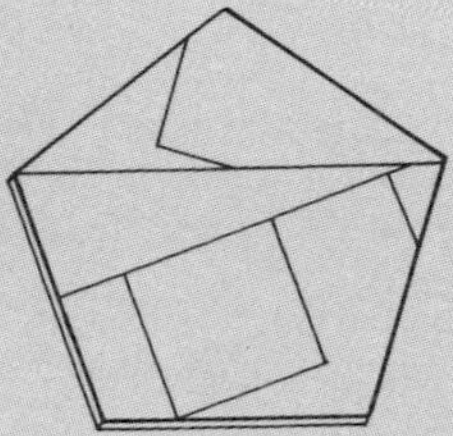

197
A Six. b 24.

198
Yes.

199
Still only 5, assuming they don't tire or lose interest!

200
A trick question! The number of grooves is irrelevant. The needle only moves from the outer edge of the playing area to the inner, or 6–(2+1)=3 inches.

201
What does Y – E – S spell?

202
Only two girls in the circle can have both red hair and green eyes. As one of them was not one of the sisters, only one of the sisters could be a green-eyed redhead.

203

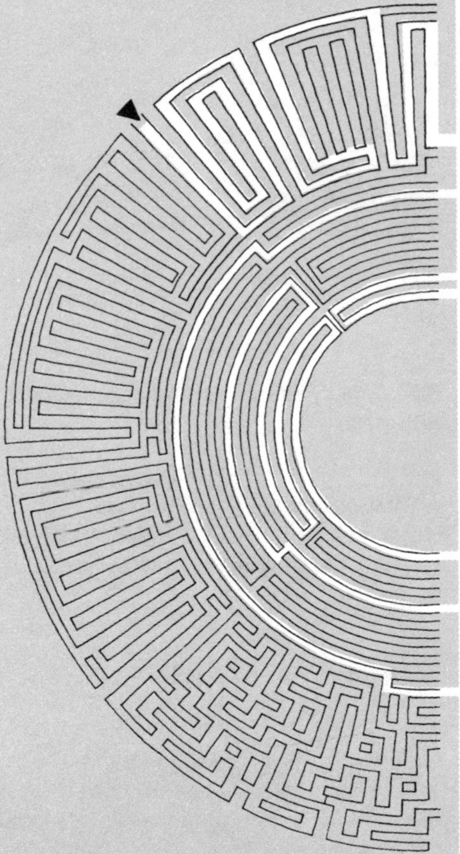

ANSWER 203

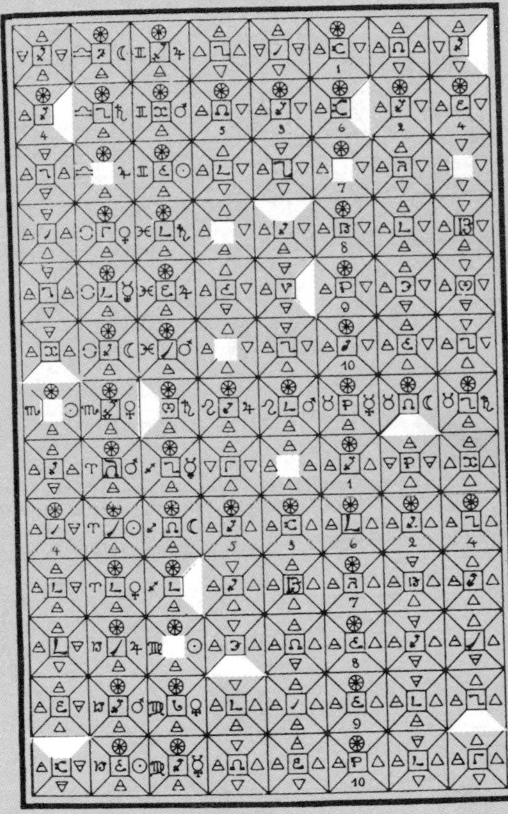

205

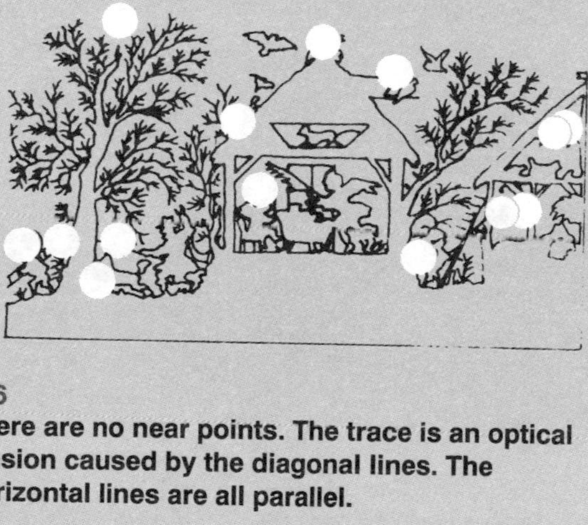

206

There are no near points. The trace is an optical illusion caused by the diagonal lines. The horizontal lines are all parallel.

207

Turn the page upside down!

208

It is physically impossible to make this item. It is an optical illusion and can exist only as a drawing.

209

210

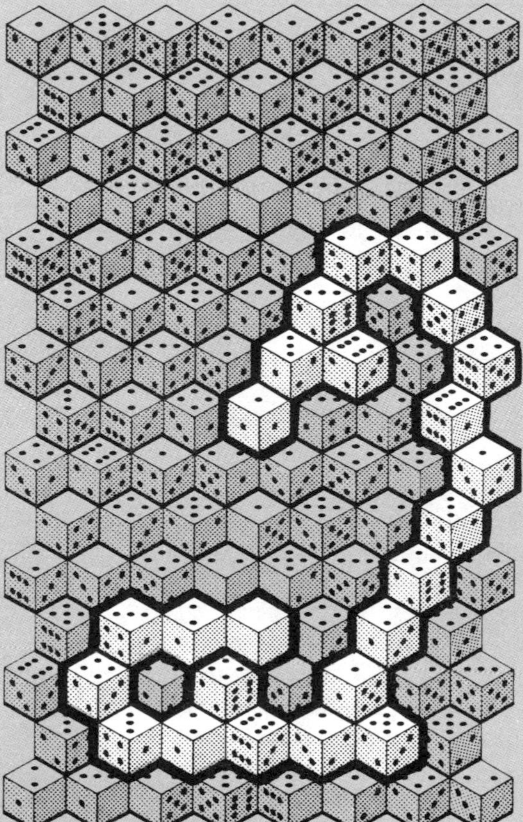

211

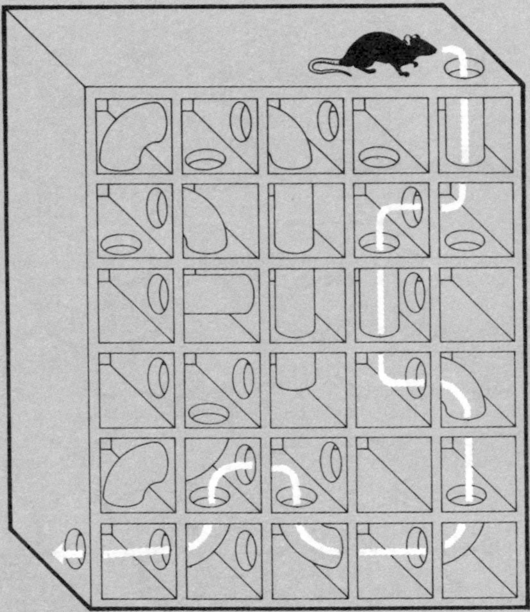

212

She was too small to be able to reach high enough to press the elevator button for the ninth floor. The highest she could reach was the button for the sixth floor.

213

The fence was 62 yards long.

214
The letter G.

215
Thirty-four tickets × 6 lines makes 304 free tickets. Using this arrangement, the manager gave away only 102.

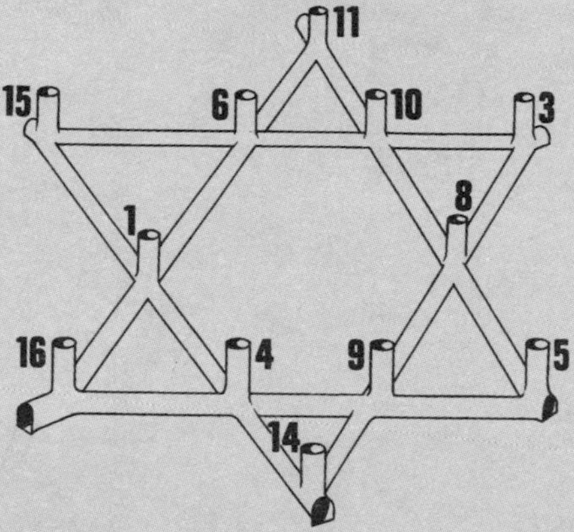

216
Five.

217
The golf ball, No. 2, is hit with a club. All the other balls shown are rolled, kicked, or thrown.

218
$2,519 per month.

219

ANSWER 219

P

221
Yes.

222
Amy was going to Australia from Heathrow;
Beth was going to Canada from Kennedy;
Jo was going to Hong Kong from Schipol;
Meg was going to Mexico from Orly.

223

Two widows each had a son. Each widow then married the son of the other and had a daughter by that marriage.

224

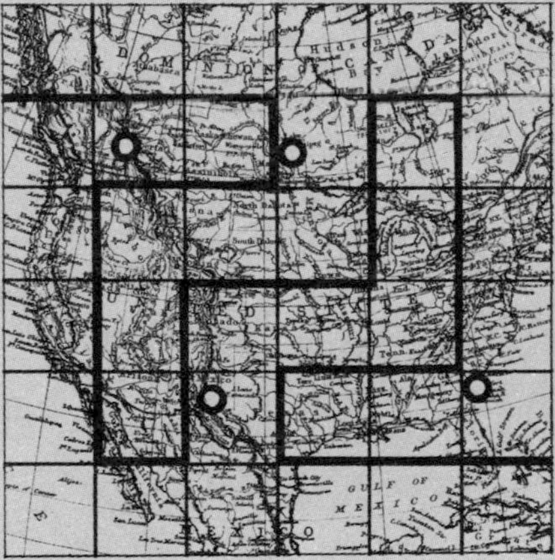

225

The workmen are from the gas company – the flame symbol is connected to the house.

226

Six ways.

227

Your lap.

228

229

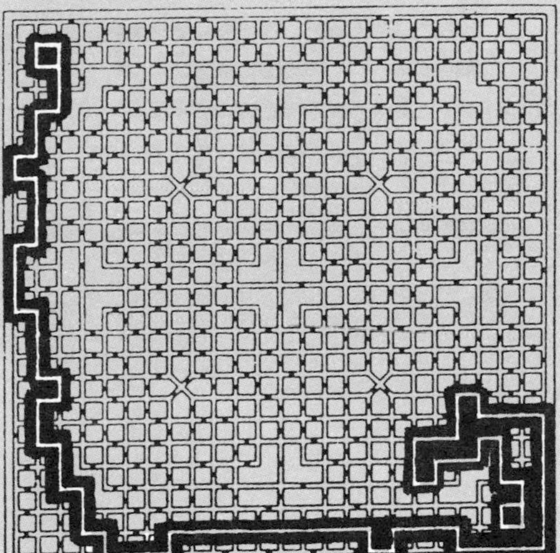

230

This route only collects eleven dots.

231
AAGON has 5 planets.
DENOS has 6 planets.
GOGON has 7 planets.
JEHAR has 8 planets.
NOSTAR has 9 planets.
RAYZOR has 10 planets.

232

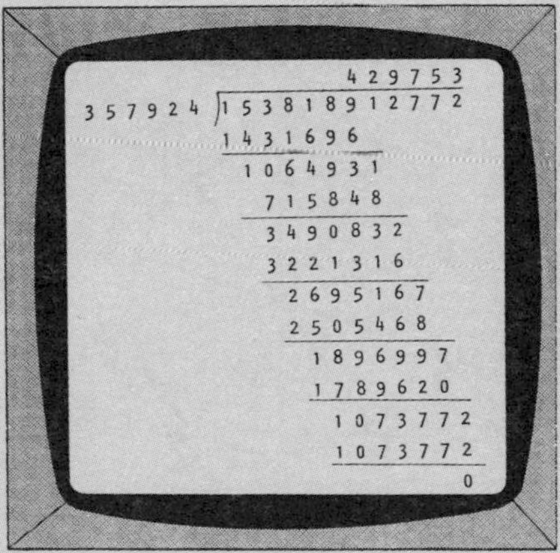

233

The *Dolphin* carried 3,600 men, allotting 60 to each of her 60 lifeboats. After the disaster, 50 boatloads of 70 men survived to tell of the sinking.

234

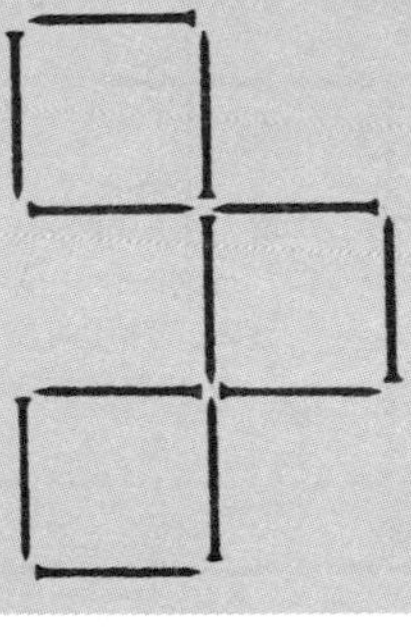

235

They would have saved $4,095.

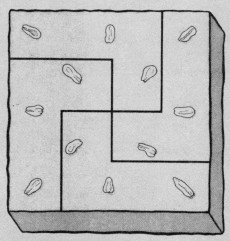

236

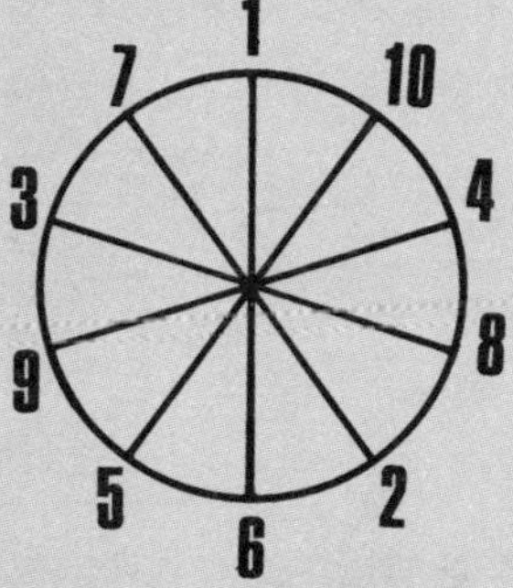

237

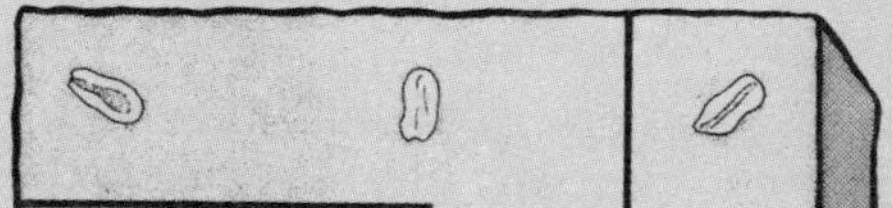

238

We said "rearrange" – so change the 8 for the 9, and then turn the 9 upside down so that it becomes a 6!

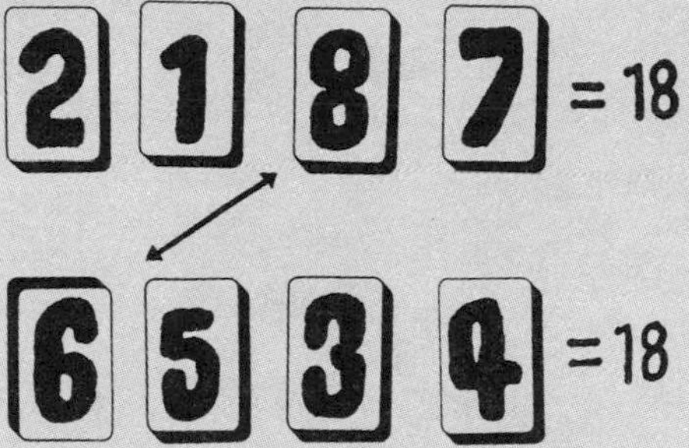

239

The correct order is 3, 2, 5, 1, 4, 6.

240

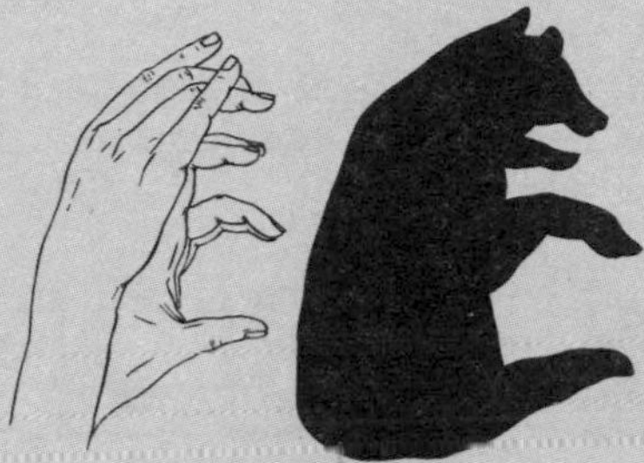

241
Sherlock Holmes. He is a character in fiction. All the others really lived.

242
A–3; B–2; C–1.

243
Weigh out 4lb of sugar with the 5lb and 9lb

weights in different pans of the scales. With the 4lb, weigh three more lots of 4lb each – the remaining sugar will also weigh 4lb.
Divide each 4lb portion equally on the two sides of the scales.

244
B is true; a, c, and d are false.

245
Three lizards.

246

247
Gull, *Egret*, *Fulmar*, *Cormorant*, *Duck*, *Barnacle*, *Albatross*.

248
The number is 342.

249
1 PLANE
2 OAK
3 ASH
4 PINE
5 SYCAMORE
6 HOLLY
7 HORSE CHESTNUT
8 POPLAR

250

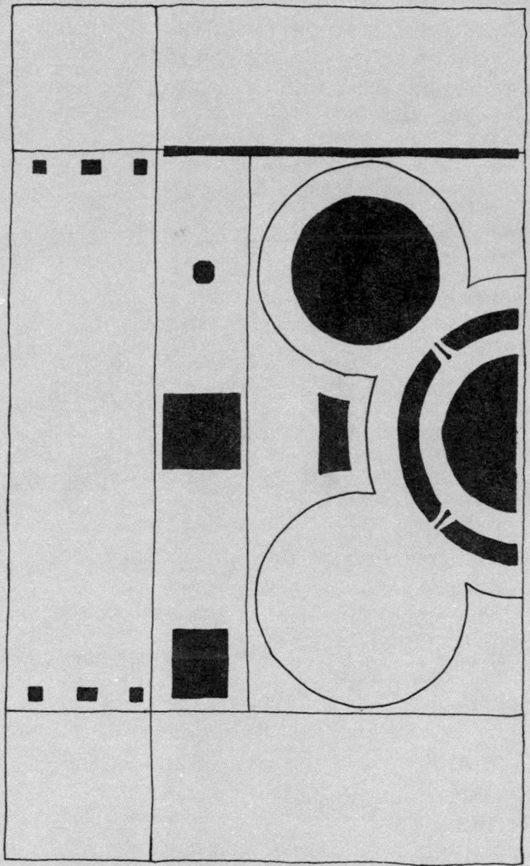

ANSWER 250

251

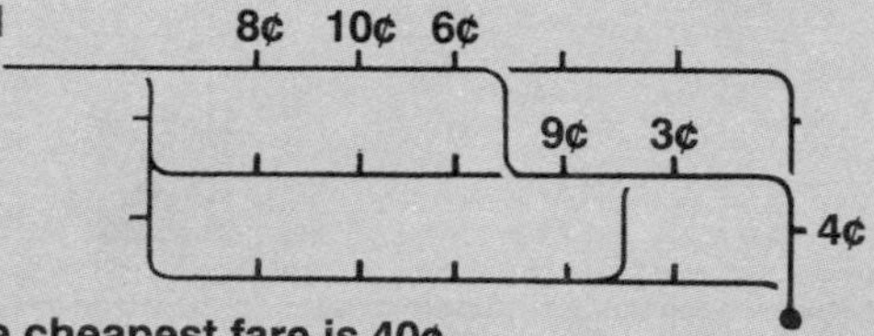

The cheapest fare is 40¢.

252

C is correct.

253

First, Nanki-Poo; 2nd, Little Buttercup; 3rd, The Gondolier; 4th, Pirate King.

254

You can ignore key ring B, because the question is only concerned with black key rings. If key ring A has an even number, the answer to the question is No. If key ring A has an odd number, C is white, and D is either black or white, the answer to the question is Yes. So as it is irrelevant if key ring D is black or white, the two key rings you should turn over are A and C.

255

B has the highest score. A scored 46, B scored 47, and C scored 43 points.

256

B completes the sequence.

257

The lizard is a reptile. The frog, toad, and newt are all amphibians.

258

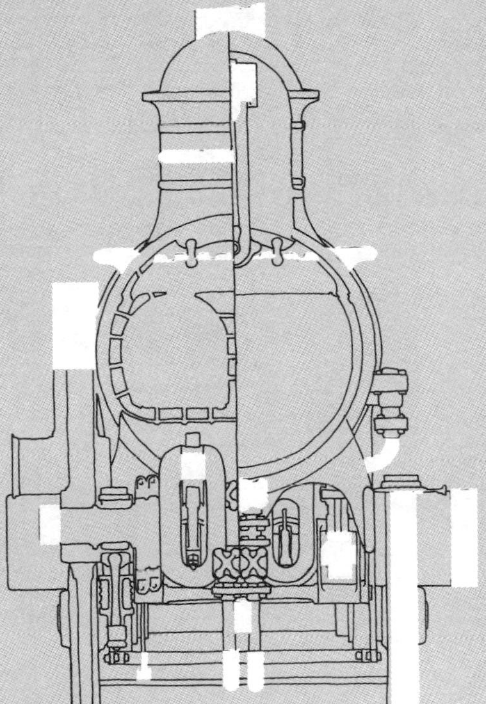

259

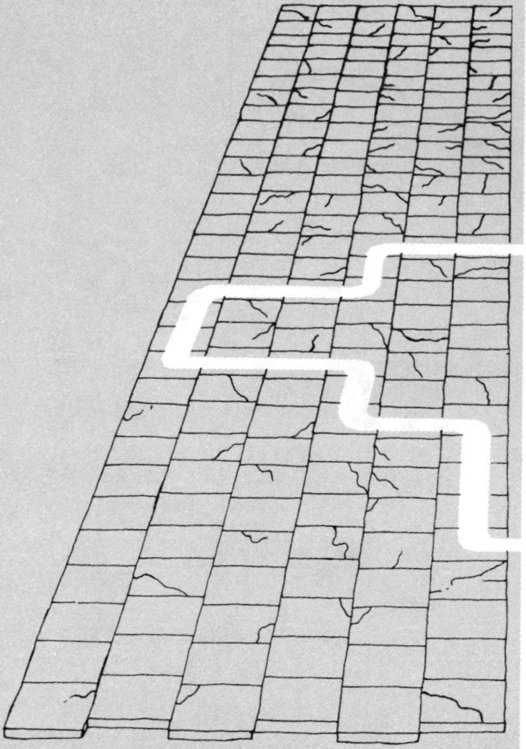

ANSWER 259

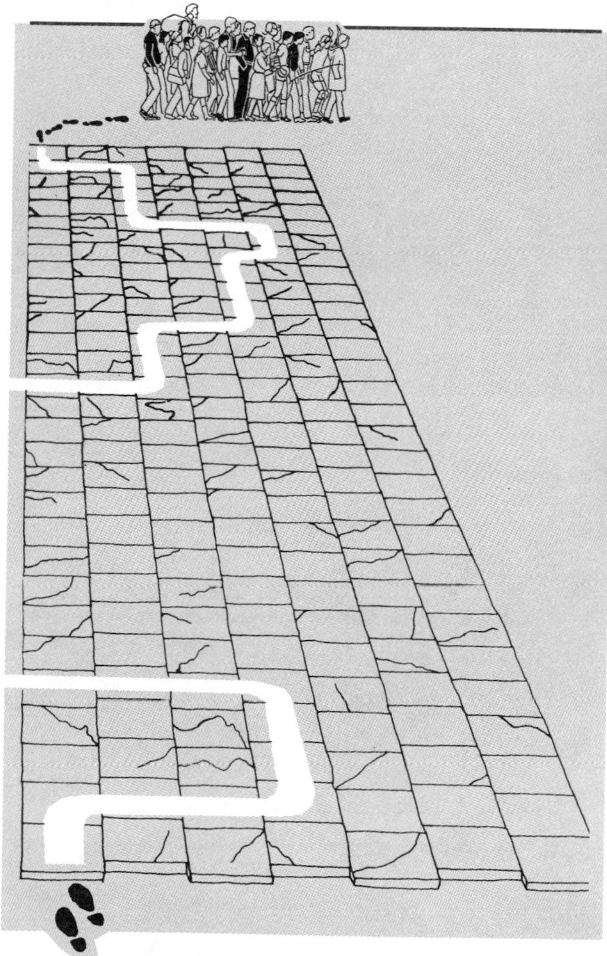

260
Here are the numbers: 954–459=495.

261
The answer is:

```
  178
  534
+ 269
  981   178x3=534
```

262
The missing number is 80. (Subtract 33 from each number in turn.)

263
Mark has 14.

264
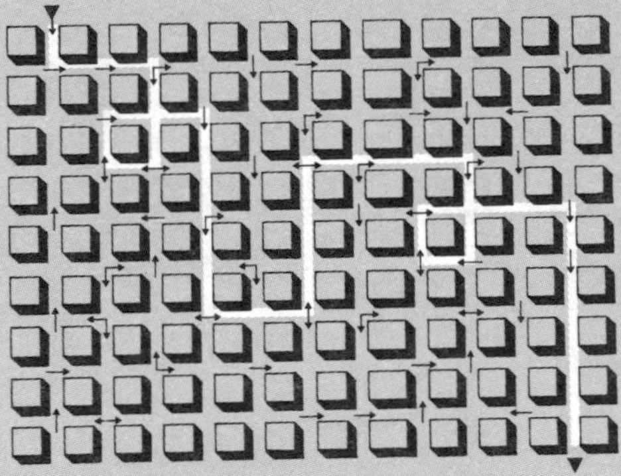

265
First the two gentlemen crossed the moat in the

boat, and one of them remained on the opposite bank. The other gentleman then brought the boat back and one of the ladies then crossed to the other side. The gentleman on that bank then brought the boat back, and the two gentlemen crossed the moat once more. Again one of them stayed behind, and the other brought the boat back for another lady to cross the moat. They then repeated these crossings until everyone was safely on the right side of the moat.

266

The ruler moves forward 10 inches.

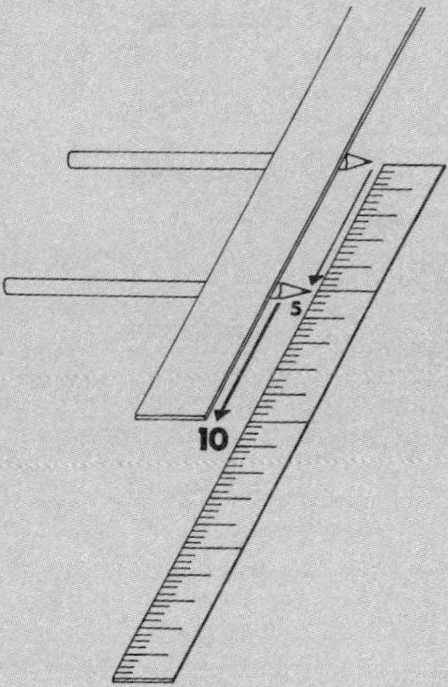

267

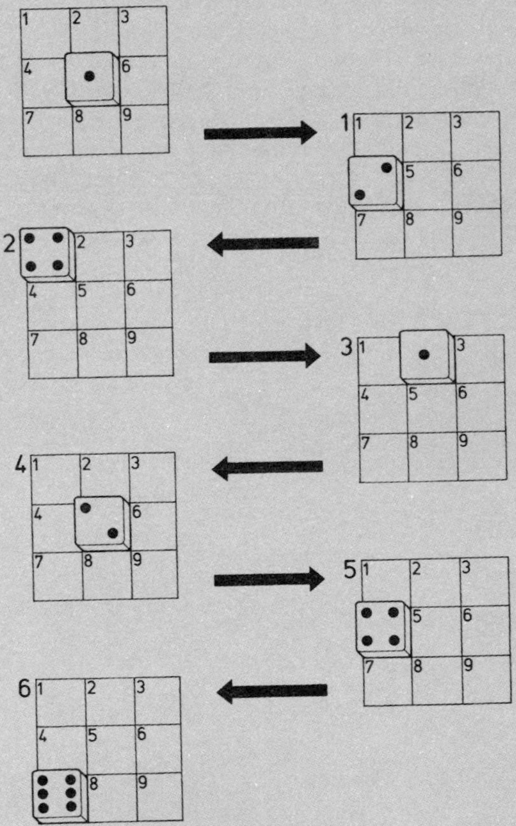

1 2 3 4 6 7 8 9
1 1 2 3 5 6 7 8 9
2 2 3 4 5 6 7 8 9
3 1 3 4 5 6 7 8 9
4 1 2 3 4 6 7 8 9
5 1 2 3 5 6 7 8 9
6 1 2 3 4 5 6 8 9

268

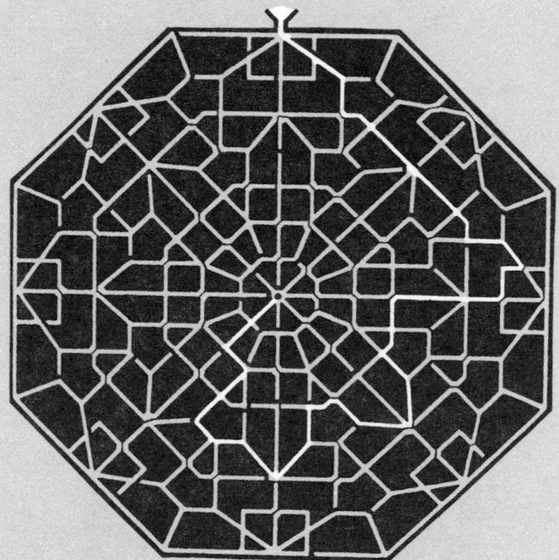

269

Ten.

270

Ten guilders. An artist cost 7 guilders, and a stonemason cost 3 guilders.

271

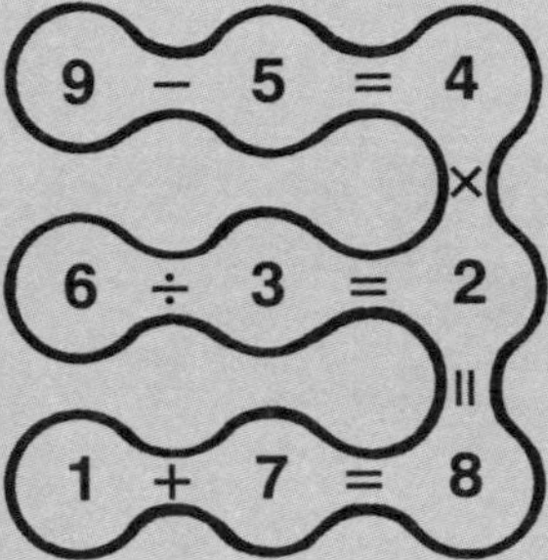

272

273

274

The next symbol would be boxed figure "a" – the only symbol with seven free ends. As an alphabet, our pioneer's invention is hardly very practical. The letter "z" would require a figure with 25 ends.

275

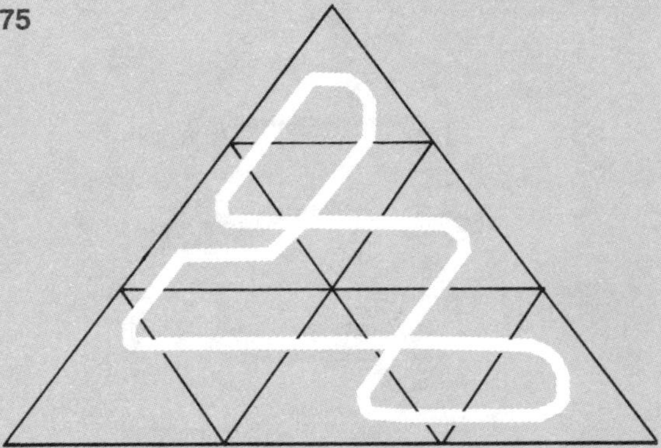

276

The boat makes 26 trips.

277

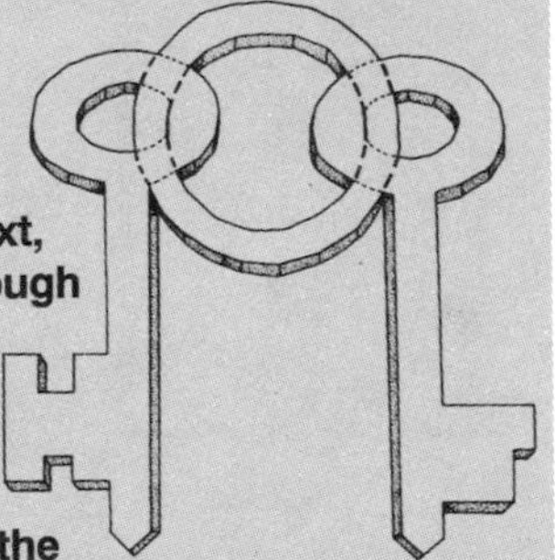

Cut out the linked key ring and keys from the cardboard, as shown. Next, carefully cut halfway through the thickness of the cardboard along the lines of dashes and then turn the cardboard over and cut halfway through the thickness of the cardboard along the dotted lines. Finally, use a penknife to split the cardboard below the four squares formed by the lines, and the keys will hang freely on the key ring.

278

$$\begin{array}{r} 11 \\ 1 \\ 1 \\ \underline{1} \\ \underline{14} \end{array}$$

We said five figures, not numbers!

279

Put the bottom cookie on the middle one!

280
You will get a twisted collar, twice the length of the original Möbius strip, to which is attached a Möbius strip that is one-third the width of the original.

281
He owned 12.

282
No. 2.

283
One of the bandits was the boy's father; the other bandit was his mother.

284
The letter L.

285

286

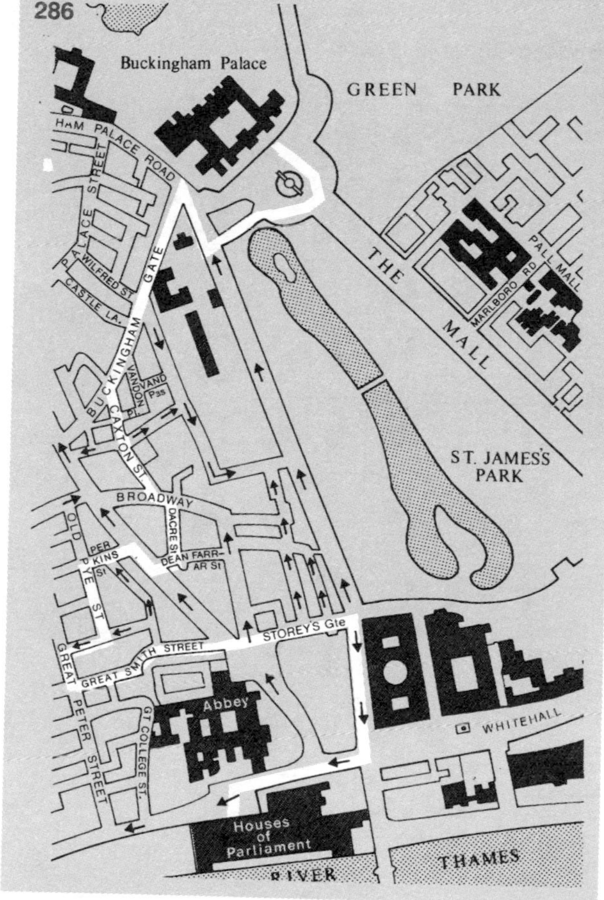
Buckingham Palace
GREEN PARK
THE MALL
PALL MALL
MARLBORO RD
ST. JAMES'S PARK
HAM PALACE ROAD
PALACE STREET
WILFRED ST
CASTLE LA.
BUCKINGHAM GATE
VANDON
VAND Pss
CAXTON ST.
BROADWAY
DACRE St
DEAN FARRAR St
OLD PYE ST
PERKINS St
STOREY'S Gte
GREAT SMITH STREET
GREAT PETER STREET
GT COLLEGE ST.
Abbey
WHITEHALL
Houses of Parliament
RIVER THAMES

287
Sixteen – here is one possible solution.

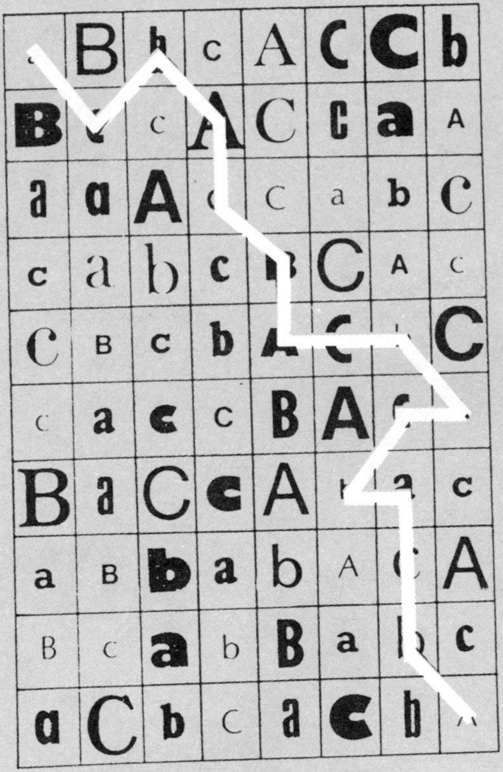

288

a) Fold the postcard in half lengthwise and cut a slit along the fold, as shown. Make sure you do not cut the card in half.
b) Cut slits at right angles from the fold almost to the edge and from the edge almost to the fold.
c) Unfold the card.
d) Gently pull the card open and climb through it – carefully!

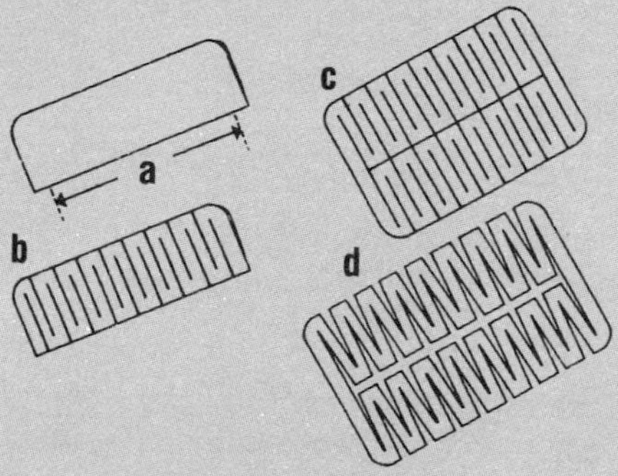

289

Maximum working depth is 84 feet below the surface. The total length of available air pipe (P) can be written like this: P = 1/8 + 2/3P + 20, which gives a value of 96 feet. We can quickly work out that the deck of the support barge is 12 feet above the water, so if all the available pipe is used the diver can reach 84 feet below the surface.

290
Five units. The value for the black balloon is found by adding the values for the other two balloons and dividing by 2.

291
Inverting the 9 would give you the simple solution: (1+2+7+8) = (3+4+5+6) = 18.

What is needed here is:

173	85
+ 4	+ 92
177	177

292 One hundred.

293
Red – an odd number plus an even number is always an odd number.

294
There are two possible winning combinations because the two pairs are interchangeable.

39571 or 39x57–1=2,222
57391 or 57x39–1=2,222

295

Three moves, as follows:

5 2 3 8 1 4 7 6 9
5 2 3 8 1 6 7 4 9
5 2 3 4 1 6 7 8 9
1 2 3 4 5 6 7 8 9

296

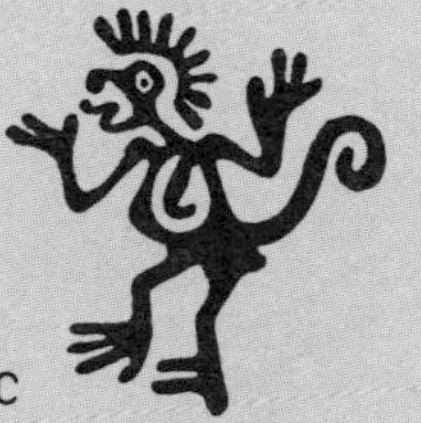

C

297

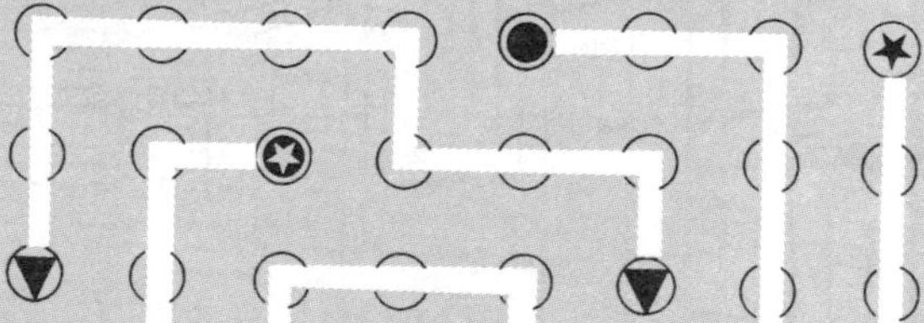

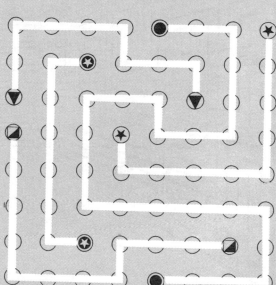

ANSWER 298

299

300

In this arrangement, all three loops are joined together, but no two are – so cut any one loop, and all three will come apart.

301

You would buy the one that didn't go at all, as it would be correct every 12 hours. The clock losing one minute every hour shows the correct time once every 30 hours, while the clock losing one minute in every 24 hours is only correct once every 720 days!

302

C is true; a and b are false.

303

304

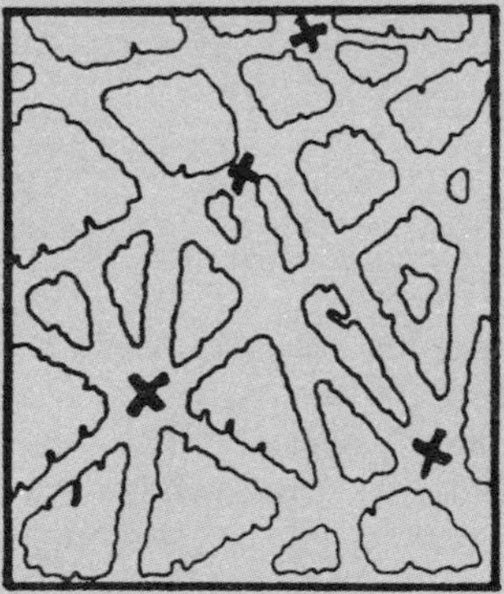

305

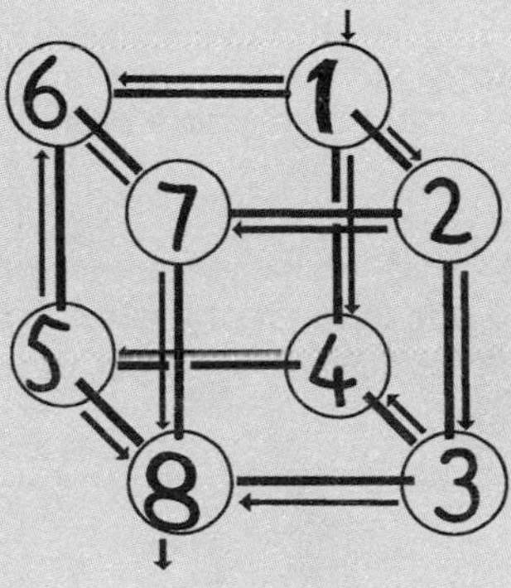

306

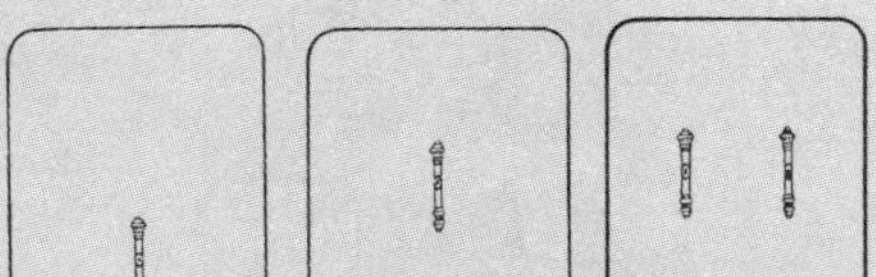

307

There were only three men – grandfather, father, and son. The father was also a son.

308

He simply divided the nuggets into three piles and placed a pile in each of the scale pans. They balanced – so Jim grabbed the third pile and ran.

309

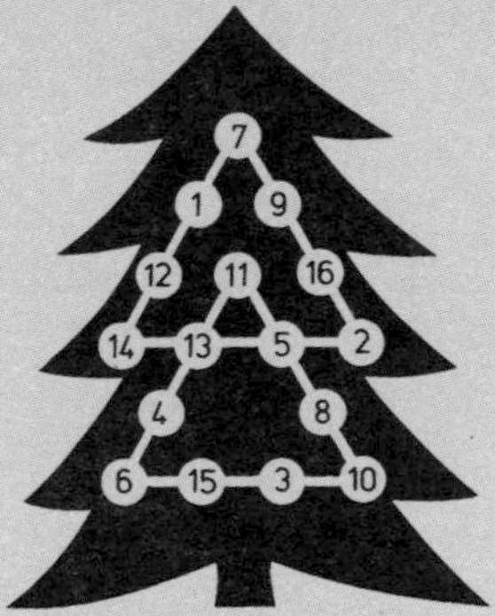

310

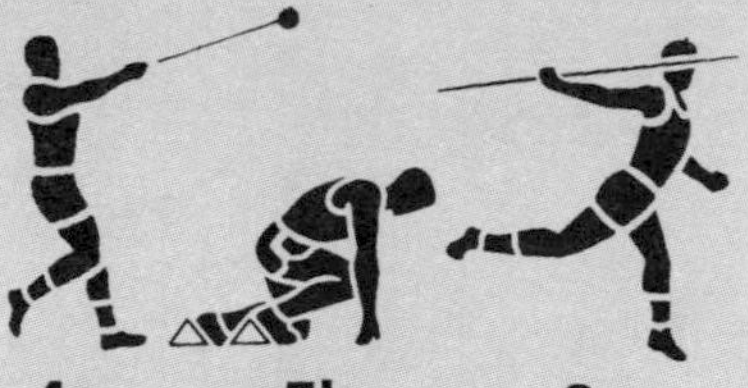

4a 5b 3c

310 (cont.)

1d

2e

311

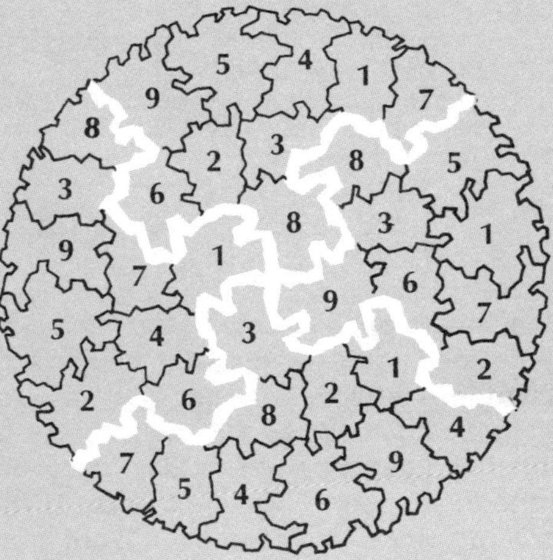

The solution is easier if you realize that the numbers 1 to 9 add up to 45.

312
Seven.

313

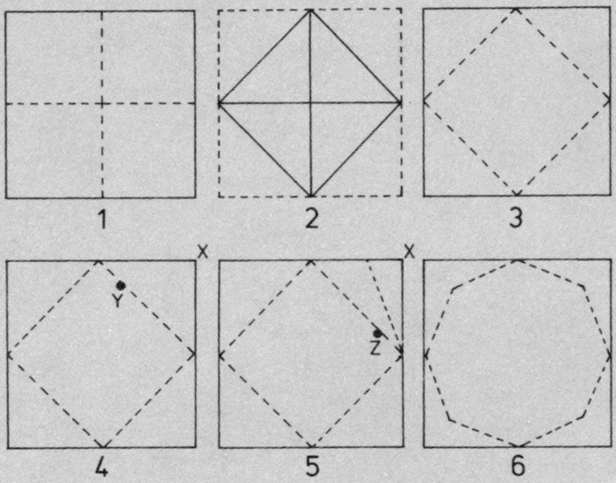

Fold the square of paper into four (1) and crease along the lines – this will mark the middle point of each of the four sides. Crease along the lines joining these points (2) so that a diamond shape is marked on your paper (3). Fold corner X of the square to touch point Y (4), and crease. Then fold corner X to point Z, and crease (5). Work around the other three corners in the same way, and you will find the regular octagon marked out by the creases (6). You can then cut it out.

314

Move seven objects from pile A to pile B, then six from pile B to pile C, and finally four from pile C to pile A.

315

If you fold the note into concertina pleats it will easily support the third glass.

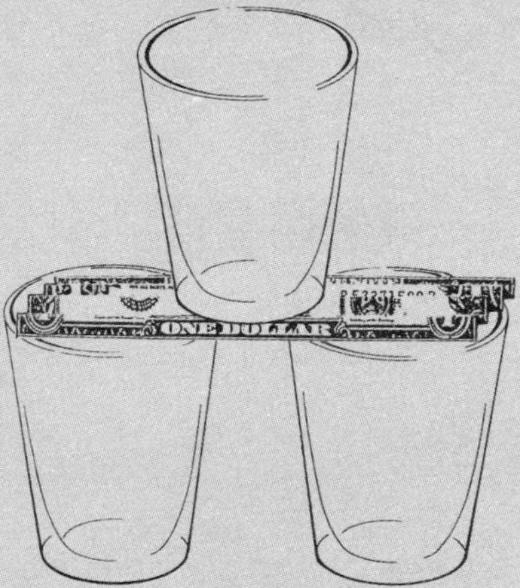

316

Make sure that your opponent takes the first pick. Watch carefully how many nuts he picks up. Then, when it is your turn, pick up enough nuts to make a total of 10 nuts for the two of you – if he picks up 3, you take 7, or if he picks up 6, you take 4. Repeat this in every round, and you will always have the last pick, and so win.

317

Mary is 10 years old, and Jane is 4 years old.

318

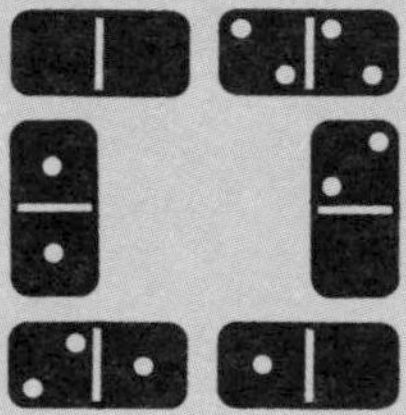

Puzzles can be classified by the method they use to challenge your intelligence. Should you like a particular type of puzzle, this index will help you locate similar puzzles in the book.

ACTIVITY PUZZLES

Animal shadows 240
Apples and oranges 2
Banknote 87
Calendar dates 238
Card moves 55, 166, 299
Card rows 81
Cardboard keys 277
Cherries in a postcard 184
Circle and dot 169
Cookie cross 279
Cross to pentagon 196
Dollar bill bridge 315
Domino square 318
Double key ring 165
Eight crosses 195
Five coins 142
Force field 36
Fudge square 237
Glasses and rulers 1
Identical shapes 224
Lettered squares 82
Magic egg 40
Mayor's postcard 288
Nail dog 70
Nail squares 234
Nuts 316
Object piles 314
Octagon construction 313
Pencil figures 56
Rolling a die 267
Ruler and pencils 266
Running men tangram 89
Scissors and cord 71
Solitaire 127
Straw triangles 112
String loops 300
Tangram cats 246
Tangram man 209
Tetrominoes 113
Three coins 141
Tied to a friend 170
Wooden shapes 10
Word pattern 167

LOGIC PUZZLES

After-dinner drink 92
Airports 222
Animal riddle 214
Antique clocks 301
Baker's shop 148
Bandit family 283
Bart's postcard 26
Baseball players 302
Bicycle thieves 18
Boy marries mother 98
Bus breakdown 173
Camper 25

Cargo boat 72
Carrying friends 226
Cat 54, 129
Cleopatra's birthday 186
Costume ball 265
Cruiser cabins 171
Daily race 152
Days of the week 30
Duel 15
Eggs 105
Egyptian gods 41
Elevator 212
Family relationships 223
Farmer's birds 139
Farmer's children 3
Fat cats 244
Fence posts 213
Fighter squadron 269
File labels 193
Fishing trip 307
Forklift truck 64
Fortune teller 306
French duelists 73
Galactic object 131
Gloves 39
Gold nuggets 308
Gold train 109
Grocer's weights 243
Highest mountain 125
Hole riddle 28
Horse race 253
Horses 53
Hotel keys 254
Identical twins 96
Letter shuffle 62
Line of trees 159
Lizards 245
Locker numbers 157
Logical pairs 38
Marching soldiers 86
Odd and even 293
Pair of stockings 37
People have it 284
Place settings 12
Red/black card 176
Riddle 130
Sail sale 194
Sentry's dream 91
Ship's cats 110
Shotgun Pete 281
Sphinx's alphabet 185
Station clock 252
Tarot cards 177
Titans 178
Toucan 63
Trolls 16
Twelve girls 202
Wee Willie Winkie 97
What gets lost? 227
Wine jugs 151
Wizards' riddle 50
Yacht race 247
Yes 201

MAZE PUZZLES
Alphabet 58
Ant labyrinth 88
Arabic floor patterns 180

Arrow maze 264
Black squares 229
Blind mice 175
Brain 124
Building 93
Bull ring 203
Bunker 126
Cable tube 146
Church window 190
Design 94
Dice 210
Dot collecting 230
Earthworm 303
Harem 59
Letter links 65
Letter sequence 287
Mayan 272
Mayan gods 221
Minotaur 140
Moorish maze 35, 285
Museum 298
Numbers maze 8, 123
Parking lot 220
Penalty points 108
Rat in a box 211
Robot 273
Roman slave 46
Royal route 286
Shortest route 114
Space invader 268
Tile-by-tile 259

NUMBER PUZZLES
Balloons 290
Bomber pilots 144
Book trunks 27
Boxes on truck 292
Bull's-eyes 122
Catching mice 199
Cathedral builders 270
Cheapest route 251
Checkout slip 261
Climbing stairs 197
College band 120
Computer bug 232
Coolant pipes 5
Cowboy and rancher 117
Data presentation 45
Diver's depth 289
Division 135
Domino multiplications 61
Dominoes 153
Empty glasses 32
Family savings 235
Father and daughter 161
Federation map 311
Free tickets 215
Girls' ages 317
Grouping figures 291
Little Boy Blue 13
Magic square 138
Magic trick 248
Marathon 80
Marbles 263
Mental arithmetic 312
Merlin's cube 305
Missile batteries 76

Missing numbers 160, 187, 188, 271
Missing signs 137
Modern art bricks 49
Mushrooms 121
Naughty pupil 83
Number maze 8
Nuts 11
Odd figures 278
One-armed bandit 294
Oogil's numbers 191
Park cats 136
Passenger ship 104
Phone code 60
Picking apples 7
Pieces of cake 33
Pig pens 79
Pills in a bottle 44
Planets 231
Pole-climbing snail 84
Processing tanks 154
Project 9
Record needle 200
Red and green apples 75
Roman-numeral matches 6
Roulette wheel 143
Row boat 276
Sequence 262
Shelf order 295
Signal post 158
Spiral shell 67
Squares and triangles 192
Steelyard 66
Storekeeper's sums 189
Superintendent's salary 218
Ten-card puzzle 236
Three digits 260
Tiles 134
Toll charges 172
Train driver 85
Tree lights 309
Upside-down numbers 155
USS *Dolphin* 233
Watch 162
Watch battery 163
Wildlife camera 43

OBSERVATION PUZZLES

Alphabet mistakes 116
Building plans 145
Calligraphy marks 133
Carpenter's tools 183
Herbal encyclopedia 182
Name search 128
Picture sequence 115
Shoe tracks 168
Silhouettes 21
Unique pottery 74
Vintage car 181
Welcome 77

SPOT THE DIFFERENCE

Blackbeard's map 78

Farm life 205, 228
Martian inscription 204
Mosaic 250
Novice scribe 34
Saints 31
Spy school 17
Steam engine 258
Woodcuts 219

VISUAL PUZZLES
Apple pie 207
Architect's models 100
Athletic equipment 310
Barracks message 149
Boats and buoys 255
Branding iron 282
Broken arrow 106
Cartoon 239
Castle wall 20
Chinese boats 304
Chinese warriors 57
Crab fishermen 4
Dot to dot 48
Dovetailed 118
Draftsman's exam 69
Farm division 111
Fuel dump 99
Great Star 103
Guards' coffee 90
Helicopter marker 19
Hexagons 47
Hidden animals 42
Hidden triangles 24, 68
House repairs 225
Ice skating 242
Leaves 249
Little men 256
Matching terminals 297
Möbius strip 280
Model 208
Modern sculpture 198
Monkey rings 296
Mystery message 174
Number cube 51
Odd animal out 23, 257
Odd ball out 217
Odd creature out 95, 257
Odd man out 156, 241
Odd woman out 147
Packager design 132
Racetrack 275
Radar scanner 206
Ribbons 107
Seahorses 216
Secret message 22
Settler's alphabet 274
Sketches 52
Spy message 119
Squares 179
Tampered cards 101
Time viewer 150
Village treasure map 102
Watch cogwheel 164
Wooden object 14
Wrong scissors 29

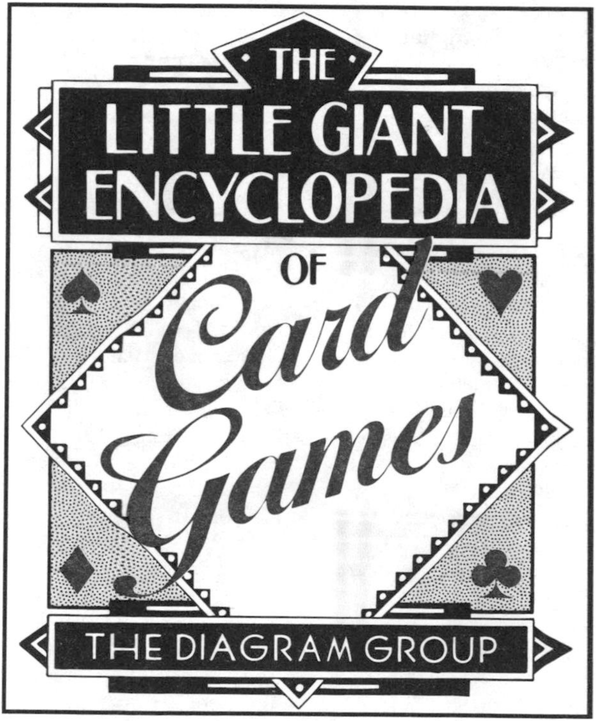
THE
LITTLE GIANT
ENCYCLOPEDIA
OF
Card
Games
THE DIAGRAM GROUP